APPLIED STATISTICAL THEORY AND APPLICATIONS

APPLIED STATISTICAL SCIENCE

APPLIED STATISTICAL THEORY AND APPLICATIONS

MOHAMMAD AHSANULLAH
EDITOR

New York

LIBRARY OF CONGRESS CATALOGING-IN-PUBLICATION DATA

Applied statistical theory and applications / [edited by] Mohammad Ahsanullah.
    pages cm. -- (Applied statistical science)
 Includes bibliographical references and index.
 ISBN 978-1-63321-858-1 (hardcover)
 1. Statistics. I. Ahsanullah, Mohammad, editor.
 QA276.A68 2014
  519.5--dc23
 2014032865

Published by Nova Science Publishers, Inc. † New York

CONTENTS

PREFACE

This book makes a significant contribution to the advancement of statistical science. It contains research in many statistical designs, compares many statistical models, and includes a theory that is oriented to real life problems.

The quasi-negative binomial distribution, characterized by three parameters, has been used to fit data arising from many fields of study. The distribution gets truncated under certain conditions. In Chapter 1 the authors investigate the truncation error by carrying out a detailed error analysis. Through this analysis, the authors determine the parameter space when the model can be used instead of using a truncated quasi-negative binomial distribution. They define a truncated quasi-negative binomial distribution that can be used when the quasi-negative binomial distribution gets truncated on the right hand side. A numerical example is used for illustration.

In Chapter 2 the authors present a new family of univariate slash distributions, which arises as the ratio of logistic distribution and independent uniform power function distribution. Slash logistic and skew Slash logistic distributions were derived and the properties were studied. Logistic and skew logistic distributions are special cases of this new family. These distributions provide us an alternative choices in simulation study and in particular, in fitting skewed data sets with heavy tails.

The distribution of the sample covariance based on a sample from a bivariate normal population has been derived in the literature by many authors. Some used conditionality principle, some used inverse Mellin transform and some used simple transformations. The main contribution of Chapter 3 is the direct derivation of the general moment structure of sample covariance via a lemma dealing with a infinite sum of product of two gamma functions. Integer valued moments of any order are also derived in terms of hypergeometric function. Some corollaries have been deduced which have potential for further use in mathematics and statistics. The probability density function, skewness and kurtosis have been graphed.

The main objective of Chapter 4 is to develop a direct Bayesian technique to determine or estimate the order of two dimensional moving average processes. The proposed technique is based on approximating the likelihood function by a matrix normal-Wishart distribution on the parameter space. Combining the approximate likelihood with a matrix normal-Wishart (or vague prior) and an indirect technique to estimate an initial value for the order, the marginal posterior probability mass function of the model order is developed in a convenient form. Then one investigates the approximate posterior probability mass function of the model order over its grid and selects the order with the maximum posterior probability to solve the identification problem. A simulation study, with three different priors, is conducted in order to inspect the numerical efficiency of the proposed Bayesian technique and compare it with the well known AIC automatic technique. The numerical results show that the proposed Bayesian technique is simple, efficient and easy to program.

Chapter 5 studies two simple approaches that are very powerful and computationally less intensive to test poisson versus zero inflated poisson distributions.

Chapter 6 proposes variables quick switching system (VQSS) where the quality characteristic follows normal distribution or lognormal distribution and has upper or lower specification limit. The variables quick switching system will be effective when testing is costly and destructive. The advantages of the variables QSS over the variables single and double sampling plans and attributes QSS are discussed. Tables are also constructed for the selection of parameters of known and unknown standard deviation VQSS for given acceptable quality level and limiting quality level. The problem is formulated as a nonlinear programming where the objective function to be minimized is the average sample number and the constraints are related to lot acceptance probabilities at acceptable quality level and limiting quality level under the operating characteristic curve .

It is well known that in a balanced incomplete block (BIB) design two treatments occur together in the same block equal number of times. Thus the restriction on triplets of treatments is the second condition for balance in the design. In Chapter 7, the authors establish some conditions on the occurrence of triplets of treatments in a BIB design, its complementary design and the design formed by the union of the BIB design and the complementary design. The authors establish the conditions in terms of the parameters of the original BIB design.

In Chapter 8, assuming that the stationary distribution in an M|M|1 balking situation is Negative Binomial, maximum likelihood estimator (MLE) and Bayes estimator of the parameter p based on the number of observations present at several sampled time points are obtained. Further, the minimum posterior risk associated with Bayes estimator and minimum Bayes risk of the estimator are obtained. In addition, the maximum likelihood and consistent asymptotically normal (CAN) estimators and $100(1-\alpha)\%$ asymptotic confidence interval for the expected number of customers in the system are obtained.

In Chapter 9, the authors demonstrate the method of construction of $100(1-\delta)\%$ confidence interval for parameter λ (scale parameter) of a Weibull distribution based on a sample of size one. The authors take a cue from this method to construct a similar $100(1-\delta)\%$ confidence intervals for these parameters based on $\{X_{1:n} = \min \{X_1, X_2, ..., X_n\}$ where $X_1, X_2, ..., X_n$ are $n(\geq 2)$ independent random variables from a Weibull distribution having parameters λ and β. For $\beta = 1$, i.e., for exponential distribution, although the proposed confidence interval for the mean λ overlaps with the confidence interval based on chi-square distribution, the former one is significantly narrower than the latter one. For $n(\geq 2)$ additional numerical results that compare proposed $100(1-\delta)\%$ confidence intervals for λ with the ones that are given in Bain and Engelhardt (1991) are provided. It is interesting to note that the former ones turn out to be significantly narrower than the latter ones for samples of sizes 1 through 5 for $\delta = 0.02$, 0.05 and 0.10.

In Chapter 10, the authors propose a truncated version of *generalized Cauchy* distribution suggested by Rider in a special setting. One possible use for the proposed model is in life-testing where the domain of definition is not only non-negative but also guarantees no failure before a given time (truncated parameter). The parameters, reliability (*RF*) and hazard rate (*HRF*) functions are estimated using the maximum likelihood and Bayes methods. The Bayes estimates (*BE's*) are obtained under the squared-error and liner exponential (*LINEX*) loss functions. The computations have been carried out using the Markov Chain Monte Carlo (MCMC) algorithm. Also, the Bayesian prediction intervals (*BPI' s*) of future observation from the proposed distribution are constructed.

In Chapter 11, a procedure is illustrated to incorporate multiple sources of prior information in the ridge regression model. The resulting model is unbiased and robust estimates of the ridge parameters are developed.

Chapter 12 focuses on three standard dose response models, namely, the multistage Weibull, logistic and log-logistic models, each involving two unknown parameters. The maximum likelihood and Berkson's modified minimum chi-square methods are employed to estimate the two unknown parameters in each model, and the mean squared errors of these estimates are derived asymptotically to the order of approximation of n^{-2}, where n is the sample size. The AIC and deviance criteria are used for model selection. One real data set is used for illustration. The results show that, as expected, the mean squared errors of the estimates behave differently for different dose groups and dose levels.

In Chapter 13, a practical approach based on the adaptive kernel density estimation (AKDE) has been applied for deriving the confidence intervals (CIs) of the generalized gamma distribution parameters based on the generalized order statistics (GOS).The efficiency of this technique has been studied comparing to the conditional inference based on the mean lengths, the covering percentages and the standard errors, via Monte Carlo simulations and some real data. From our results, it appears that the kernel approach mostly competes with the conditional approach. Finally, a numerical example is given to illustrate the inferential methods developed in this paper.

The distribution of the product of two variables is important in portfolio diversification model and in economic forecasting. In Chapter 14 the authors derive the distribution of the product of two chi-square variables when they are correlated through a bivariate chi-square distribution. Closed form expressions for raw moments, centered moments, coefficient of skewness and kurtosis are obtained. The density function is also graphed. The results match with the distribution of the product of two independent chi-square variables in case the coefficient correlation in our model vanishes. They are often extended to sample variances of bivariate normal distribution.

In Chapter 15, the problem of fixed-width Confidence Interval for the mean survival time is considered. Sequential procedures are adopted based on the maximum likelihood estimators (MLE) and uniform minimum variance unbiased estimators (UMVUE) of the scale parameter. A comparative study of the two sequential procedures is done and second-order approximations are obtained and they are proved to be 'asymptotically efficient and consistent.'

In Chapter 16 the authors have considered mixtures of exponential and geometric distributions.. Some characterizations of these distributions based on the doubly truncated mean functions are presented.

A generalization of the well-known intervened Poisson distribution (IPD) of Shanmugam (Biometrics, 1985) is discussed in Chapter 17, along with some of its important properties such as its probability mass function, mean, variance, expression for factorial moments and recurrence relation for probabilities and factorial moments. Some real life data sets are given to illustrate that the generalized version gives the best fit compared to existing models such as positive Poisson distribution, intervened Poisson distribution and intervened generalized Poisson distribution.

Generalized logistic distribution $F(x) = [1 + (m + 1) e^{-\alpha x}]^{-\frac{1}{m+1}}$ has been characterized through translation of two non-adjacent dual generalized order statistics (*dgos*) and then the characterizing results are obtained for generalized log-logistic distribution through dilation of dual generalized order statistics (*dgos*) and generalized log-logistic distribution through contraction of non-adjacent generalized order statistics (*gos*). Further in Chapter 18, the results are deduced for order statistics and adjacent generalized order statistics and dual generalized order statistics.

The maximum likelihood and moment estimators are derived for samples from the binomial distribution in the presence of outliers. The authors have shown in Chapter 19, that moment estimators are consistent. Further, it is shown that these estimators are better than MLE by using simulation technique. At the end the authors have given an example of Shooters.

In: Applied Statistical Theory and Applications
Editor: Mohammad Ahsanullah

ISBN: 978-1-63321-858-1
© 2014 Nova Science Publishers, Inc.

Chapter 1

ERROR ANALYSIS ON THE QUASI-NEGATIVE BINOMIAL DISTRIBUTION

Felix Famoye[1] and Adeyinka Ogunsanya[2]

[1]Department of Mathematics, Central Michigan University,
Mt. Pleasant, Michigan, US
[2]Department of Mathematics, University of Lagos,
Akoka-Yaba, Lagos, Nigeria

Abstract

The quasi-negative binomial distribution, characterized by three parameters, has been used to fit data arising from many fields of study. The distribution gets truncated under certain conditions. We investigate the truncation error by carrying out a detailed error analysis. Through this analysis, we determine the parameter space when the model can be used instead of using a truncated quasi-negative binomial distribution. We define a truncated quasi-negative binomial distribution that can be used when the quasi-negative binomial distribution gets truncated on the right hand side. A numerical example is used for illustration.

Keywords and phrases: Truncation error; parameter space; maximum likelihood estimates

1. Introduction

A discrete random variable X is said to have a quasi-negative binomial distribution (QNBD) if its probability function, (Li et al. 2008), is given by

$$f(x) = f_x = \begin{cases} \dfrac{\Gamma(x+\alpha)}{x!\Gamma(\alpha)} \dfrac{1}{1+cx} \left(\dfrac{1+cx}{1+b+cx} \right)^x \left(\dfrac{b}{1+b+cx} \right)^\alpha, & x = 0,1,2,\ldots \\ 0, & \text{for } x > k \text{ if } c < 0, \end{cases}$$

(1.1)

where $\alpha > 0$, $b > 0$ and k is the largest positive integer for which $1 + kc \geq 0$ when $c < 0$. The QNBD in (1.1) reduces to the negative binomial distribution (NBD) when the parameter $c = 0$. For the non-truncated QNBD, the mean and the variance as provided by Li et al. (2008) are not in closed form. The probability model in (1.1) gets truncated on the right hand side when $c < 0$. If the truncation error is negligible, one may still be able to use the model in (1.1). However, if the truncation error is substantial, it is important to consider a truncated quasi-negative binomial distribution as an alternative. This paper will study the parameter space of QNBD to identify where the truncation error is negligible. The paper will also define a truncated quasi-negative binomial distribution that can be used when the truncation error is not negligible.

In section 2, we conduct a detailed error analysis of the QNBD. In section 3, we define a truncated quasi-negative binomial distribution. In section 4, a numerical data set on the number of absenteeism among shift-workers is used for illustration. Finally in section 5, we provide some concluding remarks.

2. Error Analysis of the QNBD

Due to the truncation in QNBD, the sum of the probabilities in (1.1) may differ from unity. The difference between 1 and the sum of the probabilities (Σf_x) is the truncation error. The percentage truncation error will be computed as $100(1 - \Sigma f_x)$. Some illustrative examples for $k \leq 3$ are presented in Table 1. For two classes only, the truncation leads to only two probabilities f_0 and f_1. The sum of the two probabilities could be very small or very large as shown in Table 1. In Table 1, the sum of the non-negative probabilities could be larger than 3.0 and could be smaller than 0.2. It is hard to see a pattern in the truncation errors.

One of the motivations for this paper is to determine various conditions for which the truncation error will be negligible. For example in row 5 for $k = 2$, the sum of the probabilities is more than 3 because $f(2)$ leads to a value that is close to 3.0 on the account that $1 + 2c$ is 0.05.

When $c < 0$, we require that $1 + cx \geq 0$ in the QNBD in (1.1). If this is not satisfied, we set f_x to 0 as shown in (1.1). Thus, the largest x value can be obtained from $0 \leq 1 + cx \Rightarrow -cx \leq 1 \Rightarrow x \leq -1/c$ since $-c > 0$. Thus, the largest x value, k, is given by the integer part of $-1/c$.

Through computation, we make a detailed error analysis on the QNBD model when $c < 0$. For this analysis, we consider the values of α and b in the parameter space and the values of $c < 0$. Thus, we consider the values of $\alpha > 0$, $b > 0$ and $c < 0$. In the analysis, we compute the values of $f(x)$ for $x = 0, 1, 2, \ldots, k$ where k is such that $k \leq -1/c$ when $c < 0$. After computing the probabilities, we compute the percentage truncation error by using the formula $100(1 - \Sigma f_x)$.

In fitting the QNBD to an observed data set, the three parameters α, b and c have to be estimated. In order to have at least 1 degree of freedom for the chi-square goodness-of-fit test, we need at least five non-zero probability classes. Thus, we need the smallest value of x to be 4. Therefore, in the error analysis, the smallest x value is required to be 4. The percentage error of truncation will be said to be negligible if it is below 0.5%. Thus, the difference between 1 and the sum of all non-negative probabilities is below 0.005. This was the value used by Consul and Shoukri (1985) in their error analysis for the generalized Poisson distribution. In view of this, we will conduct the error analysis for $k \geq 4$.

The maximum truncation error for the different values of α, b and c are provided in Table 2. Since we need to have at least five non-zero probability classes, we examine the different errors for cases where x is at least 4. In the error analysis we consider the values of $\alpha = (.01)(.01)(5.0)$, $b = (0.1)(0.1)(10.0)$ and $c = (-0.25)(0.01)(-0.01)$.

Table 1. Sum of probabilities for some QNBD parameter sets

k	Parameters			Probabilities				Σf_x
	α	b	c	f_0	f_1	f_2	f_3	
1	1.0	0.1	−0.90	0.0909	2.5000			2.5909
	1.0	0.1	−0.75	0.0909	0.8163			0.9072
	1.0	0.1	−0.60	0.0909	0.4000			0.4909
	1.0	0.5	−0.90	0.3333	1.3889			1.7222
	1.0	0.5	−0.75	0.3333	0.8889			1.2222
	1.0	0.5	−0.60	0.3333	0.6173			0.9506
	1.5	0.1	−0.90	0.0274	2.6517			2.6791
	1.5	0.1	−0.75	0.0274	0.6545			0.6819
	1.5	0.1	−0.60	0.0274	0.2683			0.2957
	1.5	0.5	−0.90	0.1925	1.9018			2.0943
	1.5	0.5	−0.75	0.1925	1.0887			1.2812
	1.5	0.5	−0.60	0.1925	0.6901			0.8826
	1.5	1.0	−0.90	0.3536	1.1820			1.5356
	1.5	1.0	−0.75	0.3536	0.8587			1.2123
	1.5	1.0	−0.60	0.3536	0.6468			1.0004
	2.0	0.1	−0.90	0.0083	2.5000			2.5083
	2.0	0.1	−0.75	0.0083	0.4665			0.4748
	2.0	0.1	−0.60	0.0083	0.1600			0.1683
	2.0	0.5	−0.90	0.1111	2.3148			2.4259
	2.0	0.5	−0.75	0.1111	1.1852			1.2963
	2.0	0.5	−0.60	0.1111	0.6859			0.7970
	2.0	1.0	−0.90	0.2500	1.5026			1.7526
	2.0	1.0	−0.75	0.2500	1.0240			1.2740
	2.0	1.0	−0.60	0.2500	0.7289			0.9789
2	1.0	0.1	−.475	0.0909	0.2560	1.4815		1.8284
	1.0	0.1	−.45	0.0909	0.2367	1.2500		1.5776
	1.5	0.1	−.475	0.0274	0.1536	2.2680		2.4490
	1.5	0.1	−.45	0.0274	0.1392	1.6573		1.8239
	2.0	0.1	−.475	0.0083	0.0819	2.9630		3.0532
	2.0	0.1	−.45	0.0083	0.0728	1.8750		1.9561
3	1.0	0.1	−.33	0.0909	0.1687	0.3991	0.0683	0.7270
	1.0	0.1	−.30	0.0909	0.1563	0.3200	0.6250	1.1922
	1.5	0.1	−.33	0.0274	0.0912	0.3568	0.1425	0.6179
	1.5	0.1	−.30	0.0274	0.0829	0.2683	0.9667	1.3453
	2.0	0.1	−.33	0.0083	0.0438	0.2721	0.2484	0.5726
	2.0	0.1	−.30	0.0083	0.0391	0.1920	1.2500	1.4894

In Table 2, we report the ranges for the parameters that produce the maximum percentage error in the sum of the non-zero probabilities. In the error analysis the value of k is taken to be the integer part of $-1/c$. We also report the specific parameter values at which the maximum truncation error occurs. For example, when $0.01 < \alpha \leq 0.50$, $0.1 \leq b \leq 10.0$ and $-0.18 \leq c \leq -0.01$, the maximum truncation error with at least 5 non-zero probability classes is -0.4834. When $0.1 < b < 1.0$, the maximum truncation error in the probabilities occurs at the maximum value of α in the interval and the minimum value of $b = 0.1$. As α values increase, the range of c values decreases in order to have a maximum truncation error of less than 0.5%. For fixed α, as the number of non-zero probability classes increases, the truncation error decreases.

Table 2. Maximum percentage error and the corresponding parameter values

Range of parameters values			% Truncation error (α, b, c)	k
α	b	c		
$[0.01,0.50]$	$[0.10,1.0]$	$[-0.18,0)$	$-0.4834\ (0.50, 0.1, -0.17)$	5
$[0.51,1.00]$	$[0.10,1.0]$	$[-0.15,0)$	$-0.3314\ (1.00, 0.1, -0.15)$	6
$[1.01,1.50]$	$[0.10,1.0]$	$[-0.14,0)$	$-0.2209\ (1.50, 0.1, -0.11)$	9
$[1.51,3.00]$	$[0.10,1.0]$	$[-0.10,0)$	$-0.4571\ (3.00, 0.1, -0.10)$	10
$[3.01,6.50]$	$[0.10,1.0]$	$[-0.08,0)$	$-0.3695\ (5.06, 0.1, -0.08)$	12
$[0.01,1.00]$	$[1.01,10]$	$[-0.25,0)$	$-0.0268\ (1.00, 1.01, -.25)$	4
$[1.01,2.00]$	$[1.01,10]$	$[-0.25,0)$	$-0.1347\ (2.00, 1.01, -.25)$	4
$[2.01,3.00]$	$[1.01,10]$	$[-0.25,0)$	$-0.3663\ (0.39, 1.01, -.25)$	4
$[3.01,3.41]$	$[1.01,10]$	$[-0.25,0)$	$-0.4977\ (0.36, 1.01, -.25)$	4

When $c < 0$ and $k \geq 4$, the QNBD can be used in general when $0.01 < \alpha \leq 3.0$ for any value of $b > 1$. If $b < 1$ and $.01 < \alpha < 3$, the range of c values decreases to $-.18 \leq c < 0$. When $b < 1$ and $k \geq 4$, the QNBD can be used in general when $.01 < \alpha \leq 6.5$ and $-0.08 \leq c < 0$.

3. Truncated Quasi-Negative Binomial Distribution

A truncated quasi-negative binomial distribution (TQNBD) is defined as

$$P(X = x) = P_x = f(x)/Q_k, \; x = 0, 1, 2, ..., k, \qquad (2.1)$$

and zero otherwise, where $f(x)$ is given by (1.1), $Q_k = \Sigma_{x=0}^{k} f(x), \alpha > 0$, $b > 0$ and $-\infty < c < \infty$. The model in (2.1) is truncated on the right hand side. One may define a model that is truncated on the left hand side or truncated on both sides. However, these other truncation types will not be considered in this paper. The quantity k in (2.1) is any positive integer less than or equal to the largest observed value of x such that $1 + ck \geq 0$ when $c < 0$. We now consider the different cases for the values of c in the parameter space.

(i) When $c < -1$:

The condition $1 + ck \geq 0$ is satisfied only when $k = 0$. This case leads to a degenerate probability function as the whole probability mass is concentrated at the point $x = 0$.

(ii) When $-1 \leq c < -0.5$:

The maximum value that k can have is 1 and so the TQNBD reduces to the Bernoulli distribution with $P_0 = \left[1 + \dfrac{\alpha}{1+b+c}\left(\dfrac{1+b}{1+b+c}\right)^{\alpha}\right]^{-1}$ and $P_1 = \dfrac{\alpha}{1+b+c}\left[\dfrac{\alpha}{1+b+c} + \left(\dfrac{1+b+c}{1+b}\right)^{\alpha}\right]^{-1}$.

(iii) When $-0.5 \leq c < 0$:

The value of k can be any positive integer $\leq -1/c$. The largest observed value of x in a random sample is usually taken as an estimate of k.

(iv) When $c \geq 0$:

The quantity $f(x)$ is positive for all values of x and so the largest value of k is $+\infty$. By using Theorem 3 of Li et al. (2008), $Q_k = 1$ for $k = \infty$. Hence, $f(x)$, for $x = 0, 1, 2, \ldots$ in (2.1) will provide a true probability distribution.

For any positive integer k, the probability distribution in (2.1) represents a TQNBD and it is a true probability model for any value of c. The first two probabilities of the TQNBD are $P_0 = f_0 / Q_k = (b/(1+b))^{\alpha} / Q_k$ and $P_1 = f_1 / Q_k = \alpha b^{\alpha} / [(1+b+c)^{\alpha+1} Q_k]$. The ratio of the first two probabilities is $P_1 / P_0 = \alpha(1+b)^{\alpha}(1+b+c)^{-\alpha-1}$. The population mean μ_k and the population variance σ_k^2 of the TQNBD can be expressed as

$$\mu_k = E(X) = Q_k^{-1}\sum_{x=0}^{k} xf(x) \text{ and } \sigma_k^2 = E(X - \mu_k)^2 = Q_k^{-1}\sum_{x=0}^{k} x^2 f(x) - \mu_k^2. \quad (2.2)$$

The mean and variance in (2.2) are not in closed forms and hence it is difficult to determine the parameter region where the variance is less than (or larger than) the mean. Based on (2.2) and the ratio P_1 / P_0, it is not easy to estimate the TQNBD parameters by using the first two moments and the ratio of the first two frequencies. Suppose a random sample of size n is taken from the TQNBD in (2.1) and let the observed frequencies be denoted by n_x, $x = 0, 1, 2, \ldots, k$ for the different classes so that $\Sigma_{x=0}^{k} n_x = n$, where k is the largest observed value of x.

The log-likelihood function of the TQNBD is given by

$$\log L = \sum_{x=0}^{k} n_x \left\{\log\left(\Gamma(x+\alpha)/(x!\Gamma(\alpha))\right) - \log(1+cx) + x\log\left((1+cx)/(1+b+cx)\right)\right.$$
$$\left. + \alpha\log\left(b/(1+b+cx)\right) - \log Q_k\right\}. \quad (2.3)$$

The likelihood equations can be obtained by taking the partial derivatives of (2.3) with respect to the parameters α, b and c. The likelihood equations have to be solved numerically either by the Newton-Raphson method or some other iterative technique. We have not been able to show if the solutions to the likelihood equations are unique. The initial estimates for the parameters of TQNBD can be taken as the final estimates when a non-truncated QNBD is fitted to the data. We now describe the initial estimates for finding the maximum likelihood estimates (MLE) of the non-truncated QNBD.

Table 3. Number of absenteeism among shift-workers

Count	Observed frequency	Expected frequency			
		NBD	GNBD (GO[a])	QNBD	TQNBD
0	7	11.13	9.23	12.40	10.10
1	16	15.74	16.18	15.92	16.76
2	23	17.77	19.86	17.25	19.40
3	20	18.36	21.06	17.52	19.60
4	23	18.10	20.50	17.19	18.60
5	24	17.32	18.78	16.50	17.12
6	12	16.24	16.46	15.59	15.51
7	13	15.01	14.02	14.56	13.96
8	9	13.72	11.79	13.46	12.52
9	9	12.43	9.95	12.35	11.23
10	8	11.19	8.55	11.26	10.09
11	10	10.01	7.54	10.20	9.09
12	8	8.91	6.84	9.19	8.21
13	7	7.90	6.33	8.24	7.43
14	2	6.98	5.94	7.36	6.75
15	12	6.14	5.61	6.54	6.16
16	3	5.40	5.29	5.79	5.63
17	5	4.73	4.97	5.11	5.16
18	4	4.13	4.64	4.48	4.75
19	2	3.61	4.28	3.92	4.38
20	2	3.14	3.92	3.42	4.05
21	5	2.73	3.55	2.97	3.75
22	5	2.37	3.19	2.57	3.49
23	2	2.06	2.84	2.22	3.25
24	1	1.78	2.50	1.91	3.03
25 – 48	16	11.10	14.13	10.08	7.98
Total	248	248.00		248.00	248.00
$\hat{\alpha}$		1.679 (0.177)		1.447 (0.290)	5.188 (4.674)
$\hat{b}$		0.187 (0.022)		0.144 (0.047)	0.943 (1.219)
$\hat{c}$				−0.007 (0.008)	0.155 (0.075)
$^{c}\chi^2$		15.97	8.27	19.91	18.66
df		17	15	16	16
p-value		0.5260	0.9125	0.2243	0.2867

[a]Gupta and Ong (2004)
[c]We combined adjacent classes for chi-square values as it was done in Gupta and Ong (2004).

Since the QNBD in (1.1) reduces to the negative binomial distribution (NBD) when $c = 0$, we find the moment estimates of α and b when $c = 0$. These estimates with $c = 0$ can be used as the initial estimates for finding the MLE of QNBD parameters. Alternatively, one can take the moment estimates of α and b plus the estimate of c from equating the QNBD probability of 1 to the sample proportion of 1. This initial estimate of c is given by $\tilde{c} = (n\tilde{\alpha}\tilde{b}^{\tilde{\alpha}} / n_1)^{1/(1+\tilde{\alpha})} - 1 - \tilde{b}$, where $\tilde{\alpha}$ and $\tilde{b}$ are the moment estimates from the NBD.

4. Application to the Number of Absenteeism among Shift-Workers

Gupta and Ong (2004) defined a new generalization of the negative binomial distribution (GNBD) by mixing the mean of Poisson distribution with that of a generalized gamma distribution. The probability mass function of the new generalized negative binomial distribution, characterized by four parameters, is in terms of the confluent hyper geometric function of the second kind. The new distribution is fitted to a data set (from Arbous and Sichel (1954)) on absenteeism among shift-workers in a steel industry.

By using the SAS PROC NLMIXED, the ML estimates for the parameters of the QNBD are obtained and these are reported in Table 3. Since NBD is a special case of the QNBD, the estimates from the NBD are also reported in Table 3. The log-likelihood statistics for the NBD and the QNBD are respectively −794.00 and −793.68. In comparing the fit from NBD to the fit from QNBD, it appears there is no difference between the two fits. Furthermore, the estimate of parameter c with its standard error in the QNBD model shows that the parameter is not significantly different from zero. Thus, the QNBD model does not provide any improvement over the NBD. The results from the chi-square goodness of fit seem to suggest that the fit of the NBD is slightly better since the chi-square statistic is 15.97 compared to the 19.91 for QNBD. These chi-square values depend on how the adjacent classes are combined.

On fitting the QNBD, we compute the truncation error to see if this is negligible. The percentage truncation error is 2.366%, which is substantially larger than the 0.5% used in our error analysis. Based on this result, we fit the TQNBD to the data on number of absenteeism and the expected frequencies under the TQNBD are provided in Table 3. The final ML estimates from QNBD are used as the initial for the ML estimates of TQNBD. The log-likelihood for the TQNBD is −777.41, which is substantially smaller than the result from the QNBD. Based on the results in Table 3, the TQNBD model seems to provide better fit than the NBD and the QNBD models.

5. Conclusion

In this paper, we provide the region of the parameter space for which the percentage truncation error is below 0.5%. One needs to ensure that the number of non-zero probability classes is at least five (that is, $k \geq 4$). By using the parameter region specified in Table 2, one can determine if the estimated parameter values are in the region where the truncation error is negligible. For an observed data set, the observed value of k needs to be close to the integer part of $-1/\hat{c}$ in order for the percentage truncation error to be negligible. When $c < 0$, one can use the truncated QNBD. However, one should consider the non-truncated QNBD if the truncation error is negligible.

For the parameter estimates of QNBD in Table 3, the maximum percentage error of truncation is −0.2209%. This value is under the assumption that QNBD probabilities are computed for all integer values of $k \leq -1/\hat{c} \simeq 142$. However, the data get truncated well below 142. In view of this situation, the truncation error is no longer negligible and a TQNBD is considered.

By using the results in Li et al. (2008), the mean and variance of the QNBD in (1.1) are given by

$$\mu_* = E(X) = \sum_{i=0}^{\infty} (c/b)^i \Gamma(\alpha+i+1) / [b\Gamma(\alpha)], \qquad (4.1)$$

$$\sigma_*^2 = \sum_{i=0}^{\infty} \left(\frac{c}{b}\right)^i \frac{(i+1)(i+2)\Gamma(\alpha+i+1)}{b\Gamma(\alpha)} + \sum_{i=0}^{\infty} \left(\frac{c}{b}\right)^i \frac{(i+1)\Gamma(\alpha+i+2)}{b^2\Gamma(\alpha)} - \mu_*^2. \qquad (4.2)$$

From (4.1) and (4.2), the mean and variance do not exist when the parameter $c > 0$. The QNBD is truncated at a point k such that $1 + kc \geq 0$ when $c < 0$. When $c = 0$, QNBD reduces to the NBD and it is over-dispersed (i.e. the variance is greater than the mean). It is not easy to show if the QNBD has the property of both over-dispersion and under-dispersion. In the error analysis, we noticed that for some parameter values the mean is smaller than the variance and in others the mean is larger than the variance. Based on this, we conjecture that the QNBD has both under-dispersion and over-dispersion properties. Since the TQNBD is more difficult to estimate, one should apply the QNBD whenever the truncation error is negligible. A recommendation is to first fit the QNBD to an observed data set and check if the percentage truncation error is less than 0.5%. If not, consider fitting a TQNBD to the data set.

Acknowledgments

This work was done while Felix Famoye, Central Michigan University, was on sabbatical leave at the Department of Mathematics, University of Lagos, Nigeria. The author gratefully acknowledges the support received from the U.S. Department of State, Bureau of Education and Cultural Affairs under the grant #09-78737.

References

Arbous, A.G. & Sichel, H.S. (1954). New techniques for the analysis of absenteeism data. *Biometrika*, 41, 77-90.

Consul, P.C. & Shoukri, M.M. (1985). The generalized Poisson distribution when the sample mean is larger than the sample variance. *Communications in Statistics - Simulation and Computation*, 14(3), 667-681.

Gupta, R.C. & Ong, S.H. (2004). A new generalization of the negative binomial distribution. *Computational Statistics & Data Analysis*, 45, 287-300.

Li, S., Lee, C. & Famoye, F. (2008). On certain mixture distributions based on Lagrangian probability models. *Journal of Probability and Statistical Science*, 6(1), 91-100.

In: Applied Statistical Theory and Applications
Editor: Mohammad Ahsanullah

ISBN: 978-1-63321-858-1
© 2014 Nova Science Publishers, Inc.

Chapter 2

A New Family of Skew Slash Logistic Distributions

Bindu Punathumparambath and Sebastian George*
Department of Statistics, St. Thomas College, Pala, Kerala, India

Abstract

In this paper we present a new family of univariate slash distributions, which arises as the ratio of logistic distribution and independent uniform power function distribution. Slash logistic and skew Slash logistic distributions were derived and the properties were studied. Logistic and skew logistic distributions are special cases of this new family. These distributions provide us an alternative choices in simulation study and in particular, in fitting skewed data sets with heavy tails.

Keywords: Logistic distribution; slash distribution; skew logistic distribution; slash logistic distribution; slash skew logistic distribution

1. Introduction

Univariate skew-symmetric models have been considered by several authors. In the last two decades there has been substantial work in the area of skew-normal (SN) and related distributions (see, Azzalini (1985)). For a more detailed discussion refer to Azzalini (2005). The main feature of these models is that a new parameter λ is introduced to control skewness and kurtosis. Gupta et al. (2002) provided detailed discussion of skew-symmetric models based on the normal, Student t, Cauchy, Laplace, logistic and uniform distributions. Also similar constructions were developed by Balakrishnan and Ambagaspitiya (1994), Arnold and Beaver (2000), Branco & Dey (2001) and Jones & Faddy (2003). Symmetric distributions generalizing normality have got more attention in the statistical literature. One such extension is the class of standard slash distribution proposed by Kafadar (see, 1982 and 1988), which have heavier tails than normal distribution. Genton and Wang (2006) generalized the univariate slash normal of Kafadar to multivariate skew-slash and investigated its

---

*E-mail address: ppbindukannan@gmail.com

properties. They applied their skew-slash distributions to fit AIS and glass-fiber data. Tan and Feng (2005) introduced the multivariate slash student distributions and the skew-slash student distributions. Arslan and Genc (2009) introduced a generalization of the multivariate slash distribution. Recently Bindu (2011(a) and (b)) introduced a new family of skewed slash distributions generated by normal and Cauchy kernels. Also Bindu (2011(c)) investigated several properties of multivariate asymmetric slash Laplace distribution and Bindu (2011 (d)) introduced the multivariate skew-slash t and skew-slash Cauchy distributions.

The present paper introduces a new skewed family of distributions; skewed slash logistic distribution. This article is organized as follows. Section 2 gives the overview of the slash distribution. Section 3 defines the slash Logistic distribution and discuss various of its properties. In section 4, introduces the slash skew Logistic distribution and explore its properties. Finally, Section 5 discusses the possible applications of the model.

2. Overview of Slash Distribution

Kafadar (1988) proposed the univariate standard slash distribution as a heavy tailed alternative to the normal distribution. The standard slash distribution is obtained as the distribution of the ratio $X = \frac{Y}{U^{1/q}}$, where Y is a standard normal random variable, U is an independent uniform random variable over the interval (0,1) and $q > 0$. The probability density function (pdf) of the univariate standard slash distribution is symmetric about the origin and has heavier tails than those of the normal density. When $q = 1$ we obtain the canonical slash, which has the same tail heaviness as the Cauchy and for $q \rightarrow \infty$ yields the normal distribution. The probability density function (*pdf*) of the univariate slash distribution is given by

$$g(x;q) = \int_0^1 u^{1/q} \, f(xu^{1/q}) \, du \, , \; -\infty < x < \infty, \tag{2.1}$$

where $f(\cdot)$ is the standard normal *pdf*.
Then its *cdf* is

$$G(x;q) = \int_{-\infty}^x g(x;q) \, dx = \int_0^1 F(xu^{1/q}) \, du, \tag{2.2}$$

where $F(\cdot)$ denote the standard normal *cdf*. In terms of $v = u^{1/q}$ the *pdf* of standard slash distribution can be obtained as

$$h(x;q) = q \int_0^1 v^q \, f(xv) \, dv; -\infty < x < \infty. \tag{2.3}$$

In particular for $x = 0$ we have

$$h(0;q) = \frac{q}{(q+1)\sqrt{2\pi}}$$

The closed form expression for the *pdf* can computed for various values of q,

$$h(x,1) = \begin{cases} \frac{\phi(0)-\phi(x)}{x^2}; & x \neq 0 \\ \frac{\phi(0)}{2}; & x = 0 \end{cases}$$

$$h(x,2) = \begin{cases} \frac{2((\Phi(x)-\Phi(x))/x-\phi(x))}{x^2}; & x \neq 0 \\ \frac{2\phi(0)}{3}; & x = 0 \end{cases}$$

where $\phi(\cdot)$ and $\Phi(\cdot)$ denotes the standard normal *pdf* and *cdf* respectively.

The expectation and the variance of the standard slash distribution are given by

$$E(X) = 0, \ for \ q > 1,$$

$$Var(X) = q/(q-2), \ for \ q > 2.$$

A general slash distribution is obtained by scale multiplication and location shift of a standard slash random variable. That is, X has a general slash distribution with parameters μ, σ and q if,

$$X = \sigma \frac{Y}{U^{1/q}} + \mu,$$

Where Y is a standard normal random variable, U is an independent uniform random variable over the interval $(0, 1)$, $\mu \in \Re$, $\sigma > 0$ and $q > 0$.

General properties of this distribution are studied in Rogers and Tukey (1972) and in Mostelles and Tukey (1977). Maximum likelihood estimates (MLEs) of the related location-scale family are discussed in Kafadar (1982). Recently, Wang and Genton (2006) described multivariate and skew-multivariate extensions of the slash distribution.

3. Slash Logistic Distribution

The slash logistic distribution can be defined as the distribution of the ratio $X = \frac{Y}{U^{1/q}}$ where Y is a logistic random variable and U is an independent uniform random variable over (0,1) and $q > 0$. It is denoted by $X \sim SLO(\beta; q)$.

Definition 3.1. *A random variable X denoted by $X \sim SLO(\beta; q)$ is said to have a slash logistic distribution if its probability density function is*

$$h(x;\beta) = \frac{q}{\beta} \int_0^1 v^q \exp\left(\frac{-xv}{\beta}\right) \left\{1 + \exp\left(\frac{-xv}{\beta}\right)\right\}^{-2}, \ -\infty < x < \infty, \qquad (3.1)$$

where $\gamma > 0$, $\beta > 0$, $q > 0$ and $\lambda \in \mathbb{R}$.

The cdf is given by

$$H(x;q) = q \int_0^1 v^{q-1} \left\{1 + \exp\left(\frac{-xv}{\beta}\right)\right\}^{-1} dv. \qquad (3.2)$$

Figure (1) gives the probability density curves of the slash logistic distribution along with Logistic distribution.

We can see that the slash logistic density is symmetric, kurtosis and tail. Thus, (3.1) allows for a greater degree of flexibility and is useful in many more practical situations, such as in the modeling of detector relative efficiencies, extreme wind speeds, measurement errors, position errors in navigation, stock return, the Earths magnetic field and wind shear data.

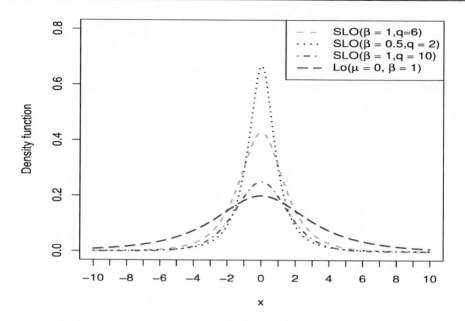

Figure 1. Slash logistic density functions for various values of parameters, along with logistic density.

Remark 3.1. *Note that the slash Logistic random variable in (3.1) is a scale mixture of the logistic random variable and so it can be represented as,*

$$\mathbf{X}|(U = u) \sim LO(0, u^{-1/q}\beta).$$

Remark 3.2. *If $X \sim SLO(0, 1; q)$ then its pdf $h(x; q)$ and cdf $H(x; q)$ has point mass at the origin. That is, when $x = 0$,*

$$h(0, q) = q \int_0^1 v^q\, f(0)\, dv = \frac{q}{4(q+1)},$$

and

$$H(0, q) = \frac{1}{4}.$$

Remark 3.3. *The limiting distribution of the standard slash logistic distribution $SLO(0, 1; q)$, $q \to \infty$, is the standard logistic distribution $LO(0, 1)$.*

    Proof. *If $X \sim CLO(0, 1; q)$ then consider the distribution function $H(x; q)$ given by (3.2).*

$$\lim_{q \to \infty} H(x; q) = \lim_{q \to \infty} \int_0^1 F(xu^{1/q})\, du = \int_0^1 F(x)\, du = F(x),$$

where $F(x)$ is the cdf of the standard logistic distribution. Hence as $q \to \infty$, the standard slash logistic yields the logistic density itself.

Remark 3.4. *If $X \sim SLO(0,1;q)$ with pdf $h(x;q)$ given by (3.1). Then $Y = |X|$, has the pdf $2\,h(y;q)\,I_{(y>0)}$.*

Proof.*If $Y = |X|$, the pdf of Y can be obtained as,*

$$f(y) = h(-y;q) + h(y;q) = 2\,h(y;q)\,I_{(y>0)},$$

which is the half slash logistic density.

4. Skew Slash Logistic Distribution

In this section we define the skewed generalization of the slash logistic distribution using the method of Azzalini (1985). A result which is central to the development of the skew-normal and related distribution appeared in Azzalini (1985), and we refer to Azzlini (2005) for a more general form, is given below.

Lemma 4.1. *Let X be a random variable with density function $f(y)$ symmetric about 0, and Z a random variable with absolutely continuous distribution function $G(y)$ such that $G'(y)$ is symmetric about 0, then for any $\lambda > 0$,*

$$h(y/\lambda) = 2f(y)G(\lambda y), \quad -\infty < y < \infty, \tag{4.1}$$

is a density function for any real λ.

For example, the skew normal distribution is obtained by taking $f \equiv \phi$ and $G \equiv \Phi$ in (4.1).

The random variable $X = \dfrac{Y}{U^{\frac{1}{q}}}$ is said to follow a skew-slash logistic distribution, if Y follow a skew-logistic distribution distribution and U is independent uniform distribution over the interval $(0,1)$. Then the probability density function of X is given by,

$$f(x;\lambda,\beta,q) = 2q \int_0^1 v^q \frac{\exp\left(\frac{-xv}{\beta}\right)}{\beta\left\{1+\exp\left(\frac{-xv}{\beta}\right)\right\}^2\left\{1+\exp\left(\frac{-\lambda xv}{\beta}\right)\right\}} dv, x \in \mathbb{R}, \tag{4.2}$$

where $\lambda \in \mathbb{R}$, $\beta > 0$ and $q > 0$.

Figure (2) gives the probability density curves of the skew-slash logistic distribution along with Laplace distribution.

We can see that the skew-slash logistic density is symmetric, negatively skewed and positively skewed for $\lambda = 0$, $\lambda < 0$ and $\lambda > 0$ respectively. The main feature of the skew-slash logistic distribution in (4.2) is that the parameters λ and q control skewness , kurtosis and tail. Thus (4.2) allows for a greater degree of flexibility and is useful in many more practical situations, such as in the modeling of detector relative efficiencies, extreme wind speeds, measurement errors, position errors in navigation, stock return, the Earths magnetic field and wind shear data.

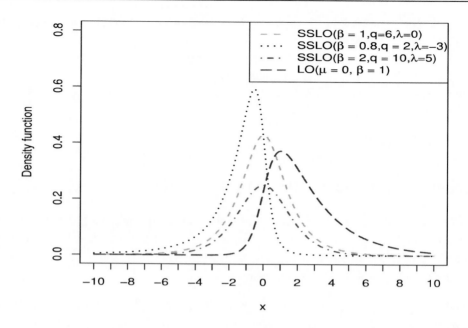

Figure 2. Skew slash logistic density functions for various values of parameters, along with logistic density.

4.1. Properties

The following properties of the probability density function (4.2) hold. For most of them the proof is immediate.

(i) If X has the skew-slash logistic distribution with skew parameter λ. Then for $\lambda = 0$, X has the slash logistic distribution.

(ii) If X has a skew-slash logistic distribution with skew parameter λ, then $-X$ also has a skew slash logistic distribution with skewness parameter $-\lambda$.

(iii) If $Y_\lambda(y)$ and $Y_0(y)$ are respectively the skew-slash logistic distribution with skewness parameter λ and the slash logistic random variables. Then

$$|Y_\lambda(y)| \to |Y_0(y)| \ as \ \lambda \to \infty.$$

That is, when $\lambda \to \infty$ the half skew-slash logistic distribution tends to half slash logistic distribution. This result implies that all even moments of $Y_\lambda(x)$ and $Y_0(x)$ are the same. This property is referred to as Perturbation invariance.

(iv) If Y_λ follows a skew-slash logistic distribution and Y is slash logistic distribution. Then for any even function h, $h(Y_\lambda) \overset{d}{=} h(Y)$, since from [p3.] we have $|Y_\lambda| \overset{d}{=} |Y|$. Also

$$Y_\lambda^2 \overset{d}{=} Y^2.$$

5. Discussion

The skew slash logistic distributions is a family of slash distributions. The logistic distribution belongs to this family, since when the skewness parameter is zero and tail parameter tends to infinity the skew slash logistic distributions reduces to the Logistic distribution. The slash Logistic family is also belongs to this family when the skewness parameter is zero. This new family of distributions has wide flexibility in tail behavior and peakedness and can be applied to data from different contexts especially for heavy-tailed data sets. Heavy-tailed distributions are commonly found in complex multi-component systems like ecological systems, biometry, economics, sociology, internet traffic, finance, business etc. Finally, skew-slash logistic distribution could be employed to deal with skewed data, heavy-tailed data and data which are both skewed and heavy-tailed.

Acknowledgment

The first author is grateful to the Department of Science & Technology, Government of India, New Delhi, for financial support under the Women Scientist Scheme (WOS-A (2008)), Project No: SR/WOS-A/MS-09/2008. The authors are very thankful to the referees and the editor of the journal for their valuable suggestions and comments.

References

[1] Arnold, B. C. and Beaver, R. J. (2000). The skew-Cauchy distribution. *Statist. Probab. Lett.* 49, 285-290.

[2] Arslan, O. and Genc, A. I. (2009). A generalization of the multivariate slash distribution. *Journal of Statistical Planning and Inference* 78, 1164-1170.

[3] Azzalini, A. (1985). A class of distributions which includes the normal ones. *Scand. J. Statist.* 12, 171-178.

[4] Azzalini, A. (2005).The Skew-normal Distribution and Related Multivariate Families. *Scand. J. Statist.* 32, 159-188.

[5] Balakrishnan, N. and Ambagaspitiya, R. S. (1994). *On skew-Laplace distributions.* Technical Report, Department of Mathematics and Statistics, McMaster University, Hamilton, Ontario, Canada.

[6] Bindu, P. P. (2011(a)). A new family of skewed slash distributions generated by the normal kernel. *STATISTICA* (to appear).

[7] Bindu, P. P. (2011(b)). A new family of skewed slash distributions generated by the cauchy kernel. *Communications in Statistics- Theory and Methods* (in press).

[8] Bindu, P. P. (2011(c)). The multivariate asymmetric slash Laplace distribution and its applications. *STATISTICA* (accepted for publication).

[9] Bindu, P. P. (2011 (d)). The multivariate skew-slash t and skew-slash Cauchy distributions. *Model Assisted Statistics and Applications* 6, 18.

[10] Branco, M. D. and Dey, D. K. (2001). A general class of multivariate skew- elliptical distributions. *J. Multivariate Anal.* 79, 99-113.

[11] Gupta, A. K., Chang, F. C., Huang, W. J. (2002). Some skew-symmetric models. *Random Operators and Stochastic Equations.* 10, 133140.

[12] Jones, M.C., Faddy, M.J. (2003).A skew extension of the t distribution, with applications. *J. Roy. Statist. Soc. Series B*, 65, 159-174.

[13] Kafadar, K. (1982). A biweight approach to the one-sample problem. *J. Amer. Statist. Assoc.* 77, 416-424.

[14] Kafadar, K. (1998). Slash Distribution. *Encyc. Statist. Sciences* 8.

[15] Rogers, W.H., Tukey, J.W. (1972). Understanding some long-tailed symmetrical distributions. *Statist. Neerlandica* 26, 211-226.

[16] Tan, F., Peng, H. (2005). The slash and skew-slash student t distribution. Pre-print.

[17] Wang, J., Genton, M. G. (2006). The multivariate skew-slash distribution. *Journal of Statistical Planning and Inference* 136, 209-220.

In: Applied Statistical Theory and Applications
Editor: Mohammad Ahsanullah

ISBN: 978-1-63321-858-1
© 2014 Nova Science Publishers, Inc.

Chapter 3

ON THE MOMENTS OF SAMPLE COVARIANCE FROM A BIVARIATE NORMAL POPULATION

Anwar H. Joarder[1] and M. Hafidz Omar[2]
Department of Mathematics and Statistics
King Fahd University of Petroleum and Minerals
Dhahran, Saudi Arabia

Abstract

The distribution of the sample covariance based on a sample from a bivariate normal population has been derived in the literature by many authors. Some used conditionality principle, some used inverse Mellin transform and some used simple transformations. The main contribution of the paper is the direct derivation of the general moment structure of sample covariance via a lemma dealing with a infinite sum of product of two gamma functions. Integer valued moments of any order are also derived in terms of hypergeometric function. Some corollaries have been deduced which have potential for further use in mathematics and statistics. The probability density function, skewness and kurtosis have been graphed.

AMS Mathematics Subject Classification: 60E05, 60E10, 62E15

Keywords and Phrases: Sample covariance, Wishart distribution, Macdonald function, hypergeometric function

1. Introduction

Let a_{11} and a_{22} be the mean centered sum of squares, and a_{12}, the mean centered sum of products for samples of size $N \, (> 2)$ drawn from a bivariate normal distribution with means

---

[1] E-mail address: anwarj@kfupm.edu.sa
[2] E-mail address: omarmh@kfupm.edu.sa

θ_1 and θ_2, variances σ_1^2 and σ_2^2, and covariance $\sigma_{12} = \rho\sigma_1\sigma_2$. Then $a_{ii} = ms_i^2$, $a_{12} = mrs_1s_2$, $m = N-1, (i = 1,2)$, s_1^2 and s_2^2 are sample variances and r is the product moment correlation coefficient. The joint density function of mean centered sum of squares and sum of products at a_{11} and a_{22} a_{12}, originally due to Fisher (1915), is given by

$$f(a_{11}, a_{22}, a_{12}) = \frac{(1-\rho^2)^{-m/2}(\sigma_1\sigma_2)^{-m}}{2^m\sqrt{\pi}\Gamma(m/2)\Gamma((m-1)/2)} \left(a_{11}a_{22} - a_{12}^2\right)^{(m-3)/2}$$

$$\times \exp\left(-\frac{a_{11}}{2(1-\rho^2)\sigma_1^2} - \frac{a_{22}}{2(1-\rho^2)\sigma_2^2} + \frac{\rho a_{12}}{(1-\rho^2)\sigma_1\sigma_2}\right),$$

(1.1)

$a_{11} > 0$, $a_{22} > 0$, $-\infty < a_{12} < \infty$, $m > 2$ and $-1 < \rho < 1$ (Anderson, 2003, 123).

Because of the importance of Wishart distribution in multivariate statistical analysis, various authors have given different derivations. See Gupta and Nagar (2000, 87-88) and the references therein for a good update on the Wishart distribution.

The distribution of the sample covariance based on a sample from a bivariate normal population has been known. Pearson, Jeffery, and Elderton (1929) used simple transformation on the distribution of sample variances and covariance. Wishart and Bartlett (1932) also studied the distribution of covariance by inverting the characteristic function of sample variances and covariance. Mahalanobis, Bose and Roy (1937) reviewed the distribution of the generalized variance (determinant of variance covariance matrix) due to Wilks (1932), distribution of the ratio of correlated standard deviations due to Bose (1935), the distribution of sample covariance due to Pearson, Jeffery, and Elderton (1929) and many other aspects of the distribution of sample variances and correlation coefficient. Springer, (1979, 343) derived the distribution of sample covariance by inverse Mellin transform.

We sketch the derivation of the density function of sample covariance by making simple transformations on the distribution of sample variances and covariance as was done by Pearson, Jeffery, and Elderton (1929) just to make the paper self-contained for today's readers. Standard notations have been used throughout the paper. The main contribution of the paper is the derivation of general moments of the distribution with the help of a lemma that involves infinite sum of a product of gamma functions. Integer valued moments of sample covariance of any order have been derived in terms of hypergeometric function. A number of corollaries have been deduced which has potential for applications in mathematics and statistics. The probability density function, the coefficient of skewness and coefficient of kurtosis have been graphed.

The following results will be used in sequel:

$$(2z)!\sqrt{\pi} = 2^{2z}z!\Gamma(z + \tfrac{1}{2}).$$

(1.2)

The modified Bessel function of the second kind or the Macdonald function admits the following integral representation (Watson, 1993, 183):

$$K_\alpha(y) = \tfrac{1}{2}(\tfrac{1}{2}y)^\alpha \int_0^\infty t^{-(\alpha+1)} \exp\left(-t - \frac{y^2}{4t}\right) dt. \tag{1.3}$$

The hypergeometric function $_pF_q(a_1, a_2, \cdots, a_p; b_1, b_2, \cdots, b_q; z)$ is defined by

$$_pF_q(a_1, a_2, \cdots, a_p; b_1, b_2, \cdots, b_q; z) = \sum_{k=0}^\infty \frac{(a_1)_{\{k\}}(a_2)_{\{k\}}\cdots(a_p)_{\{k\}}}{(b_1)_{\{k\}}(b_2)_{\{k\}}\cdots(b_p)_{\{k\}}} \frac{z^k}{k!}, \tag{1.4}$$

where $a_{\{k\}} = a(a+1)\cdots(a+k-1)$.

2. Distribution of the Sample Covariance

In this section, we derive the distribution of sample covariance $W = (a_{12}/m)$ by integrating out a_{11} and a_{22} from the density function (1.1) as was done by Pearson, Jeffery and Elderton (1929).

Theorem 2.1. Let $w = a_{12}/m$, be the sample covariance based on a sample from a bivariate normal distribution. Then the density function of W is given by

$$f_1(w) = \frac{(m/\sigma_1\sigma_2)^{(m+1)/2}}{2^{(m-1)/2}\sqrt{\pi(1-\rho^2)}\Gamma(m/2)} |w|^{(m-1)/2} \exp\left(\frac{\rho m w}{(1-\rho^2)\sigma_1\sigma_2}\right) K_{(m-1)/2}\left(\frac{m|w|}{(1-\rho^2)\sigma_1\sigma_2}\right), \tag{2.1}$$

where $\sigma_1 > 0, \sigma_2 > 0, -1 < \rho < 1,\ m > 2$ and $K_\alpha(x)$ is the modified Bessel function of the second kind represented by (1.3).

Proof. It follows from (1.1) that the density function of $a_{12} = Z$ is given by

$$f_2(z) = \frac{(1-\rho^2)^{-m/2}(\sigma_1\sigma_2)^{-m}}{2^m\sqrt{\pi}\Gamma\left(\dfrac{m}{2}\right)\Gamma\left(\dfrac{m-1}{2}\right)} \exp\left(\frac{\rho z}{(1-\rho^2)\sigma_1\sigma_2}\right) I(m,\rho), \tag{2.2}$$

where $I(m,\rho) = \iint\limits_{z^2 \le xy} \left(xy - z^2\right)^{(m-3)/2} \exp\left(-\frac{x}{2(1-\rho^2)\sigma_1^2} - \frac{y}{2(1-\rho^2)\sigma_2^2}\right) dydx$.

Letting $xy - z^2 = u$, i.e., $y = (z^2 + u)/x$ with Jacobian $J(y \to u) = 1/x$, we have

$$I(m,\rho) = \int\limits_{x=0}^{\infty} \int\limits_{u=0}^{\infty} u^{(m-3)/2} \exp\left(-\frac{x}{2(1-\rho^2)\sigma_1^2} - \frac{z^2+u}{2(1-\rho^2)\sigma_2^2 x}\right)\frac{1}{x}\,du\,dx.$$

Completing the integral in u and substituting $[2(1-\rho^2)\sigma_1^2]^{-1}x = t$ in the resulting integral, we have

$$I(m,\rho) = \Gamma\left(\frac{m-1}{2}\right)[2(1-\rho^2)\sigma_1\sigma_2]^{m-1} \int\limits_{t=0}^{\infty} t^{(m-3)/2} \exp\left(-t - \frac{z^2}{4(1-\rho^2)^2\sigma_1^2\sigma_2^2 t}\right)dt.$$

Putting $-(\alpha+1) = (m-3)/2$ and $y^2 = [(1-\rho^2)\sigma_1\sigma_2]^{-2}z^2$, in the Bessel function of the second kind given by (1.3), and using the property $K_{-\alpha}(z) = K_\alpha(z)$, we have

$$I(m,\rho) = 2^{(m+1)/2}\Gamma\left(\frac{m-1}{2}\right)[(1-\rho^2)\sigma_1\sigma_2]^{(m-1)/2} \times |z|^{(m-1)/2} K_{(m-1)/2}\left(\frac{|z|}{(1-\rho^2)\sigma_1\sigma_2}\right). \quad (2.3).$$

By using (2.3) in (2.2) and performing a bit of simplification, we have (2.1).
The probability density function in (2.1) has been graphed in Figure 1 below:

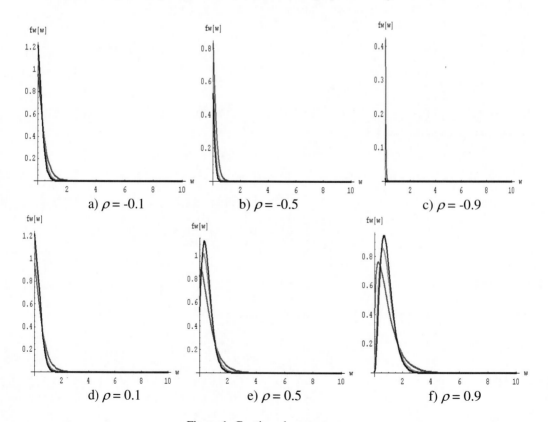

Figure 1. Continued on next page.

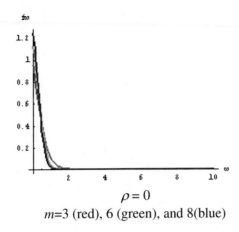

$$\rho = 0$$

$m=3$ (red), 6 (green), and 8(blue)

Figure 1. Density function for the sample covariance at various values of ρ and m.

The density function of $\Upsilon = m[(1-\rho^2)\sigma_1\sigma_2]^{-1}W$ at υ is given by

$$f_2(\upsilon) = \frac{(1-\rho^2)^{m/2}}{2^{(m-1)/2}\sqrt{\pi}\Gamma(m/2)}|\upsilon|^{(m-1)/2} e^{\rho} K_{(m-1)/2}(|\upsilon|),$$

which was obtained by Springer (1979, 343) by inverse Mellin transform. Some interesting forms of the density function of sample covariance are pointed by Press (1967).

3. Moments of the Sample Covariance

The higher order moments of the sample covariance $W = S_1 S_2 R$ can be calculated directly from the density function derived in Theorem 2.1. In this section we will derive them from (1.1). Since the moments of sample covariance involves infinite sum of product of gamma functions, we have the following lemma to have closed form expressions.

Lemma 3.1. Let $-1 < \rho < 1$, $m > 2$, and c and d are real numbers. Also let

$$g(k;c,d) = \frac{(2\rho)^k}{k!}\Gamma\left(\frac{k+m+2h+c}{2}\right)\Gamma\left(\frac{k+2h+d}{2}\right).$$

Then

a. $\sum_{j=0}^{\infty} g(2j;c,d) = \Gamma\left(h+\frac{m+c}{2}\right)\Gamma\left(h+\frac{d}{2}\right){}_2F_1\left(h+\frac{m+c}{2}, h+\frac{d}{2};\frac{1}{2};\rho^2\right),$

$$2h+m+c \geq 0,$$

b. $\sum_{j=0}^{\infty} g(2j+1;c,d) = 2\rho\Gamma\left(h+\dfrac{m+c+1}{2}\right)\Gamma\left(h+\dfrac{d+1}{2}\right){}_2F_1\left(h+\dfrac{m+c+1}{2},h+\dfrac{d+1}{2};\dfrac{3}{2}\right),$

$$2h+m+c+1\geq 0, \ \ 2h+d+1\geq 0.$$

Proof. By using (1.2) in $g(k;c,d)$, we have

$$\sum_{j=0}^{\infty} g(2j;c,d) = \sum_{j=0}^{\infty} \frac{\sqrt{\pi}\rho^{2j}}{j!\,\Gamma\left(j+(1/2)\right)}\Gamma\left(j+h+\frac{m+c}{2}\right)\Gamma\left(j+h+\frac{d}{2}\right)$$

which can be expressed as what we have in part (a) by virtue of (1.4). By using (1.2) in $g(k;c,d)$, we have

$$\sum_{j=0}^{\infty} g(2j+1;c,d) = \sum_{j=0}^{\infty} \frac{\sqrt{\pi}\rho^{2j+1}}{j!\,\Gamma\left(j+(3/2)\right)}\Gamma\left(j+h+\frac{m+c+1}{2}\right)\Gamma\left(j+h+\frac{d+1}{2}\right),$$

which can be written as part (b) by virtue of (1.4).

Theorem 3.1. Let W be the sample covariance based on a bivariate normal distribution. Then, for any real number h, the h-th moment of W is given by

$$E(W^h) = \frac{2^{h-1}(1-\rho^2)^{h+(m/2)}(\sigma_1\sigma_2)^h}{m^h\Gamma(m/2)\sqrt{\pi}} \sum_{k=0}^{\infty}\{1+(-1)^{k+h}\}\frac{(2\rho)^k}{k!}\Gamma\left(\frac{k+m+h}{2}\right)\Gamma\left(\frac{k+1+h}{2}\right),$$

where $\sigma_1 > 0$, $\sigma_2 > 0$, $-1 < \rho < 1$ and $m > 2$.

Proof. Under the transformation $a_{11} = ms_1^2, a_{22} = ms_2^2, a_{12} = mrs_1s_2$ in (1.1) with Jacobian $4m^3s_1^2s_2^2$, the joint density function of the sample standard deviations (S_1,S_2) and correlation coefficient R is given by

$$f_2(s_1,s_2,r) = \frac{m^m\left(1-\rho^2\right)^{-m/2}(\sigma_1\sigma_2)^{-m}}{\pi\,\Gamma(m-1)}\exp\left(-\frac{m}{2-2\rho^2}\left(\frac{s_1^2}{\sigma_1^2}+\frac{s_2^2}{\sigma_2^2}\right)\right) \quad (3.1)$$

$$\times\sum_{k=0}^{\infty}\frac{(m\rho)^k(s_1s_2)^{m-1+k}}{(1-\rho^2)^k(\sigma_1\sigma_2)^k k!}r^k\left(1-r^2\right)^{(m-3)/2}.$$

Since $W = S_1S_2R$, the h-th moment of W is given by $E(W^h) = E(S_1^h S_2^h R^h)$ which is (h,h,h)-th moment of the joint density function of S_1, S_2 and R. Hence, we have

$$E(W^h) = \frac{m^m (1-\rho^2)^{-m/2} (\sigma_1 \sigma_2)^{-m}}{\pi\, \Gamma(m-1)} \sum_{k=0}^{\infty} \frac{(m\rho)^k}{(1-\rho^2)^k (\sigma_1 \sigma_2)^k\, k!}$$

$$\times \int_0^{\infty} s_1^{(m+k+h)/2} \exp\left(\frac{-ms_1^2}{(2-2\rho^2)\sigma_1^2}\right) ds_1^2 \int_0^{\infty} s_2^{(m+k+h)/2} \exp\left(-\frac{1}{2}\frac{ms_2^2}{(1-\rho^2)\sigma_2^2}\right) ds_2^2$$

$$\times \{1+(-1)^{k+h}\} \int_0^1 u^{(k+h-1)/2} (1-u)^{(m-3)/2} \frac{1}{2}\, du.$$

Having evaluated the gamma and beta integrals, we have the theorem.

Theorem 3.2. Let W, be the sample covariance based on a sample from a bivariate normal distribution. Then for any real number h, the $(2h)$-**th** moment of W is given by

$$E(W^{2h}) = \frac{2^{2h-1}(1-\rho^2)^{2h+(m/2)}}{m^{2h}\Gamma(m/2)\sqrt{\pi}} (\sigma_1\sigma_2)^{2h}$$

$$\times \left[\{1+(-1)^{2h}\}\Gamma\left(h+\frac{m}{2}\right)\Gamma\left(h+\frac{1}{2}\right) {}_2F_1\left(h+\frac{m}{2}, h+\frac{1}{2}; \frac{1}{2}; \rho^2\right) \right. \tag{3.2}$$

$$\left. + 2\{1-(-1)^{2h}\}\rho\Gamma\left(h+\frac{m+1}{2}\right)\Gamma(h+1)\, {}_2F_1\left(h+\frac{m+1}{2}, h+1; \frac{3}{2}; \rho^2\right) \right],$$

where $\sigma_1 > 0, \sigma_2 > 0, -1 < \rho < 1,\ m > 2$ and ${}_pF_q(a_1, a_2; b_1; z)$ is the generalized hypergeometric function defined by (1.4).

Proof. From Theorem 3.1, we have

$$E(W^{2h}) = \frac{2^{2h-1}(1-\rho^2)^{2h+(m/2)}}{m^{2h}\Gamma(m/2)\sqrt{\pi}} (\sigma_1\sigma_2)^{2h} \sum_{k=0}^{\infty} \{1+(-1)^{2h}(-1)^k\} g(k; 0, 0)$$

where $g(k; 0, 0)$ is defined in Lemma 3.1. Note that

$$\sum_{k=0}^{\infty} \{1+(-1)^{2h}(-1)^k\} g(k; 0, 1) = \{1+(-1)^{2h}\}\sum_{j=0}^{\infty} g(2j; 0, 1) + \{1-(-1)^{2h}\}\sum_{j=0}^{\infty} g(2j+1; 0, 1).$$

Since

$$E(W^{2h}) = \frac{2^{2h-1}(1-\rho^2)^{2h+(m/2)}}{m^{2h}\Gamma(m/2)\sqrt{\pi}} (\sigma_1\sigma_2)^{2h} \left[\{1+(-1)^{2h}\}\sum_{j=0}^{\infty} g(2j; 0, 1) + \{1-(-1)^{2h}\}\sum_{j=0}^{\infty} g(2j+1; 0, 1) \right],$$

the proof is complete by using Lemma 3.1.

Corollary 3.1. Let W be the sample covariance based on a sample from a bivariate normal distribution, and h be an integer. Then the $2h$-th moment of sample covariance is given by

$$E(W^{2h}) = \frac{(1-\rho^2)^{(m+4h)/2}}{\Gamma(m/2)\sqrt{\pi}} \left(\frac{2\sigma_1\sigma_2}{m}\right)^{2h} \Gamma\left(\frac{m}{2}+h\right)\Gamma\left(\frac{1}{2}+h\right){}_2F_1\left(\frac{1}{2}+h,\frac{m+2h}{2};\frac{1}{2};\rho^2\right), \quad (3.3)$$

where $\sigma_1 > 0, \sigma_2 > 0, -1 < \rho < 1, \ m > 2$.

Proof. If h is an integer in (3.2), then $1+(-1)^{2h} = 2$, and $1-(-1)^{2h} = 0$. Then the corollary follows from Theorem 3.2.

Theorem 3.3. Let W, be the sample covariance based on a sample from a bivariate normal distribution. Then for any real number h, the $(2h+1)$-th moment of W is given by

$$\begin{aligned}
E(W^{2h+1}) = &\frac{2^{2h}(1-\rho^2)^{(2h+1)+(m/2)}}{\Gamma(m/2)\sqrt{\pi}} \left(\frac{\sigma_1\sigma_2}{m}\right)^{2h+1} \\
&\times \left[\{1-(-1)^{2h}\}h\Gamma\left(h+\frac{m+1}{2}\right)\Gamma(h){}_2F_1\left(h+\frac{m+1}{2},h+1;\frac{1}{2};\rho^2\right) \right. \\
&\left. +2\{1+(-1)^{2h}\}\rho\Gamma\left(h+\frac{m+2}{2}\right)\Gamma\left(h+\frac{3}{2}\right){}_2F_1\left(h+\frac{m+2}{2},h+\frac{3}{2};\frac{1}{2};\rho^2\right)\right],
\end{aligned} \quad (3.4)$$

where $\sigma_1 > 0, \ \sigma_2 > 0, \ -1 < \rho < 1$ and $m > 2$.

Proof. From Theorem 3.1, we have

$$E(W^{2h+1}) = \frac{2^{2h}(1-\rho^2)^{(2h+1)+(m/2)}}{m^{2h+1}\Gamma(m/2)\sqrt{\pi}} (\sigma_1\sigma_2)^{2h+1} \sum_{k=0}^{\infty} \{1+(-1)^k(-1)^{2h+1}\}\frac{(2\rho)^k}{k!}g(k;1,2)$$

where $g(k;1,2)$ is given by Lemma 3.1. Since

$$\sum_{k=0}^{\infty}\{1+(-1)^k(-1)^{2h+1}\}g(k;1,2) = \{1-(-1)^{2h}\}\sum_{j=0}^{\infty}g(2j;1,2)+\{1+(-1)^{2h}\}\sum_{j=0}^{\infty}g(2j+1;1,2),$$

we have

$$\begin{aligned}
E(W^{2h+1}) = &\frac{2^{2h}(1-\rho^2)^{(2h+1)+(m/2)}}{\Gamma(m/2)\sqrt{\pi}} \left(\frac{\sigma_1\sigma_2}{m}\right)^{2h+1} \\
&\times \left[[1+(-1)^{2h}]\sum_{j=0}^{\infty}g(2j;1,2)+[1-(-1)^{2h}]\sum_{j=0}^{\infty}g(2j+1;1,2)\right],
\end{aligned}$$

the proof is then complete by Lemma 3.1.

Corollary 3.2. Let W be the sample covariance based on a sample from a bivariate normal distribution. Then for any integer h, the $(2h+1)$-th moment of sample covariance is given by

$$E(W^{2h+1}) = \frac{\rho(1-\rho^2)^{(2h+1)+(m/2)}}{\Gamma(m/2)\sqrt{\pi}} \left(\frac{2\sigma_1\sigma_2}{m}\right)^{2h+1}$$
$$\times \Gamma\left(h+\frac{m+2}{2}\right)(2h+1)\Gamma\left(h+\frac{1}{2}\right){}_2F_1\left(h+\frac{m+2}{2}, h+\frac{3}{2}; \frac{1}{2}; \rho^2\right)\Bigg],$$

(3.5)

where $\sigma_1 > 0$, $\sigma_2 > 0$, $-1 < \rho < 1$ and $m > 2$.

Proof. If h is an integer in (3.4), then $1+(-1)^{2h} = 2$, and $1-(-1)^{2h} = 0$. Then the corollary follows from Theorem 3.3.

Corollary 3.3. Let h be an integer, $m > 2$ and $-1 < \rho < 1$. Then we have the following integrals:

a. $\displaystyle\int_{-\infty}^{\infty} w^{2h} \, |w|^{(m-1)/2} \, \exp\left(\frac{\rho m w}{(1-\rho^2)\sigma_1\sigma_2}\right) K_{(m-1)/2}\left(\frac{m|w|}{(1-\rho^2)\sigma_1\sigma_2}\right) dw$

$$= \frac{2^{2h+(m-1)/2}(1-\rho^2)^{(m+4h+1)/2}}{m^{2h+(m+1)/2}(\sigma_1\sigma_2)^{2h-(m+1)/2}}\Gamma\left(\frac{m}{2}+h\right)\Gamma\left(\frac{1}{2}+h\right){}_2F_1\left(\frac{1}{2}+h, \frac{m+2h}{2}; \frac{1}{2}; \rho^2\right),$$

(3.6)

b. $\displaystyle\int_{-\infty}^{\infty} w^{2h+1} \, |w|^{(m-1)/2} \, \exp\left(\frac{\rho m w}{(1-\rho^2)\sigma_1\sigma_2}\right) K_{(m-1)/2}\left(\frac{m|w|}{(1-\rho^2)\sigma_1\sigma_2}\right) dw$

$$= \frac{2^{2h+(m+1)/2}\rho\{(1-\rho^2)\sigma_1\sigma_2\}^{2h+(m+3)/2}}{m^{2h+(1-m)/2}}$$
$$\times \Gamma\left(h+\frac{m+2}{2}\right)(2h+1)\Gamma\left(h+\frac{1}{2}\right){}_2F_1\left(h+\frac{m+2}{2}, h+\frac{3}{2}; \frac{1}{2}; \rho^2\right)\Bigg].$$

(3.7)

Proof. Part (a) follows from Corollary 3.1. Part (b) follows from Corollary 3.2.

A more general integral can be derived from Theorem 3.1 for any real h.

Corollary 3.4. Let W be the sample covariance based on a sample from a bivariate normal distribution. Then first four moments of sample covariance are given below:

a. $E(W) = \rho\sigma_1\sigma_2$,

b. $E(W^2) = \dfrac{1}{m}[(m+1)\rho^2 + 1]\sigma_1^2\sigma_2^2$,

c. $E(W^3) = \dfrac{(m+2)\rho}{m^2}[(m+1)\rho^2 + 3]\sigma_1^3\sigma_2^3,$

d. $E(W^4) = \dfrac{(m+2)}{m^3}[(m+1)(m+3)\rho^4 + 6(m+3)\rho^2 + 3]\sigma_1^4\sigma_2^4,$

where $\sigma_1 > 0, \sigma_2 > 0, -1 < \rho < 1$, and $m > 2$.

The centered moments of sample covariance of order a is given by $\mu_a = E(W - \mu)^a$, $a = 1, 2, \cdots$, that is the second, third and fourth order mean corrected moments are given by $\mu_2 = E(W^2) - \mu^2$, $\mu_3 = E(W^3) - 3E(W^2)\mu + 2\mu^3$, and $\mu_4 = E(W^4) - 4E(W^3)\mu + 6E(W^2)\mu^2 - 3\mu^4$.

Corollary 3.5. The first three non-zero centered moments of sample covariance based on bivariate normal distribution are given by

a. $\mu_2 = \dfrac{1}{m}(1 + \rho^2)\sigma_1^2\sigma_2^2,$

b. $\mu_3 = \dfrac{2}{m^2}\rho(3 + \rho^2)\sigma_1^3\sigma_2^3,$

c. $\mu_4 = \dfrac{3}{m^3}[(m+2)\rho^4 + (2m+12)\rho^2 + (m+2)]\sigma_1^4\sigma_2^4,$

where $\sigma_1 > 0$, $\sigma_2 > 0$, $-1 < \rho < 1$ and $m > 2$ which matches with (32.126b) of Johnson, Balakrishnan and Johnson (1995, 601).

The skewness and kurtosis are given by the moment ratios $\alpha_i(W) = \mu_i \mu_2^{-i/2}$, $i = 3, 4$. That is, they are given by

$$\alpha_3(W) = \dfrac{2\rho(3 + \rho^2)}{\sqrt{m}\,(1 + \rho^2)^{3/2}}\ , \text{ and } \alpha_4(W) = 3 + \dfrac{6(1 + 6\rho^2 + \rho^4)}{m(1 + \rho^2)^2}\ \text{ respectively.}$$

Note that the moment ratios match with Johnson, Kotz and Balakrishnan (1995, 601).

If $\rho = 0$, then $\alpha_3(W) = 0$ and $\alpha_4(W) = 3$. Moreover if $m \to \infty$, then $\alpha_3(W) = 0$ and $\alpha_4(W) = 3$.

The graph of skewness as a function of ρ at different values of m is produced in Figure 2 below.

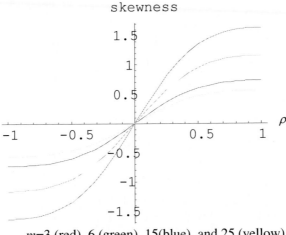

skewness

m=3 (red), 6 (green), 15(blue), and 25 (yellow)

Figure 2. Coefficient of Skewness for different ρ and m.

The graph of kurtosis as a function of ρ at different values of m is produced in Figure 3 below.

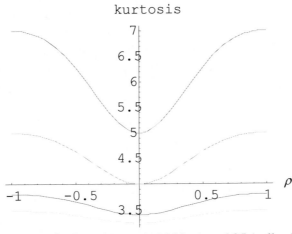

kurtosis

$m = 3$ (red), 6 (green), 15(blue), and 25 (yellow)

Figure 3. Coefficient of Kurtosis for different ρ and m.

4. Conclusion

In this paper we have derived closed form expressions of integer valued moments of higher order. This may lead to further investigation in statistical inference.

Acknowledgments

The authors gratefully acknowledge the research support provided by King Fahd University of Petroleum & Minerals, Saudi Arabia.

References

Anderson, T.W. (2003). An *Introduction to Multivariate Statistical Analysis*. John Wiley and Sons. New York.

Fisher, R.A. (1915). Frequency distribution of the values of the correlation coefficient in samples from an indefinitely large population. *Biometrika*, 10, 507-521.

Gupta, A.K. and Nagar, D.K. (2000). *Matrix Variate Distributions*. Chapman and hall, London, UK.

Bose, S.S. (1935). On the distribution of the ratio of variances of two samples drawn from a given normal bivariate correlated population. Sankhya, 2, 65-72.

Johnson, N.L., Kotz, S. and Balakrishnan, N. (1995). *Continuous Univariate Distributions*, v2. John Wiley.

Mahalanobis, P.C., Bose, R.C. and Roy, S.N. (1937). Normalization of statistical variates and the use of rectangular coordinates in the use of sampling distributions. *Sankhya*, 3, 1-40.

Pearson, K., Jeffery, G.B. and Elderton, E.M. (1929). On the distribution of the first product moment-coefficient in samples drawn from an indefinitely large normal population. *Biometrika*, 21, 164-193. (tables computed by E.M. Elderton, pp 194-201).

Press, S.J. (1967). On the sample covariance from a bivariate normal distribution. *Annals of the Institute of Statistical Mathematics,* 19, 355-361.

Springer, M.D. (1979). *The Algebra of Random Variables*. John Wiley and Sons.

Watson, G.N. (1993). *A Treatise on the Theory of Bessel Functions.* Cambridge University Press.

Wilks, S.S. (1932). Certain generalizations in the Analysis of variance. *Biometrika*, 24, 476-477.

Wishart, J. and Bartlett, M.S. (1932). The distribution of second order moment statistics in a normal system. *Proceedings of the Cambridge Philosophical Society*, 28, 455-459.

In: Applied Statistical Theory and Applications
Editor: Mohammad Ahsanullah

ISBN: 978-1-63321-858-1
© 2014 Nova Science Publishers, Inc.

Chapter 4

BAYESIAN IDENTIFICATION OF TWO DIMENSIONAL MOVING AVERAGE PROCESSES

Samir M. Shaarawy[1,*], *Mohammad S. Albassam*[2] *and Sherif S. Ali*[2,†]

[1]Department of Mathematical Sciences,
Umm Al-Qura University, Makkah, Saudi Arabia
[2]Department of Statistics, King Abdulaziz University,
Jeddah, Saudi Arabia

Abstract

The main objective of this article is to develop a direct Bayesian technique to determine or estimate the order of two dimensional moving average processes. The proposed technique is based on approximating the likelihood function by a matrix normal-Wishart distribution on the parameter space. Combining the approximate likelihood with a matrix normal-Wishart (or vague prior) and an indirect technique to estimate an initial value for the order, the marginal posterior probability mass function of the model order is developed in a convenient form. Then one investigates the approximate posterior probability mass function of the model order over its grid and selects the order with the maximum posterior probability to solve the identification problem. A simulation study, with three different priors, is conducted in order to inspect the numerical efficiency of the proposed Bayesian technique and compare it with the well known AIC automatic technique. The numerical results show that the proposed Bayesian technique is simple, efficient and easy to program.

Keywords: Identification, Two dimensional moving average processes, likelihood function, matrix normal-Wishart distribution, Probability mass function, AIC technique

1. Introduction

Moving average processes have been widely used successfully to model time series data arise in many areas of application such as economics, business, agriculture, engineering,

---

*Permanent Address: Department of Statistics, Faculty of Economics and Political Science, Cairo University, Egypt
†Permanent Address: Department of Statistics, Faculty of Economics and Political Science, Cairo University, Egypt

biometrics, geophysics, chemistry and environmental studies. The statistical analysis of such data often requires modeling two time series jointly. In a study of consumer behavior , as an example, one may record spending on education $y_1(t)$ and spending on health services $y_2(t)$. In a study of traffic accidents ,as another example , one may record the number of accidents $y_1(t)$ and the number of fatalities because of the accidents $y_2(t)$. As a third example, one may record the temperature $y_1(t)$ and humidity $y_2(t)$. These variables are modeled and examined jointly in order to understand the nature of dynamic relationship among the variables and to increase the precision of the estimates of the parameters and future observations.

Of great importance in analyzing the two dimensional time series is identifying the order of the process. In identification process , a time series analyst constructs the tools that will be used to absorb information from the data to determine or estimate the model order. However, it is well known that the solution of identification problem depends on subjective opinions as well as mathematical and statistical arguments. It is well known also that there is no optimum method is completely agreed upon to identify the model order.

With respect to univariate moving average processes, one may trace three different non-Bayesian approaches to identify the model order . In 1970, Box and Jenkins presented the first and most popular approach by matching the autocorrelation function computed from the data with its theoretical counterpart. Their technique has been widely used bay many others such as Chatfield (1980), Harvey (1981), Priestely (1981) and Liu (2009). The second non-Bayesian approach to identify the order of univariate moving average processes is what so called the automatic approach. Assuming the maximum order of the process is known, the automatic approach is to fit all possible moving average models and compute a certain criterion for each model. The identified model is then the model for which the proposed criterion attains its optimal value. However, one may say that there is no complete agreement on the form of the criterion to be optimized. Examples of the automatic identification technique may be found in Akaike (1974), Schwarz (1978), Rissanen (1978), Hannan and Quinn (1979), Terasvirta and Mellin (1986), Mills and Passad (1992), and Beveridge and Oickle (1994). A third non-Bayesian approach is called a goodness of fit approach. Assuming the correct value of the order q, the asymptotic distribution of the residual correlations have a zero mean. Box and Pierce (1970) proposed a chi-square test to identify the order of the process. The Chi-square test has been modified and improved by Ljung and Box (1978).

On the other hand, Bayesian identification of univarate moving average processes is being developed and the Bayesian literature devoted to the identification of moving average processes is sparse. One of the most important Bayesian contribution has been done by Monahan (1983) who found a way to work with univariate autoregressive moving average processes with low order. Assuming stationarity and invertibilty, he has developed a numerical technique to implement the identification phase of low order autoregressive moving average processes which include moving average processes as a special case. Broemeling and shaarawy (1988) have developed an approximate technique to identify the order of ARMA processes. Shaarawy and Ali (2003) have developed a direct Bayesian technique to identify seasonal autoregressive models. Shaarawy et. al. (2007) found a direct way to identify the order of moving average processes. They developed an approximate posterior probability mass function of the model order in a convenient form. Then, one may choose the order at which the posterior probability mass function attains its maximum to be the identified order of the time series being analyzed.

With respect to the two dimensional and multivariate versions, the identification problem, from a non-Bayesian view point, has been studied by Granger and Newbold (1973), Tiao and Box (1981) and Tiao and Tsay (1983) by matching the cross correlation functions of the data with their theoretical counterparts. On the other hand, Shaarawy et. al. (2006) have introduced a direct Bayesian technique to identify the order of bivariate autoregressive processes. Their technique has been extended by Shaarawy and Ali (2008) to the case of general vector autoregressive processes. However, one may say that the direct Bayesian approach to identify the order of two dimensional moving average processes has not been explored yet.

The main objective of this article is to develop an approximate direct Bayesian technique to determine or estimate the order of two dimensional moving average processes. Using n vectors of 2×1 observations, the marginal posterior probability mass function of the model order is derived in an approximate convenient form using an approximate likelihood function and a matrix normal-Wishart prior class of densities or a vague prior. Then the time series analyst may inspect the approximate marginal posterior mass function of the model order over its grid and selects the order with the maximum posterior probability to be the identified or estimated order. A simulation study is conducted, using the modern specialized package SCA, in order to inspect the numerical efficiency of the proposed Bayesian technique and compare it with some popular non-Bayesian technique.

The rest of this paper is structured as follows: Section 2 introduces the definition of the two dimensional moving average model of order q in matrix notations. Section 3 presents an indirect Bayesian technique to identify an initial order for the two dimensional moving average processes. Section 4 develops an approximate marginal posterior probability mass function of the order q and explains the idea of the proposed identification technique. Section 5 is devoted to investigate the numerical efficiency of the proposed Bayesian technique in solving the identification problems. The performance of the proposed Bayesian technique is compared with the AIC in the same section.

2. Two Dimensional Moving Average Processes

As Box and Tiao (1981) have shown, a very useful class of models is the two dimensional moving average processes, denoted by $MA_2(q)$ for short, defined by

$$\underline{y}(t) = \theta_q(B)\, \varepsilon(t) \qquad (2.1)$$

where $\underline{y}(t)$ is the vector of (2×1) observations at time t, $t = \dots, -1, 0, 1, 2, \dots$, $\varepsilon(t)$ is a sequence of independent and normally distributed (2×1) unobservable random vector with zero mean and a (2×2) unknown precision matrix T,

$$\theta_q(B) = I - \theta_1\, B - \theta_2\, B^2 - \dots - \theta_q\, B^q$$

is a matrix polynomial in B, the $\theta's$ are (2×2) matrices of real unknown constants, q is a positive integer, and the backshift operator B is such that

$$B^j y(t) = y(t - j) \quad j = 1, 2, \dots$$

The $MA_2(q)$ processes are always stationary no matter the parameters matrices $\theta's$ are, and are invertible if the roots of the determinant $|\theta_q(B)|$, which is a polynomial in B, lie outside the unit circle. The parameter space is constrained by invertibility conditions for identifiability reasons, see Box and Jenkins (1970) and Box and Tiao (1981).

In general, one can write the $MA_2(q)$ process as

$$\underline{y}(t) = \varepsilon(t) - \theta_1\,\varepsilon(t-1) - \theta_2\,\varepsilon(t-2) - \ldots - \theta_q\,\varepsilon(t-q)$$

Thus, if we have n observations, we can express the general class of $MA_2(q)$ model as

$$Y = X_1\,\theta_1' + X_2\,\theta_2' + \ldots + X_q\,\theta_q' + U \tag{2.2}$$

where

$$Y = \begin{bmatrix} y(1) & y(2) & \ldots & y(n) \end{bmatrix}' = \begin{bmatrix} y(1,1) & y(1,2) \\ y(2,1) & y(2,2) \\ \vdots & \vdots \\ y(n,1) & y(n,2) \end{bmatrix}_{n\times2}$$

$$X_1 = \begin{bmatrix} -\varepsilon'(0) \\ -\varepsilon'(1) \\ \vdots \\ -\varepsilon'(n-1) \end{bmatrix}_{n\times2}, X_2 = \begin{bmatrix} -\varepsilon'(-1) \\ -\varepsilon'(0) \\ \vdots \\ -\varepsilon'(n-2) \end{bmatrix}_{n\times2}, \ldots, X_q = \begin{bmatrix} -\varepsilon'(1-q) \\ -\varepsilon'(2-q) \\ \vdots \\ -\varepsilon'(n-q) \end{bmatrix}_{n\times2}$$

In more compact form, one may write the general class of $MA_2(q)$ models as

$$Y_{n\times2} = X_{n\times2q}\,\Theta_{2q\times2} + U_{n\times2} \tag{2.3}$$

where

$$X = \begin{bmatrix} X_1 & X_2 & \cdots & X_q \end{bmatrix} = \begin{bmatrix} -\varepsilon'(0) & -\varepsilon'(-1) & \ldots & -\varepsilon'(1-q) \\ -\varepsilon'(1) & -\varepsilon'(0) & \ldots & -\varepsilon'(2-q) \\ \vdots & \vdots & \vdots & \vdots \\ -\varepsilon'(n-1) & -\varepsilon'(n-2) & \ldots & -\varepsilon'(n-q) \end{bmatrix},$$

$$\Theta = \begin{bmatrix} \theta_1' \\ \theta_2' \\ \vdots \\ \theta_q' \end{bmatrix} = \begin{bmatrix} \theta_{11}^{(1)} & \theta_{21}^{(1)} \\ \theta_{12}^{(1)} & \theta_{22}^{(1)} \\ \ldots & \ldots \\ \theta_{11}^{(2)} & \theta_{21}^{(2)} \\ \theta_{12}^{(2)} & \theta_{22}^{(2)} \\ \ldots & \ldots \\ \vdots & \vdots \\ \theta_{11}^{(q)} & \theta_{21}^{(q)} \\ \theta_{12}^{(q)} & \theta_{22}^{(q)} \end{bmatrix}_{2q\times2}$$

$$U = \begin{bmatrix} \varepsilon(1) & \varepsilon(2) & \ldots & \varepsilon(n) \end{bmatrix}' \quad and \quad \varepsilon(t) = \begin{bmatrix} \varepsilon(t,1) & \varepsilon(t,2) \end{bmatrix}'$$

The expression (2.3) represents the general class of two dimensional moving average models of order q. This class of model is quite useful in modelling and forecasting a lot of two dimensional time series arise in many fields of application. In real applications, the order q is usually unknown and should be identified or determined using the observed data about the two time series being analyzed. For Bayesians the order q is considered, in effect, as additional unknown parameter for which the posterior probability mass function should be developed in a convenient form. The main objective of this research is to develop such mass function.

In order to achieve our main objective, let $S_n = \begin{bmatrix} y(1) & y(2) & \ldots & y(n) \end{bmatrix}'$ be a matrix of $n \times 2$ observations generated from the two dimensional moving average process of order q on the form (2.3) where the order q is an unknown positive integer. Assuming that $\varepsilon(1-q) = \varepsilon(2-q) = \ldots = \varepsilon(0) = \underline{0}$, (see Hillmer and Tiao (1979)), the likelihood function of the parameters $\Theta(q)$, q, and T can be written as

$$L(\Theta(q), q, T | S_n) \quad \propto \quad |T|^{\frac{n}{2}} \exp(-\frac{1}{2} tr \sum_{t=1}^{n} \varepsilon(t) \varepsilon'(t) T) \tag{2.4}$$

where $\Theta(q) \in \mathbb{R}^{2q \times 2}$, $T > 0$, $q = 1, 2, \ldots, Q$, and Q is the maximum order of the process. In general the likelihood function (2.4) is very complicated because the disturbances $\varepsilon(t)$ are non-linear function of the coefficients Θ. To see this, one may write the disturbances vectors, form (2.2), as

$$\varepsilon'(t) = y'(t) - x'_q(t-1) \Theta(q), \quad t = 1, 2, \ldots, n \tag{2.5}$$

where

$$x'_q(t-1) = \begin{bmatrix} -\varepsilon'(t-1) & -\varepsilon'(t-2) & \ldots & -\varepsilon'(t-q) \end{bmatrix}$$

Thus, one may write the mth component of the residual vector $\varepsilon(t)$ as

$$\varepsilon(t, m) = y(t, m) + \sum_{k=1}^{q} \sum_{j=1}^{2} \theta_{mj}^{(k)} \varepsilon(t-k, j) \quad, m = 1, 2. \tag{2.6}$$

The expression (2.6) is a recurrence relation for the residuals. This recurrence causes the main problem in developing the exact Bayesian solution for the identification problem of the two dimensional moving average processes. However (2.6) can be used to evaluate the residuals recursively if one knows Θ and initial value of the residuals.

Using (2.6), the likelihood function (2.4) can be rewritten in the form

$$L(\Theta(q), q, T | S_n) \quad \propto \quad |T|^{\frac{n}{2}} \exp(-\frac{1}{2} tr \sum_{t=1}^{n} H(\Theta(q), q, t) T) \tag{2.7}$$

where $H(\Theta(q), q, t) = (h_{rs})$ is 2×2 matrix and

$$h_{rs} = \left[y(t, r) + \sum_{k=1}^{q} \sum_{j=1}^{2} \varepsilon(t-k, j) \theta_{rj}^{(k)} \right] \left[y(t, s) + \sum_{k=1}^{q} \sum_{j=1}^{2} \varepsilon(t-k, j) \theta_{sj}^{(k)} \right] \tag{2.8}$$

The form (2.8) is not quadratic in the parameters θ's because $\varepsilon(t-k, j)$ is a function of θ's through the recurrence (2.6). If $\varepsilon(t-k, j)$ are known, $H(\Theta(q), q, t)$ would be a quadratic form in the parameters. The proposed approximation is based on replacing the exact residuals $\varepsilon(t)$ by their least squares estimates. The least square estimates, say $\hat{\varepsilon}(t)$, are obtained by searching over the parameter space for the value of Θ, say Θ_0, which minimizes the residual sum of squares $\sum_{t=1}^{n} \hat{\varepsilon}^2(t,i)$, $i = 1,2$. Before doing this process, one should have an initial adequate value for the order q. It is proposed to obtain such value, say q_0, by the indirect technique presented in the next section. The least squares estimate $\Theta_0(q_0)$ and the assumed initial values, namely zero, are then substituted in (2.6) to obtain the least squares estimates of the residuals recursively. Substituting theses estimates in $x_q'(t-1)$, one can write (2.5) as

$$\hat{\varepsilon}'(t) = y'(t) - \hat{x}_{q_0}'(t-1)\,\Theta(q) \tag{2.9}$$

where $t = 1, 2, \ldots, n$ and $\hat{x}_q'(t-1)$ is the same as $x_q'(t-1)$ but using the residuals estimates instead of the exact ones,

Using the estimates of the residuals, one may rewrite the likelihood function (2.7) approximately as

$$L^*(\Theta(q), q, T|S_n) \;\propto\; |T|^{\frac{n}{2}} \exp(-\frac{1}{2}\,tr\,\{\sum_{t=1}^{n}$$

$$[\underline{y}(t) - \Theta'(q)\,\hat{x}_q(t-1)][\underline{y}(t) - \Theta'(q)\,\hat{x}_q(t-1)]'\,T\}) \tag{2.10}$$

A convenient choice of the conditional prior of $\Theta(q)$ given q and T is

$$f_1(\Theta(q)|q,T) \;=\; (2\pi)^{\frac{-4q}{2}}\,|\,R(q)\,|^{\frac{2}{2}}\,|T|^{\frac{2q}{2}}\,\exp(-\frac{1}{2}$$

$$tr\,[\Theta(q) - D(q)]'\,R(q)\,[\Theta(q) - D(q)]T) \tag{2.11}$$

where the hyperparameters $D(q) \in \mathbb{R}^{2q \times 2}$ and $R(q)$ is a $(2q \times 2q)$ positive definite matrix. The precision matrix T is assigned, a priori, the following Wishart distribution

$$f_2(T) \;\propto\; |\,T\,|^{(a-3)/2}\,\exp\left(-\frac{1}{2}\,tr\,\mathbf{V}\,T\right)$$

where $\mathbf{V}$ is a (2×2) positive definite matrix. Thus the joint prior distribution of $\Theta(q)$ and T give q is assumed to be

$$f_3(\Theta(q), T|q) \;\propto\; f_1(\Theta(q)|q,T)\,f_2(T) \tag{2.12}$$

The class of prior distribution (2.12) is called matrix normal-Wishart class of distributions. Let β_i be the prior probability that the time series realization Y is generated from a two dimensional moving average process of order i. Thus the prior probability mass function of q is

$$\beta_i = P_r[q = i]\,, \qquad i = 1, 2, \ldots, Q \tag{2.13}$$

From (2.12) and (2.13), the joint prior distribution of the parameters $\Theta(q)$, T, and q is

$$f(\Theta(q), q, T) \;\propto\; \beta_i\,(2\pi)^{\frac{-4q}{2}}\,|\,R(q)\,|^{\frac{2}{2}}\,|T|^{\frac{1}{2}[2q+a-3]}\,\exp(-\frac{1}{2}$$

$$tr\,\{[\Theta(q) - D(q)]'\,R(q)\,[\Theta(q) - D(q)] + \mathbf{V}\}T) \tag{2.14}$$

If one can not or unwilling to specify the hyperparameters $D(q)$, $R(q)$, a, $\mathbf{V}$ and β_i, one might use Jeffrey's vague prior

$$f(\Theta(q), q, T) \;\propto\; |\,T\,|^{-3/2} \tag{2.15}$$

3.   Indirect Bayesian Identification Technique

The $MA_2(q)$ class of models is quite useful in modeling two dimensional time series data and frequently q is not excess of 4. In practice the value of the model order q is unknown and one has to identify it using the observed n vectors of 2×1 observations. The direct Bayesian approach to identify the order q is to find the marginal posterior probability mass function of the unknown q and use its mode to be the identified value. The approach taken here is somewhat different from the direct approach. Instead of working directly with the posterior distribution of q, it is proposed to focus on the marginal posterior distribution of the coefficients

$$
\Theta = \begin{bmatrix} \theta_1 \\ \theta_2 \\ \vdots \\ \theta_Q \end{bmatrix}_{2Q \times 2}
\tag{3.1}
$$

where θ_i is a square matrix of order 2, $i = 1, 2, ..., Q$. The maximum order Q is assumed to be known.

Assuming that $\varepsilon(0) = \varepsilon(-1) = ... = \varepsilon(1-Q) = 0$, the likelihood function of the parameters Θ and T is

$$
L(\Theta, T | S_n) \quad \propto \quad |T|^{\frac{n}{2}} \exp(-\frac{1}{2} tr\{\sum_{t=1}^{n} \varepsilon(t)\, \varepsilon'(t)\, T\})
\tag{3.2}
$$

where $\Theta \in \mathbb{R}^{2Q \times 2}$, T is positive definite matrix, and

$$
\varepsilon'(t) = y'(t) - x'(t-1)\, \Theta, \quad t = 1, 2, ..., n
\tag{3.3}
$$

where

$$
x'(t-1) = \begin{bmatrix} -\varepsilon'(t-1) & -\varepsilon'(t-2) & \cdots & -\varepsilon'(t-Q) \end{bmatrix}
$$

The expression (3.3) is a recurrence relation for the residuals and the m-th component of the residual $\varepsilon(t)$ can be written as

$$
\varepsilon(t, m) = y(t, m) + \sum_{k=1}^{Q} \sum_{j=1}^{2} \theta_{mj}^{(k)} \varepsilon(t-k, j) \quad , m = 1, 2
\tag{3.4}
$$

The recurrence relation (3.4) causes the main problem in developing the exact Bayesian analysis of two dimensional moving average processes. However, this recurrence may be used to evaluate the residuals recursively if one knows Θ and the initial values of the residuals. The proposed approximation is based on replacing the exact residuals by their least squares estimated and assuming that $\varepsilon(0) = \varepsilon(-1) = ... = \varepsilon(1-Q) = 0$. Thus, we estimate the residuals recursively by

$$
\hat{\varepsilon}(t, m) = y(t, m) + \sum_{k=1}^{Q} \sum_{j=1}^{2} \hat{\varepsilon}(t-k, j)\, \hat{\theta}_{mj}^{(k)}
\tag{3.5}
$$

where $t = 1, 2, \ldots, n$; $m = 1, 2$, and $\hat{\theta}_{mj}^{(k)}$ are the nonlinear least squares estimates of $\theta_{mj}^{(k)}$. Using the estimates of the residuals, one may rewrite the likelihood function (3.2) approximately as

$$L^*(\Theta, T | S_n) \; \propto \; |T|^{\frac{n}{2}} \, \exp(-\frac{1}{2} \, tr \, \{\sum_{t=1}^{n}$$

$$[\underline{y}(t) - \Theta' \, \hat{x}(t-1)][\underline{y}(t) - \Theta' \, \hat{x}(t-1)]' \, T\}) \qquad (3.6)$$

where $\hat{x}(t-1)$ is the same as $x(t-1)$ but using the estimate residuals instead of the exact ones.

A convenient choice of the prior density of the parameters Θ and T is the following matrix normal-Wishart distribution:

$$\xi(\Theta, T) \; \propto \; \xi_1(\Theta | T) \, \xi_2(T) \qquad (3.7)$$

where

$$\xi_1(\Theta | T) \propto |T|^{\frac{2Q}{2}} \, \exp(-\frac{1}{2} \, tr \, [\Theta - D]' \, W \, [\Theta - D]T)$$

and

$$\xi_2(T) \; \propto \; |T|^{(a-3)/2} \, \exp\left(-\frac{1}{2} \, tr \, \mathbf{V} \, T\right)$$

where the hyperparameters $D \in \mathbb{R}^{2Q \times 2}$, W is a $(2Q \times 2Q)$ positive definite matrix, $a > 0$ and Σ is a (2×2) positive definite matrix. If one has "little" information about the parameters, a priori, he may use the Jeffreys' prior

$$\xi(\Theta, T) \; \propto \; |T|^{-3/2}, \quad \Theta \in \mathbb{R}^{2Q \times 2}, T > 0 \qquad (3.8)$$

Theorem 3.1. *Using the approximate likelihood function (3.6) and the matrix normal-Wishart prior density (3.7), the marginal posterior distribution of Θ is a matrix t with parameters $(A^{-1} B, A^{-1}, C - B' A^{-1} B, \nu)$ where*

$$A \;=\; W + \sum_{t=1}^{n} \hat{x}(t-1) \, \hat{x}'(t-1),$$

$$B \;=\; WD + \sum_{t=1}^{n} \hat{x}(t-1) \, y'(t),$$

$$C \;=\; D' W D + \mathbf{V} + \sum_{t=1}^{n} y(t) \, y'(t),$$

and $\quad \nu = n + a - 1$

Corollary 3.1. *Using the approximate likelihood function (3.6) and the Jeffreys' prior density (3.8), the marginal posterior distribution of Θ is a matrix t with parameters $(A^{-1} B, A^{-1}, C - B' A^{-1} B, \nu)$. However, A, B, C and ν will be modified by letting $W \longrightarrow 0_{2Q \times 2Q}$, $a \longrightarrow -2Q$, and $\mathbf{V} \longrightarrow 0_{2 \times 2}$.*

The reader is referred to Box and Tiao (1973) for the form and the properties of the matrix t density function. Since Θ has a matrix t distribution, any subset of 2 rows has a matrix t distribution. Also, the conditional distribution of a subset of rows given any other subset of rows is a matrix t distribution, see Box and Tiao (1973). Furthermore, one can test any subset of rows to be zero (marginally or conditionally) using exact F statistics. The forms of the F statistics can be found in Box and Tiao (1973, pp. 451-453).

The proposed indirect Bayesian procedure to identify the order q is to do the backward elimination procedure. One first tests $H_0 : \theta_Q = 0$ versus $\theta_Q \neq 0$ using the marginal posterior distribution of θ_Q which is a matrix t distribution. If H_0 is not rejected, one tests $H_0 : \theta_{Q-1} = 0$ given $\theta_Q = 0$ using the conditional posterior distribution of θ_{Q-1} given $\theta_Q = 0$ which is also a matrix t distribution. If the last H_0 is not rejected, one tests $H_0 : \theta_{Q-2} = 0$ given $\theta_Q = \theta_{Q-1} = 0$ using the conditional posterior distribution of θ_{Q-2} given $\theta_Q = \theta_{Q-1} = 0$ which is also a matrix t distribution. The procedure is continued in this fashion until the hypothesis $H_0 : \theta_{q_0} = 0$ is rejected for some q_0 where $0 < q_0 \leq Q$. The value q_0 is the proposed indirect Bayesian solution of the two dimensional identification problem and the proposed initial value of our proposed direct Bayesian approach.

4. The Posterior Probability Mass Function of the Model Order

The main objective of this section is to develop an approximate posterior probability mass function of the order q under the conditions outlined above. In order to do that, one must combine the approximate likelihood function (2.10), via Bayes theorem, with the prior distribution of the parameters (2.14). Thus the joint posterior distribution of the parameters $\Theta(q)$, T, and q is

$$g(\Theta(q), T, q | S_n) \propto \beta_i (2\pi)^{\frac{-4q}{2}} |R(q)|^{\frac{2}{2}} |T|^{\frac{\alpha(q)}{2}}$$
$$\exp(-\frac{1}{2} tr \{[\Theta(q) - D(q)]' R(q) [\Theta(q) - D(q)] + \mathbf{V}$$
$$+ \sum_{t=1}^{n} [y(t) - \Theta'(q) \hat{x}_q(t-1)][y(t) - \Theta'(q) \hat{x}_q(t-1)]'\}T) \quad (4.1)$$

where

$$\alpha(q) = n + 2q + a - 3 \quad (4.2)$$

Theorem 4.1. *Using the approximate likelihood function (2.10) and prior distribution (2.14), the marginal posterior probability mass function of the order q is*

$$h(q | S_n) \propto \beta_i |R(q)| |A(q)|^{-1} |C(q)|^{-\frac{1}{2}(n+a)} \prod_{j=1}^{k} \Gamma(\frac{n+a+j-2}{2}), \quad n > 1 - a$$

where

$$A(q) = R(q) + \sum_{t=1}^{n} \hat{x}_q(t-1) \hat{x}_q'(t-1) \quad (4.3)$$

$$B(q) = R(q) D(q) + \sum_{t=1}^{n} \hat{x}_q(t-1) y'(t) \quad (4.4)$$

and

$$C(q) = D'(q)\,R(q)\,D(q) + \mathbf{V} + \sum_{t=1}^{n} y(t)\,y'(t) - B'(q)\,A^{-1}(q)\,B(q) \qquad (4.5)$$

It might be noted that the proof of Theorem (4.1.) can be done by integrating (4.2) with respect to $\Theta(q)$ and T respectively. However, the integral with respect to $\Theta(q)$ is done using the matrix normal integral and the integral with respect to T is done using the generalized gamma function. The reader is referred to Box and Tiao (1973) for the forms of the matrix normal density and the generalized gamma function.

Theorem 4.2. *Using the approximate likelihood function (2.10) and the non-informative prior distribution (2.15), the marginal posterior probability mass function of the model order q is*

$$h_1(q|S_n) \propto (\pi)^{2q}\,|A^*(q)|^{-1}\,|C^*(q)|^{-\frac{1}{2}[n-2q]}\,\prod_{j=1}^{2}\Gamma(\frac{n+j-2q-2}{2}),\quad n > 1+2q$$

where

$$A^*(q) = \sum_{t=1}^{n}\hat{x}_q(t-1)\,x_q'(t-1)\,,$$

$$B^*(q) = \sum_{t=1}^{n}\hat{x}_q(t-1)\,y'(t)\,,$$

and

$$C^*(q) = \sum_{t=1}^{n}y(t)\,y'(t) - B^{*'}(q)\,A^{*-1}(q)\,B^*(q)$$

The proof of Theorem (4.2.) can be done using the same procedures used to prove Theorem(4.1.).

The forms of the posterior probability mass function given by Theorem (4.1.) and (4.2.) are convenient and could be easily programmed. Then one may inspect the posterior probability mass function over the grid of the order q and select the value of q at which the posterior mass function attains its maximum to be the identified order of the two dimensional time series data being analyzed.

5. A Numerical Study

One of the main objectives of this research is to study the effectiveness of the proposed technique in identifying the order of two dimensional moving average processes. In order to achieve this goal, six simulations have been conducted. The proposed technique is employed, with three different prior distributions, to identify the order of $MA_2(1)$ model with various parameter values. All computations were performed by using the modern package SCA.

Our main concern is to study the effectiveness of the proposed Bayesian technique by calculating the percentage of correct identification. Such effectiveness will be examined with respect to the time series length (sample size) as well as the parameters of the selected model. For all sample sizes and parameters, the covariance matrix of the noise term is fixed at $\begin{pmatrix} 2 & 1 \\ 1 & 1 \end{pmatrix}$.

Simulation 1, as an illustration, begins with the generation of pairs of 500 data sets of bivariate normal variates, each of size 300 to represent $\varepsilon_1(t)$ and $\varepsilon_2(t)$ respectively. These data sets are then used to generate a pair of 500 realizations, each of size 300, from MA$_2$(1) process with $\Theta = \begin{pmatrix} 0.5 & -0.4 \\ -0.3 & 0.2 \end{pmatrix}$ assuming the starting values are zero. For a specific prior, the second step of simulation 1 is to carry out all computations, assuming the maximum order $Q = 4$, required to identify each of the 500 realizations and finding the percentage of correct identification. Note that the computations include the application of the indirect Bayesian technique in order to get an adequate initial value q_0, and use it on applying our proposed direct Bayesian technique. Such computations are done for a specific time series length n using the first n observations of each generated set. This second step is repeated for each chosen sample size, maximum order, and prior combinations. The sample size is taken to be 50, 100, 150, 200 and 300, while the maximum order Q is taken to be 4. With respect to the prior probability mass of the order q, which is combined with the vague prior $\Theta(q)$ and T, the following three priors are used

Prior 1 : $\xi(q) = \frac{1}{Q}$, $q = 1, 2, \ldots, Q$
Prior 2 : $\xi(q) \propto (0.5)^q$, $q = 1, 2, \ldots, Q$
Prior 3 : $\xi(q = 1) = 0.4$; $\xi(q = 2) = 0.3$; $\xi(q = 3) = 0.2$; $\xi(q = 4) = 0.1$,

The first prior assigns equal probabilities to the all possible values of the order q. The second prior is chosen in such a way to give probabilities that decline exponentially with the order, while the third prior is chosen in such a way to give probabilities that decrease with an absolute amount 0.1 as the order increases.

Simulation 2 is done in a similar way but using $\Theta = \begin{pmatrix} -0.5 & 0.4 \\ 0.3 & -0.2 \end{pmatrix}$. The results of simulations 1 and 2 are presented in Table 1. The other simulations are done in similar way but using different values of Θ and their results are presented in Tables 2 and 3. The parameters of the simulations have been chosen in such a way to satisfy the invertibility conditions, see Harvey (1981). In some simulations, the parameters are chosen to be close from non-invertibility region, see Table 3.

An inspection of the numerical results shows an increasing trend for the efficiency of the proposed Bayesian technique as the sample size n increases. The percentages of correct identification are reasonably high, being greater than 68%, for all models and priors, for samples of size 150 or more no matter what the parameters are. In addition, the percentages of correct identification achieved using the third prior is higher than the corresponding percentages achieved by the first prior, while the corresponding percentages achieved by the second prior are the highest. Finally, for sufficiently large n, it is to be noticed that the posterior results are not very sensitive to the minor changes between the second and third prior distributions.

For the matter of comparison, the well known Akaik's information criterion, denoted by AIC, has been used to identify the data sets, which have been used with simulations 1-6, and the percentages of choosing the correct orders have been calculated. For all considered models, the results of the proposed technique are less than the results of AIC if a small

Table 1. Percentages of Correct Identification of the proposed Bayesian Technique and AIC for $MA_2(1)$ Processes for Simulations 1 and 2

PARAMETERS	n	PRIOR1	PRIOR2	PRIOR3	AIC
$\Theta = \begin{bmatrix} 0.5 & -0.4 \\ -0.3 & 0.2 \end{bmatrix}$	50	53.8	60.4	57.2	66.2
	100	76.4	82.6	79.8	83.2
	150	88.4	92.2	90.4	84.4
	200	92.8	95.2	94.0	89.2
	300	93.6	94.6	94.2	90.0
$\Theta = \begin{bmatrix} -0.5 & 0.4 \\ 0.3 & -0.2 \end{bmatrix}$	50	56.6	61.6	59.2	73.6
	100	75.4	81.8	78.8	82.8
	150	87.4	90.8	88.8	85.2
	200	93.4	95.6	94.6	88.6
	300	96.2	97.0	96.8	88.2

Table 2. Percentages of Correct Identification of the proposed Bayesian Technique and AIC for $MA_2(1)$ Processes for Simulations 3 and 4

PARAMETERS	n	PRIOR1	PRIOR2	PRIOR3	AIC
$\Theta = \begin{bmatrix} 0.3 & 0.5 \\ 0.4 & 0.3 \end{bmatrix}$	50	63.4	68.0	65.4	70.0
	100	75.2	81.4	79.2	81.6
	150	88.8	92.6	91.0	83.6
	200	95.2	96.4	95.6	86.4
	300	95.8	97.0	96.8	88.6
$\Theta = \begin{bmatrix} 0.7 & 0.5 \\ 0.4 & 0.3 \end{bmatrix}$	50	64.6	69.8	67.4	76.4
	100	76.8	83.0	79.8	84.6
	150	85.6	89.6	88.2	85.8
	200	88.8	92.0	90.8	87.0
	300	88.6	90.6	89.6	88.4

sample size is used. As the sample size increases, the results of the proposed technique become superior to the results of AIC. It might be important to mention that the correct percentages achieved by the proposed technique, with simulations 1-4, were higher than

Table 3. Percentages of Correct Identification of the proposed Bayesian Technique and AIC for MA$_2$(1) Processes for Simulations 5 and 6

PARAMETERS	n	PRIOR1	PRIOR2	PRIOR3	AIC
$\Theta = \begin{bmatrix} 1 & -0.2 \\ 1.1 & -1 \end{bmatrix}$	50	52.6	58.6	54.6	76.0
	100	58.0	64.6	62.4	80.6
	150	68.4	74.2	71.6	84.4
	200	80.0	83.6	82.0	85.0
	300	84.8	88.2	86.4	88.2
$\Theta = \begin{bmatrix} 0.9 & -0.2 \\ 1.1 & -0.9 \end{bmatrix}$	50	46.8	52.2	48.6	71.8
	100	58.0	64.0	60.2	82.4
	150	76.6	81.8	79.8	84.2
	200	84.8	88.2	86.8	88.6
	300	89.8	92.8	91.4	88.4

the correct percentages achieved by AIC for $n \geq 200$, regardless of the prior distribution.

In general the numerical results support the adequacy of using the proposed Bayesian technique in solving the identification problems of two dimensional moving average processes. The percentages of correct identification depends on the sample size and the choice of the prior distribution. A moderate sample size is needed in order to have a better chance of getting correct identification no matter what the parameters are.

Summary and Conclusion

The main objective of this article is to develop a Bayesian methodology to choose the order q of two dimensional moving average processes. The marginal posterior probability mass function of the model order is developed in a convenient form using an approximate conditional likelihood function and a matrix- normal Wishart or Jeffreys' vague prior. Then one may easily calculate the posterior probabilities of all possible values of the order q and choose the value of q at which the posterior probability mass function attains its maximum to be the identified order.

In order to demonstrate the performance of the proposed Bayesian procedure and test its adequacy in identifying the order of two dimensional moving average processes, a simulation study with three different prior mass functions has been carried out. The numerical results show that the proposed procedure can efficiently identify the orders of two dimensional moving average processes with high precision for moderate and large sample size.

Acknowledgment

The project was funded by the Deanship of Scientific Research (DSR), King Abdulaziz University, Jeddah, under grant no. 3-013/429. The authors, therefore, acknowledge with thanks DSR support for Scientific Research.

References

[1] Akaike, H. (1974). A New Look at Statistical Model Identification. *IEEE Transaction on Automatic Control,* Vol. 19, pp. 716-723.

[2] Beveridge, S. and Oickle, C. (1994). A Comparison of Box-Jenkins and Objectives Methods for Determining the Order of a Non-seasonal ARMA Model. *Journal of Forecasting,* Vol. 13, pp. 419-434, (1994).

[3] Box, G. and Jenkins, G. (1970). *Time Series Analysis, Forecasting and Control.* Holden-Day, San Francisco.

[4] Box, G. and Pierce, D.A. (1970). Distribution of residual autocorrelation in autoregressive integrated moving average time series models. *J. of the American Stats. Associ,* Vol. 65,pp. 1509-1526.

[5] Box, G. and Tiao, G. (1973). *Bayesian Inference in Statistical Analysis.* Addison-Wesley, Reading, MA.

[6] Broemling, L.D. and Shaarawy, S. (1988). Time Series Analysis:Bayesian Analysis in the Time Domain. *Bayesian Analysis of Time Series and Dynamic Models*, edited by Spall, J.

[7] Chatfield, C. (1980). *The Analysis of Time Series: Theory and Practice.* Chapman and Hall Ltd., London.

[8] Granger, C.W.J and Newbold, P. (1973). *Forecasting Economic Time Series.* New York: Academic Press.

[9] Hannan, E. J. and Quinn, B. G. (1979). The Determination of an Autoregression. *Journal of the Royal Statistical Society, Series B*, Vol. 42, pp. 190-195.

[10] Harvey, A.C. (1981). *Time Series Models.* Wiley, New York.

[11] Hillmer, S.C. and Tiao, G.C. (1979). Likelihood function of stationary multiple autoregressive moving average models. *J. Am. Stat. Assoc.* 74, 652-660.

[12] Liu, L.M. (2009). *Time Series Analysis and forecasting.* 2nd edition. Scientific Computing Association Corp.

[13] Ljung, G. and Box, G.E. (1978). On a measure of lack of fit in time series models. *Biometrika*, Vol. 65, pp. 297-303.

[14] Mills, J. and Prasad, K.(1992). A Comparison of Model Selection Criteria. *Econometric Reviews*, Vol. 11, p. 201-233, (1992).

[15] Monahan, J.E. (1983). Fully Bayesian Analysis of ARIMA Time Series Models. *Journal of Econometrics*, Vol. 21, pp. 307-331.

[16] Rissanen, J. (1978). Modelling by Shortest Data Description. *Automatica*, Vol. 14, pp. 465-471.

[17] Schwarz, G. (1978). Estimating the Dimension of a Model. *Annals of the Institute of Statistical Mathematics*, Vol. 6, pp. 461-464.

[18] Shaarawy, S. and Ali, S. (2003). Bayesian Identification of Seasonal Autoregressive Models. *Communications in Statistics- Theory and Methods*, Vol. 32, Issue 5, pp. 1067-1084.

[19] Shaarawy, S., Albassam, M. and and Ali S. (2006). A Direct Bayesian Identification to Select the Order of Bivariate Autoregressive Processes. *The Egyptian Statistical Journal*, Institute of Statistical Studies and Research, Cairo University, Vol. 50, Issue 1.

[20] Shaarawy, S., Soliman, E. and Ali S. (2007). Bayesian Identification of Moving Average Models. *Communications in Statistics- Theory and Methods*, Vol. 36, Issue 12.

[21] Shaarawy, S. and Ali S.(2008). Bayesian Identification of Multivariate Autoregressive Processes. *Communications in Statistics- Theory and Methods*, Vol. 37, Issue 5, (2008).

[22] Terasvirta, T. and Mellin, I. (1986). Model Selection Criteria and Model Selection Tests in Regression Models. *Scandinavian Journal of Statistics: Theory and Applications*, Vol. 13, pp. 159-171.

[23] Tiao, G. and Box, G. (1981). Modeling Multiple Time Series with Multiplications. *Journal of the American Statistical Association*, Vol. 76, No. 376, pp.802-816.

[24] Tiao, G. C. and Tsay, R.(1983). Multiple Time Series Modeling and Extended Sample Cross Correlation. *Journal of Business and Economic Statistics*, Vol.1, No.1, (1983).

In: Applied Statistical Theory and Applications
Editor: Mohammad Ahsanullah

ISBN: 978-1-63321-858-1
© 2014 Nova Science Publishers, Inc.

Chapter 5

ON THE USE OF MOMENT ESTIMATORS TO TEST FOR A ZERO INFLATED POISSON (ZIP) DISTRIBUTION

A. Nanthakumar[1] *and Z. Govindarajulu*[2]
[1]Department of Mathematics, SUNY-Oswego, Oswego, New York, US
[2]Department of Statistics, University of Kentucky, Lexington, Kentucky, US

Abstract

The paper studies two simple approaches that are very powerful and computationally less intensive to test poisson versus zero inflated poisson distributions.

AMS Subject Classification: 62F03

Keywords: Moment Estimator, Hypothesis Test, Distance, Zero Inflated Poisson

1.   Introduction

For a long time, the occurrence of large number of zeroes was observed in the context of counting processes which otherwise could be easily found to follow a regular Poisson distribution. This phenomenon occurs regularly in physical and biological systems where the Poison counts appear when a system functions properly and additional zeroes are observed when the system malfunctions. Cochran (1954) was the first to develop a hypothesis-test for testing Poissonness against ZIP and later Rao and Chakravarty (1956), Singh (1963) developed their own tests for testing Poissonness against ZIP. The test developed by Cochran (1954) was later shown to be equivalent to the score test developed by Van den Broeck (1995). El-Shaarawi (1985) conducted a simulation study for comparing the power of all the tests that existed until that time to test for Poissonness, and based on his study, he concluded that the score test is more powerful while being computationally less intensive. Most of the hypothesis tests, for example by Lambert (1992), Van den Broeck (1995) were developed in the context of regression models where the parameters depend on the covariates. Recently, Thas and Rayner (2005) developed a partial sum based score tests for testing Poissonness against a class of alternatives (including ZIP as a possible alternative) and their test seems to be reasonably powerful.

In this paper, we present two simple tests which are very simple and at the same time very powerful. One of these tests use the idea of "distance" to perform the test. The other one is a locally most powerful test (LMP). The LMP test (also called likelihood derivative test) is due to Rao (1948). According to Moran (1970), the LMP test is very powerful for testing mixing proportions. One can describe a ZIP distribution (indeed a mixture distribution) as follows.

$$P(Y=0) \;=\; \theta+(1-\theta)e^{-\lambda} \tag{1}$$

$$P(Y=y) \;=\; \theta+(1-\theta)\frac{e^{-\lambda}\lambda^{y}}{y!} \;,\; y>0 \tag{2}$$

where θ is the mixing proportion.

2. Methodology

We use the method of moments for deriving the estimator. For the above described ZIP distribution, one can easily show that

$$E(Y) \;=\; (1-\theta)\lambda \tag{3}$$

and

$$E(Y^2) \;=\; (1-\theta)(\lambda+\lambda^2) \tag{4}$$

This clearly implies that the moment estimator of and are as follows.

$$\hat{\lambda}_n = \left(\frac{\sum_1^n y_i^2}{\sum_1^n y_i} \right) - 1 \tag{5}$$

and

$$\hat{\theta}_n = 1 - \left(\frac{\left(\sum_1^n y_i\right)^2}{n\left(\sum_1^n y_i^2 - \sum_1^n y_i\right)} \right) \tag{6}$$

We are led to the following results as $n \to \infty$.

Theorem 1.

$\left(\dfrac{\sum_1^n y_i^2}{n} , \dfrac{\sum_1^n y_i}{n} \right)$ follows a bivariate normal distribution with mean = (μ_1, μ_2) and variance-covariance matrix $\begin{bmatrix} \dfrac{\sigma_{11}}{n} & \dfrac{\sigma_{12}}{n} \\[2mm] \dfrac{\sigma_{12}}{n} & \dfrac{\sigma_{22}}{n} \end{bmatrix}$ as n tends to ∞, where

$$\mu_1 = (1-\theta)\lambda(1+\lambda), \quad \mu_2 = (1-\theta)\lambda \tag{7}$$

$$\sigma_{11} = (1-\theta)\lambda\left(1+6\lambda+4\lambda^2+\theta\lambda(1+\lambda)^2\right) \tag{8}$$

$$\sigma_{22} = (1-\theta)\lambda(1+\theta\lambda) \tag{9}$$

and

$$\sigma_{12} = (1-\theta)\lambda\left(1+2\lambda+\theta\lambda(1+\lambda)\right) \tag{10}$$

Proof. Since each component in the vector is a linear combination of iid random variables, the result follows due to the multivariate central limit theorem.

Theorem: Suppose that $X_n = (X_{n1}, X_{n2}, \ldots, X_{nk})$ is $AN\left(\mu, \dfrac{1}{n}\Sigma\right)$ as n tends to ∞ then for any continuous function $g(x)$,

$$g(X_n) = AN\left(g(\mu), \frac{1}{n}\sum_{1}^{k}\sum_{1}^{k}\sigma_{ij}\left.\frac{\partial g}{\partial x_i}\right|_{x=\mu}\left.\frac{\partial g}{\partial x_j}\right|_{x=\mu}\right) \text{ as } n \text{ tends to } \infty.$$

where AN means asymptotically normally distributed.

Corollary 1.
$$\hat{\lambda} \sim AN\left(\lambda, \frac{(\lambda+2)}{n(1-\theta)}\right) \text{ as } n \text{ tends to } \infty$$

Proof: In order to apply the above quoted theorem, let us define
$X_{nl} = \sum_{i}^{n} y_i^2$ and $X_{n2} = \sum_{i}^{n} y_i$. Note that $\hat{\lambda} = \dfrac{X_{nl}}{X_{n2}} - 1 = g(X_{n1}, X_{n2})$.

Note that

$$\left.\frac{\partial g}{\partial X_{n1}}\right|_{x_{n1}=\mu,\, x_{n2}=\mu_2} = \frac{1}{n(1-\theta)\lambda} \tag{11}$$

$$\left.\frac{\partial g}{\partial X_{n2}}\right|_{x_{n1}=\mu,\, x_{n2}=\mu_2} = \frac{-(1+\lambda)}{n(1-\theta)\lambda} \tag{12}$$

After simplification, the asymptotic variance of $\hat{\lambda}$ is seen to be $\dfrac{\lambda+2}{n(1-\theta)}$.

Proof. The proof can be mimicked along the same lines as in Corollary 1.

Corollary 2.

Let $D = \dfrac{\overline{Y^2} - \overline{Y}^2}{\overline{Y}}$

Then, $D \sim AN\left(1 + \theta\lambda, \dfrac{2 + \theta^2\lambda + \theta(1-\theta)^2\lambda^2)}{n(1-\theta)}\right)$ as n tends to ∞.

Proof. The proof can be mimicked along the same lines as in Corollary 1.

3. Hypothesis Testing Procedures

3.1. Distance Based Testing

Suppose that we want to test $H_0 : \theta = 0$ (Poisson) versus $H_1 : \theta > 0$ (ZIP)

$$\text{Under } H_0, \ \hat{\lambda} = \overline{Y} \ \text{ and } \ \text{Under } H_1, \ \hat{\lambda} = \frac{\overline{Y^2}}{\overline{Y}} - 1 \tag{13}$$

Now, let us define the distance between these estimates as follows.

$$\text{Distance, } D = \overline{Y^2} - \overline{Y}^2 - \overline{Y} \tag{14}$$

We aim to derive a decision rule based on this distance Note that when is close to 0 then this supports the null hypothesis. However, this distance measure can be negative and moreover the null distribution for this distance measure depends on the nuisance parameter which is unknown. Therefore, we re-define the distance measure as follows.

$$D = \frac{(\overline{Y^2} - \overline{Y}^2)}{\overline{Y}} \tag{15}$$

Corollary 3.

For the distance measure D given by (15), the null distribution is asymptotically normal with mean = 1 and variance = $\dfrac{2}{n}$ as n tends to ∞.

4. Locally Most Powerful Test (LMP Test)

The likelihood function L is given by

$$L = \left(\theta + (1-\theta)e^{-\lambda}\right)^{n_1} \cdot (1-\theta)^{n-n_1} \cdot \frac{e^{(-n-n_1)\lambda}\lambda^{\sum y_i}}{\prod y_i!} \tag{16}$$

Note that n_1 represents the number of '0's in a sample of size = n. Next, evaluate the partial derivative of the natural logarithm of L with respect to θ at $\theta = 0$.

$$\frac{\partial lnL}{\partial \theta} = \frac{n1(1 - e^{-\lambda})}{(\theta + (1-\theta)e^{-\lambda})} - \frac{(n-n_1)}{(1-\theta)} \tag{17}$$

Reject the null hypothesis H_0 when $n_1 > C_1$, where n_1 represents the number of '0's in the sample and C_1 is the critical value for the test.

Example. (Leroux and Puterman (1992))

Count data for fetal lamb movements.

Outcome:	0	1	2	3	4	5	6	7
Count:	182	41	12	2	2	0	0	1

Based on this data, $\overline{Y} = 0.358$, $\overline{Y^2} = 0.783$.

For the LMP test, the number of '0's = 182. The critical value at 5% significance level is C_1 179. Hence, we reject the null hypothesis. For the distance based test, the distance measure $D = 1.829$ and the critical value at 5% level is 1.126 for the exact test. So, we reject H_0 and accept H_1. These results agree with the findings of Thas and Rayner (2005) and Leroux and Puterman (1992).

5. Power Computation

We computed the power for both the locally most powerful (LMP) test and this distance based test for different choices of λ and θ where $0 \leq \theta \leq 1$ The power is nearly the same for both tests. These tests are far less computationally intensive while being very powerful. As λ and θ move away from 0, the power of both these tests is almost 1.

6. Conclusion

In this paper, we have presented two simple approaches that are very powerful and less computationally intensive for testing Poisson versus Zero Inflated Poisson (ZIP). The locally most powerful test (LMP test) seems to be very powerful for testing Poisson versus Zero Inflated Poisson (ZIP). Also, the power of the distance based test seems to be very high except for values of in the neighborhood of 1. This could be due to the difficulty in separating an observation '0' as coming from either regular Poisson or ZIP, but the power of separation seems to get better for large values of the Poisson mean λ. Note that when is equal to 1 this results in a degenerate distribution. Also note that the null distribution (when $\theta = 0$) for the distance based test does not require any knowledge about the nuisance parameter λ and so the critical value for testing Poisson versus ZIP does not involve λ. Although, the power of the partial sum score test developed by Thas and Rayner (2005) and the score test developed by Van den Broeck (1995) seems to have a similar power pattern as our distance based test, the distance based test and the Locally most powerful test (LMP test) seem to outperform the partial sum score test and the score test on the basis of power.

In fact, the LMP is a better test for testing the mixing proportions in the context of mixture distributions.

Acknowledgment and Dedication

I wish to dedicate this paper to the memory of my PhD advisor and my mentor, Professor Zakkula Govindarajulu for his contribution to the development of Statistics as a subject. Professor Govindarajulu joined me in writing this paper at his old age of 77 before his sudden death on December 5, 2010. Also, I wish to thank the Editor and the referees for their comments to improve the presentation of this paper on behalf late Professor Z. Govindarajulu and myself. Thank you.

References

Cochran, W. (1954). Some methods of strengthening tests, *Biometrics* 10, 417 - 451.

El-Shaarawi, A. (1985). Some goodness-of-fit methods for the Poisson plus added zero distribution, *Applied and Environmental Microbiology* 49, 1304 - 1306.

Lambert, D. (1992). Zero-inflated Poisson regression, with an application to defects in manufacturing, *Technometrics* 34, 1 - 13.

Leroux, B. and Puterman, M. (1992). Maximum-penalized likelihood estimation for independent and Markov dependent mixture models, *Biometrics*, 48, 545 - 588.

Moran, P.A.P. (1970). On asymptotically optimal tests for composite hypothesis, *Biometrika*, 57, 47 - 55.

Rao, C.R. (1948). Large sample tests of statistical hypothesis concerning several parameters with applications to problems of estimation, *Proceedings of the Cambridge Philosophical Society*, 44, 50 - 57.

Rao, C.R. and Chakravarti, I.M. (1956). Some small sample tests of significance for a Poisson distribution, *Biometrics*, 12, 264 - 282.

Serfling, R.J. (1980). *Approximation Theorems of Mathematical Statistics*, Wiley.

Singh, S. (1963). A note on inflated Poisson distribution, *Journal of the Indian Statistical Association*, 1, 140 - 144.

Thas, O. and Rayner, J.C.W. (2005). Smooth Tests for the Zero-Inflated Poisson distribution, *Biometrics*, 61, 808 - 815.

Van den Broeck, J. (1995). A score test for zero inflation in a Poisson distribution, *Biometrics*, 51, 738 - 743.

In: Applied Statistical Theory and Applications
Editor: Mohammad Ahsanullah

ISBN: 978-1-63321-858-1
© 2014 Nova Science Publishers, Inc.

Chapter 6

OPTIMAL DESIGNING OF A VARIABLES QUICK SWITCHING SAMPLING SYSTEM BY MINIMZING THE AVERAGE SAMPLE NUMBER

S. Balamurali and M. Usha

Department of Mathematics, Kalasalingam University,
Krishnan Koil, TN, India

Abstract

This article proposes variables quick switching system (VQSS) where the quality characteristic follows normal distribution or lognormal distribution and has upper or lower specification limit. The variables quick switching system will be effective when testing is costly and destructive. The advantages of the variables QSS over the variables single and double sampling plans and attributes QSS are discussed. Tables are also constructed for the selection of parameters of known and unknown standard deviation VQSS for given acceptable quality level and limiting quality level. The problem is formulated as a nonlinear programming where the objective function to be minimized is the average sample number and the constraints are related to lot acceptance probabilities at acceptable quality level and limiting quality level under the operating characteristic curve .

1. Introduction

A sampling system consists of two or more sampling plans and the rules for switching between the sampling plans to achieve a blending of the advantageous features of each of the sampling plans. In general, any sampling system of sampling inspection involving only normal and tightened inspection will be referred to as a two-plan system. Quick switching system (QSS) developed by Dodge (1967) is one of the two-plan systems for the application of attributes quality characteristics. In any two plan system, the tightened inspection can be used when the quality of a product deteriorated and normal inspection are used when the quality is found to be good. Dodge (1965), Hald and Thyregod (1965) and Stephen and Larson (1967) have investigated the two-plan systems using different switching criteria to achieve the desired discrimination on the operating characteristic (OC) curve. Romboski (1969) has investigated the quick switching system of type QSS-1 by taking single sampling plan as the reference plan.

Whenever the normal distribution for the quality characteristic is justifiable, variables sampling plans are used. The main advantage of the variables sampling plan is that the same operating characteristic (OC) curve can be obtained with a smaller sample size than would be required by an attributes sampling plan. Thus, a variables acceptance sampling plan would require less sampling. The measurements data required by a variables sampling plan would probably cost more per observation than the collection of attributes data. However, the reduction in sample size obtained may more than offset this increased cost. When destructive testing is employed, variables sampling is particularly useful in reducing the costs of inspection. Another advantage is that measurements data usually provide more information about the manufacturing process or lot than do attributes data. Generally, numerical measurements of quality characteristics are more useful than simple classification of the item as conforming or non-conforming. Another advantage of the variables sampling plan is that when acceptable quality levels (AQLs) are very small, the sample size required by it is very less than the attributes sampling plans. Under these circumstances, the variables sampling plans have significant advantages.

For compliance testing of a measurable characteristic, a variable sampling plan may be preferred. Based on this idea, Govindaraju and Balamurali (1998) extended the concept of chain sampling of Dodge (1955) to the measurable quality characteristics. Later, Balamurali and Jun (2006) developed a sampling plan called variables repetitive group sampling for the application variables inspection. Soundararajan and Palanivel (1997) extended the concept of QSS to the normally distributed quality characteristics. They have also developed tables for selecting parameters of the variables QSS, but they didn't follow any optimization techniques. So, this paper attempts to design a variables QSS by minimizing average sample number (ASN). Obviously, a sampling plan having smaller ASN would be more desirable. For the selection of the parameters of the VQSS, the problem is formulated by a nonlinear programming where the objective function to be minimized is the ASN and the constraints are related to lot acceptance probabilities at acceptable quality level (AQL) and limiting quality level (LQL). Comparisons are also made to show the advantages of the proposed system with other conventional variables plans such as single and double sampling plans.

2. Conditions of Application and Operating Procedure

The following assumptions should be valid for the application of the variables quick switching system.

(i) Production is in a steady state, so that results of past, present and future lots are broadly indicative of a continuing process.
(ii) Lots are submitted for inspection serially either in the order of production or in the order of being submitted for inspection.
(iii) Inspection is by measurements, with quality is defined as the fraction nonconforming, p.

In addition, the usual conditions for the application of single sampling variables plans with known or unknown standard deviation should also be valid. The operating procedure of the VQSS is as follows.

Suppose that the quality characteristic of interest has the upper specification limit U and follows a normal distribution with known standard deviation σ. Then the following two procedures of the variables QSS are proposed.

2.1. Procedure 1: k Method

Step 1. Start with normal inspection. During normal inspection, take a random sample of size n_σ, say $\left(X_1, X_2 ... X_{n_\sigma}\right)$ and compute $v = \dfrac{\left(U - \overline{X}\right)}{\sigma}$, where $\overline{X} = \dfrac{1}{n_\sigma}\sum_{i=1}^{n_\sigma} X_i$.

Step 2. Accept the lot if $v \geq k_{N\sigma}$ and reject the lot if $v < k_{N\sigma}$. If a lot is rejected on normal inspection, then switch to tightened inspection as in Step 3.

Step 3. During tightened inspection, take a random sample of size n_σ, say $\left(X_1, X_2 ... X_{n_\sigma}\right)$ and compute $v = \dfrac{\left(U - \overline{X}\right)}{\sigma}$, where $\overline{X} = \dfrac{1}{n_\sigma}\sum_{i=1}^{n_\sigma} X_i$.

Step 4. Accept the lot if $v \geq k_{T\sigma}$ and reject the lot if $v < k_{T\sigma}$ $(k_{T\sigma} > k_{N\sigma})$. If a lot is accepted on tightened inspection, then immediately switch to normal inspection as in Step 1.

Thus, the variables QSS system is characterized by three parameters, namely n_σ, $k_{N\sigma}$ and $k_{T\sigma}$. If $k_{N\sigma} = k_{T\sigma}$, then the system will reduce to the variables single sampling plan.

2.2. Procedure 2: M Method

Step 1. Start with normal inspection. During normal inspection, take a random sample of size n_σ, say $\left(X_1, X_2 ... X_{n_\sigma}\right)$ and compute $Q_U = \dfrac{\left(U - \overline{X}\right)}{\sigma}\sqrt{\dfrac{n}{n-1}}$, where $\overline{X} = \dfrac{1}{n_\sigma}\sum_{i=1}^{n_\sigma} X_i$.

Also determine the minimum variance unbiased estimate of the fraction non-conforming p, as

$$\hat{p}_U = \int_{Q_U}^{\infty} \frac{1}{\sqrt{2\pi}} e^{-t^2/2} dt .$$

Step 2. Accept the lot if $\hat{p}_U \leq M_{N\sigma}$ and reject the lot if $\hat{p}_U > M_{N\sigma}$. Where $M_{N\sigma}$ is the proportion of the area under the normal curve beyond $k_{N\sigma}\sqrt{\dfrac{n}{n-1}}$. If the lot is rejected on normal inspection, then switch to tightened inspection as in Step 3.

Step 3. During tightened inspection, take a random sample of size n_σ, say $\left(X_1, X_2 ... X_{n_\sigma}\right)$ and compute $Q_U = \dfrac{\left(U - \overline{X}\right)}{\sigma}\sqrt{\dfrac{n}{n-1}}$, where $\overline{X} = \dfrac{1}{n_\sigma}\sum_{i=1}^{n_\sigma} X_i$. Also determine the minimum variance unbiased estimate of the fraction non-conforming p, as

$$\hat{p}_U = \int_{Q_U}^{\infty} \frac{1}{\sqrt{2\pi}} e^{-t^2/2} dt .$$

Step 4. Accept the lot if $\hat{p}_U \leq M_{T\sigma}$ and reject the lot if $\hat{p}_U > M_{T\sigma}$. Here $M_{T\sigma}$ is the

proportion of the area under the normal curve beyond $k_{T\sigma} \sqrt{\dfrac{n}{n-1}}$. (Note: $M_{T\sigma} < M_{N\sigma}$). If a

lot is accepted on tightened inspection then immediately switch to normal inspection as in Step 1.

Thus, the parameters of the variables QSS under the M method are the sample size n_σ, acceptable criterion $M_{T\sigma}$ and $M_{N\sigma}$.

It is also worthwhile to note that the same VQSS can be applied to the case where the quality characteristic follows a log-normal distribution, since the logarithmic transformation leads to a normal distribution. Let $\hat{\mu}$ be an estimate of mean which is calculated from the logarithmic transformation of the data. Then the VQSS is employed as follows.

Step 1. Start with the normal inspection level. Select a random sample of size n_σ and

compute $v = \dfrac{\log(U) - \hat{\mu}}{\sigma}$. Accept the lot if $v \geq k_{N\sigma}$ and reject the lot if $v < k_{N\sigma}$. If a lot is

rejected under normal inspection, then switch to tightened inspection.

Step 2. During the tightened inspection, inspect the lots using the single sampling variables plan with a sample size n_σ and the acceptance criterion $k_{T\sigma}(>k_{N\sigma})$. Accept the lot if

$v \geq k_{T\sigma}$ and reject the lot if $v < k_{T\sigma}$, where $v = \dfrac{\log(U) - \hat{\mu}}{\sigma}$. If a lot is accepted on

tightened inspection, then switch to normal inspection as in Step 1.

Thus, the parameters of the VQSS under the log-normal distribution are the sample size n_σ, acceptable criterion $k_{T\sigma}$ and $k_{N\sigma}$. The rest of the paper deals with k method under normal distribution only.

3. Operating Characteristics of a Variables Quick Switching System

The OC function of the variables QS system, which gives the proportion of lots that are expected to be accepted for given product quality, p under known sigma case is given by

$$P_a(p) = \frac{P_T}{1 - P_N + P_T} = \frac{\Pr(v \geq k_{T\sigma})}{1 - \Pr(v \geq k_{N\sigma}) + \Pr(v \geq k_{T\sigma})} \tag{1}$$

where $P_N = \Pr(v \geq k_{N\sigma})$ is the probability of accepting a lot based on a single sample with parameters $(n_\sigma, k_{N\sigma})$ and $P_T = \Pr(v \geq k_{T\sigma})$ is the probability of accepting a lot based on a single sampling plan with parameters $(n_\sigma, k_{T\sigma})$. Under type B situation (i.e. a series of lots of the same quality), forming lots of N items from a process and then drawing random sample of size n_σ from these lots is equivalent to drawing random samples of size n_σ directly from the process. Hence the derivation of the OC function is straightforward. The fraction non-conforming in a lot will be determined as

$$p = 1 - \Phi\left(\frac{U - \mu}{\sigma}\right) = 1 - \Phi(v) = \Phi(-v) \tag{2}$$

where $\Phi(y)$ is given by

$$\Phi(y) = \int_{-\infty}^{y} \frac{1}{\sqrt{2\pi}} \exp\left(\frac{-z^2}{2}\right) dz, \tag{3}$$

provided that the quality characteristic of interest is normally distributed with mean μ and standard deviation σ, and the unit is classified as non-conforming if it exceeds the upper specification limit U. Then its probability of acceptance is written as

$$P_a(p) = \frac{\Phi(w_T)}{1 - \Phi(w_N) + \Phi(w_T)} \tag{4}$$

where $w_T = (v - k_{T\sigma})\sqrt{n_\sigma}$ and $w_N = (v - k_{N\sigma})\sqrt{n_\sigma}$

4. Designing of a Known Sigma Variables Quick Switching System

The OC function of a known sigma VQSS is given in (4). If two points on the OC curve namely, AQL(=p_1), LQL(=p_2), the producer's risk α and the consumer's risk β are prescribed then the OC function can be expressed as

$$\frac{\Phi(w_{T1})}{1 - \Phi(w_{N1}) + \Phi(w_{T1})} = 1 - \alpha \tag{5}$$

and

$$\frac{\Phi(w_{T2})}{1 - \Phi(w_{N2}) + \Phi(w_{T2})} = \beta \tag{6}$$

Here w_{T1} is the value of w_T at p=p_1, w_{N1} is the value of w_N at p=p_1, w_{T2} is the value of w_T at p=p_2 and w_{N2} is the value of w_N at p=p_2. That is,

$$w_{T1} = (v_1 - k_{T\sigma})\sqrt{n_\sigma} \ , w_{N1} = (v_1 - k_{N\sigma})\sqrt{n_\sigma}$$

$$w_{T2} = (v_2 - k_{T\sigma})\sqrt{n_\sigma} \ \text{and} \ w_{N2} = (v_2 - k_{N\sigma})\sqrt{n_\sigma} \qquad (7)$$

where v_1 is the value of v at AQL and v_2 is the value of v at LQL. For given AQL or LQL, the values of $k_{N\sigma}$, $k_{T\sigma}$ and the sample size n_σ are determined by using a search procedure.

The average sample number (ASN), by definition, means the expected number of sampled units required for making decisions about the lot. The concept of ASN is meaningful under Type B sampling situations. It is also known that the ASN of the known sigma VQSS is

$$ASN(p) = \frac{n\xi + n\delta}{\xi + \delta} = n \qquad (8)$$

The ASN given above can be used as an objective function to solve for the parameters $(n_\sigma, k_{N\sigma}, k_{T\sigma})$. Since there are several choices to obtain the objective function, it is considered here to minimize ASN at AQL. If the objective is to minimize the ASN at AQL, then the problem will be reduced to the following nonlinear optimization problem.

Minimize ASN(p_1)=n_σ
Subject to
$$P_a(p_1) \geq 1 - \alpha$$
$$P_a(p_2) \leq \beta$$
$$n_\sigma > 1, \ k_{1\sigma} > k_{2\sigma} > 0 \qquad (9)$$

where $P_a(p_1)$ and $P_a(p_2)$ are the lot acceptance probabilities at AQL and LQL respectively and are given in (5) and (6) respectively.

5. Designing of Unknown Sigma Variables QS System

Whenever the standard deviation is unknown, we should use the sample standard deviation S instead of σ. In this case, the operation of the scheme is as follows.

Step 1. Start with the normal inspection level using the single sampling variables plan with a sample size n_S and the acceptance criterion k_{NS}. Accept the lot if $v \geq k_{NS}$ and reject the lot if $v < k_{NS}$, where $v = \dfrac{(U - \bar{X})}{S}$, $\bar{X} = \dfrac{1}{n_S}\sum_{i=1}^{n_S} X_i$ and $S = \sqrt{\dfrac{\sum(X_i - \bar{X})^2}{n_S - 1}}$. If a lot is rejected under normal inspection, then switch to tightened inspection.

Step 2. During the tightened inspection, inspect the lots using the single sampling variables plan with a sample size n_S and the acceptance criterion $k_{TS}(>k_{NS})$. Accept the lot if

$v \geq k_{TS}$ and reject the lot if $v < k_{TS}$, where $v = \dfrac{(U - \overline{X})}{S}$, $\overline{X} = \dfrac{1}{n_S} \sum\limits_{i=1}^{n_S} X_i$ and

$S = \sqrt{\dfrac{\sum (X_i - \overline{X})^2}{n_S - 1}}$. If a lot is accepted on tightened inspection, then immediately switch to normal inspection as in Step 1.

Thus, the unknown sigma VQSS has the parameters namely the sample size n_S, and the acceptable criterion k_{NS} and k_{TS}. If $k_{NS} = k_{TS}$, then the VQSS reduced to the variables single sampling plan with unknown standard deviation. The relationship between known and unknown sigma plan parameters is true only for single sampling plan. Hamaker (1979) has given an approximation for finding the parameters of the unknown sigma single sampling plan from the parameters of the known sigma single sampling plan. Soundarajan and Palanivel (1997) have followed the same approximation for selecting the parameters of unknown sigma variables QSS. However it is to be pointed out that Hamaker's (1979) results must be extended to variables QS system rather than wrongly assuming that the same approximation is valid for VQSS. So the entire design of unknown sigma schemes provided in Soundararajan and Palanivel (1997) seems faulty. So we will follow a different procedure for the unknown sigma case. The determination of parameters for the unknown sigma case namely (n_S, k_{NS}, k_{TS}) is slightly different from the known sigma case. It is known that $\overline{X} \pm k_{NS} S$ is approximately normally distributed with mean $\mu \pm k_{NS} E(S)$ and variance $\dfrac{\sigma^2}{n_S} + k_{NS} Var(S)$ (see Duncan (1986)).

That is,

$$\overline{X} + k_{NS} S \sim N\left(\mu + k_{NS}\sigma, \frac{\sigma^2}{n_S} + k_{NS}{}^2 \frac{\sigma^2}{2n_S} \right)$$

Therefore, the probability of accepting a lot under normal inspection is given by

$$P\{\overline{X} \leq U - k_{NS} S \mid p\} = P\{\overline{X} + k_{NS} S \leq U \mid p\}$$

$$= \Phi\left(\frac{U - k_{NS}\sigma - \mu}{(\sigma/\sqrt{n_S})\sqrt{1 + \dfrac{k_{NS}{}^2}{2}}} \right) = \Phi\left((v - k_{NS})\sqrt{\dfrac{n_S}{1 + \dfrac{k_{NS}{}^2}{2}}} \right)$$

If we let, $w_{NS} = \left((v - k_{NS})\sqrt{\dfrac{n_S}{1 + \dfrac{k_{NS}{}^2}{2}}} \right)$ then the probability of acceptance under tightened inspection is considered $\Phi(w_{NS})$.

Similarly if we let, $w_{TS} = \left((v - k_{TS}) \sqrt{\dfrac{n_S}{1 + \dfrac{k_{TS}^2}{2}}} \right)$ then the probability of acceptance under

tightened inspection is taken as $\Phi(w_{TS})$. Hence the lot acceptance probability for sigma unknown case under two-point situation is given by

$$P_a(p_1) = \frac{\Phi(w_{T1S})}{1 - \Phi(w_{N1S}) + \Phi(w_{T1S})} \qquad (10)$$

and

$$P_a(p_2) = \frac{\Phi(w_{T2S})}{1 - \Phi(w_{N2S}) + \Phi(w_{T2S})} \qquad (11)$$

We obtain $w_{N1S}, w_{T1S}, w_{N2S}, w_{T2S}$ corresponding to $w_{N1}, w_{T1}, w_{N2}, w_{T2}$ respectively by

$$w_{N1S} = \left((v_1 - k_{NS}) \sqrt{\dfrac{n_S}{1 + \dfrac{k_{NS}^2}{2}}} \right), \quad w_{T1S} = \left((v_1 - k_{TS}) \sqrt{\dfrac{n_S}{1 + \dfrac{k_{TS}^2}{2}}} \right)$$

$$w_{N2S} = \left((v_2 - k_{NS}) \sqrt{\dfrac{n_S}{1 + \dfrac{k_{NS}^2}{2}}} \right) \text{ and } w_{T2S} = \left((v_2 - k_{TS}) \sqrt{\dfrac{n_S}{1 + \dfrac{k_{TS}^2}{2}}} \right)$$

In this case, the optimization problem becomes,

$$
\begin{aligned}
&\text{Minimize } ASN(p_1) = n_S \\
&\text{Subject to} \\
&P_a(p_1) \geq 1 - \alpha \\
&P_a(p_2) \leq \beta \\
&n_\sigma > 1, \; k_{NS} > k_{TS} > 0
\end{aligned} \qquad (12)
$$

where $P_a(p_1)$ and $P_a(p_2)$ are the lot acceptance probabilities at AQL and LQL respectively and are described in (10) and (11).

We may determine the parameters of the known sigma and unknown sigma VQSS by solving the nonlinear equation given in (9) and (12) respectively. There may exist multiple solutions since there are three unknowns with only two equations. Generally a sampling would be desirable if the required number of sampled is small. So, in this paper, we consider the ASN as the objective function to be minimized with the probability of acceptance along with the corresponding producer's and consumer's risks as constraints. To solve the above nonlinear optimization problems given in (9) and (12), the sequential quadratic programming (SQP) proposed by Nocedal and wright (1999) can be used. The SQP is implemented in Matlab software using the routine "fmincon". By solving the nonlinear problem mentioned above, the parameters (n_σ, $k_{N\sigma}$ and $k_{T\sigma}$) for known sigma plan and the parameters (n_S, k_{NS} and k_{TS}) for unknown sigma plan are determined and these values are tabulated in Table 2.

6. Examples

6.1. Selection of Known Sigma VQSS Indexed by AQL and LQL

Table 1 is used to determine the parameters of the known σ variables quick switching system for specified values of AQL and LQL when $\alpha = 5\%$ and $\beta = 10\%$. For example, if $p_1 = 2\%$, $p_2 = 8\%$, $\alpha = 5\%$ and $\beta = 10\%$, Table 2 gives the parameters as $n_\sigma = 12$, $k_{N\sigma} = 1.552$ and $k_{T\sigma} = 1.817$.

For the above example, the operation of the VQSS is as follows.

Step 1. Take a random sample of size 12 and compute $v = \dfrac{(U - \bar{X})}{\sigma}$, where $\bar{X} = \dfrac{1}{12}\sum_{i=1}^{12} X_i$.

Accept the lot if $v \geq 1.552$ and reject the lot if $v < 1.552$. If a lot is rejected, then switch to tightened inspection as in step 2.

Step 2. Select a random sample of size 12 and compute $v = \dfrac{(U - \bar{X})}{\sigma}$, where $\bar{X} = \dfrac{1}{12}\sum_{i=1}^{12} X_i$.

Accept the lot if $v \geq 1.817$ and reject the lot if $v < 1.817$. Switch to normal inspection as in step 1, if a lot accepted on this inspection phase.

6.2. Selection of Unknown Sigma VQSS Indexed by AQL and LQL

Table 1 can also be used for the selection of the parameters of the unknown σ VQSS for given values of AQL and LQL. Suppose that AQL=1%, LQL=5%, α=5% and β=10%. From Table 2, the parameters of the VQSS can be determined as $n_S = 24$, $k_{NS} = 1.729$ and $k_{TS} = 2.214$.

7. Advantages of the Variables Quick Switching System

In this section, we will discuss the advantages of the variables QSS over attributes QSS and variables single sampling plans. For the purpose of comparison, we will consider the plans which have the same AQL and LQL. Suppose that for given values of AQL=0.01, α=5%, LQL=0.02 and $\beta = 10\%$, one can find the parameters of the attributes quick switching system under the application of Poisson model as

(i) n = 251, $c_T = 5$ and $c_N = 9$

For the same AQL and LQL, we can determine the parameters of the variables single sampling plan (from Sommers (1981)) and variables QSS (from Table 2) respectively as follows.

(ii) $n_\sigma = 116$ and $k = 2.17$
(iii) $n_\sigma = 28$, $k_{N\sigma} = 1.923$ and $k_{T\sigma} = 2.418$

By comparing the above, it is clear that the variables QS System achieves a reduction of over 89% in sample size than the attributes QSS and about 76% than the variables single sampling plan with same AQL and LQL conditions. In order to show the better efficiency of the variables QSS, three OC curves are considered. Fig.1. shows the OC curves of the variables single sampling plans with parameters (10, 1.754) and (10, 2.179) and the variables QSS with parameters (10; 1.754, 2.179). The variables quick switching system (10; 1.754, 2.179) is selected in such a way that it satisfies the two-points on the OC curve condition ($p_1 = 0.01$, $1-\alpha = 0.95$) and ($p_2 = 0.045$, $\beta = 0.10$).

Table 1. Variables Quick Switching Sampling Systems Indexed by AQL and LQL for α=5% and β=10% Involving Minimum ASN

p_1	p_2	MinASN(p_1) Known Sigma			MinASN(p_1) Unknown Sigma		
		n_σ	$k_{T\sigma}$	$k_{N\sigma}$	n_S	k_{TS}	k_{NS}
0.001	0.002	134	2.998	2.943	234	3.193	2.773
	0.003	45	2.958	2.833	108	3.166	2.666
	0.004	31	2.899	2.784	104	2.999	2.704
	0.005	14	2.994	2.599	71	2.998	2.628
	0.006	11	2.985	2.535	60	2.955	2.600
	0.007	10	2.939	2.519	45	2.985	2.525
	0.008	14	2.769	2.639	38	2.982	2.482
	0.009	8	2.897	2.457	35	2.947	2.467
	0.010	7	2.899	2.409	32	2.926	2.446
	0.012	9	2.710	2.525	28	2.880	2.415
	0.015	6	2.751	2.381	24	2.819	2.379
	0.025	4	2.672	2.222	16	2.715	2.260
0.0025	0.004	96	2.841	2.596	326	2.917	2.542
	0.005	35	2.917	2.432	156	2.945	2.445
	0.006	26	2.878	2.398	113	2.910	2.410
	0.0075	23	2.773	2.413	82	2.861	2.371
	0.010	14	2.762	2.302	56	2.809	2.309
	0.015	9	2.693	2.193	37	2.710	2.235
	0.020	8	2.572	2.182	33	2.563	2.233
	0.025	6	2.569	2.079	28	2.490	2.200
	0.030	8	2.353	2.213	19	2.564	2.074
	0.040	5	2.374	2.039	15	2.485	2.010

Table 1. Continued

p_1	p_2	MinASN(p_1) Known Sigma			MinASN(p_1) Unknown Sigma		
		n_σ	$k_{T\sigma}$	$k_{N\sigma}$	n_S	k_{TS}	k_{NS}
0.005	0.0075	100	2.626	2.361	330	2.679	2.329
	0.010	31	2.683	2.183	123	2.705	2.205
	0.012	23	2.641	2.146	89	2.664	2.169
	0.015	19	2.549	2.139	63	2.617	2.122
	0.020	9	2.657	1.897	45	2.533	2.073
	0.030	9	2.377	1.982	28	2.443	1.978
	0.035	7	2.385	1.895	23	2.424	1.929
	0.040	7	2.298	1.913	20	2.394	1.894
	0.060	6	2.109	1.884	15	2.224	1.834
0.0075	0.010	149	2.499	2.244	575	2.502	2.252
	0.012	58	2.527	2.137	209	2.549	2.144
	0.015	34	2.485	2.080	107	2.549	2.059
	0.020	23	2.391	2.041	64	2.486	1.996
	0.025	14	2.402	1.922	47	2.426	1.951
	0.030	11	2.367	1.867	36	2.395	1.900
	0.035	11	2.263	1.893	31	2.337	1.877
	0.040	11	2.179	1.909	26	2.313	1.838
	0.050	8	2.151	1.816	20	2.266	1.776
	0.060	7	2.086	1.781	17	2.196	1.741
	0.070	6	2.036	1.686	14	2.175	1.685
0.010	0.015	68	2.427	2.047	243	2.434	2.064
	0.020	28	2.418	1.923	94	2.441	1.946
	0.025	21	2.334	1.899	62	2.393	1.893
	0.030	15	2.314	1.829	47	2.344	1.854
	0.035	13	2.255	1.810	38	2.304	1.819
	0.040	14	2.141	1.856	32	2.268	1.788
	0.045	10	2.179	1.754	27	2.247	1.752
	0.050	14	2.005	1.875	24	2.214	1.729
	0.060	7	2.123	1.648	20	2.148	1.693
	0.070	6	2.084	1.599	17	2.100	1.655
	0.080	6	1.987	1.617	14	2.089	1.599
	0.090	6	1.904	1.629	11	2.138	1.513
	0.100	3	1.906	1.557	11	2.027	1.532
0.015	0.020	129	2.236	1.971	402	2.248	1.973
	0.025	43	2.265	1.835	121	2.317	1.827
	0.030	26	2.252	1.757	78	2.279	1.779
	0.035	23	2.163	1.768	59	2.233	1.748
	0.040	22	2.082	1.795	48	2.188	1.723
	0.045	21	2.012	1.787	39	2.167	1.687
	0.050	13	2.083	1.658	34	2.131	1.666
	0.060	11	2.009	1.629	26	2.088	1.613
	0.070	8	2.021	1.526	22	2.025	1.585
	0.080	7	1.952	1.526	18	2.005	1.535
	0.090	7	1.888	1.508	16	1.956	1.511
	0.100	5	1.856	1.376	14	1.927	1.477

Table 1. Continued

p_1	p_2	MinASN(p_1) Known Sigma			MinASN(p_1) Unknown Sigma		
		n_σ	$k_{T\sigma}$	$k_{N\sigma}$	n_S	k_{TS}	k_{NS}
0.020	0.030	87	2.070	1.840	170	2.167	1.772
	0.035	33	2.158	1.673	96	2.172	1.702
	0.040	26	2.108	1.653	68	2.153	1.658
	0.045	21	2.076	1.621	54	2.120	1.630
	0.050	17	2.060	1.580	50	2.046	1.636
0.020	0.060	17	1.926	1.618	33	2.044	1.554
	0.070	17	1.813	1.638	26	2.004	1.510
	0.080	12	1.817	1.552	24	1.910	1.510
	0.090	8	1.877	1.417	19	1.911	1.451
	0.100	7	1.851	1.376	16	1.897	1.407
	0.120	5	1.700	1.345	18	1.664	1.474
0.030	0.040	116	1.934	1.679	269	1.965	1.665
	0.045	57	1.957	1.592	133	1.999	1.584
	0.050	33	1.998	1.493	89	1.999	1.535
	0.060	22	1.947	1.442	54	1.974	1.469
	0.070	17	1.894	1.404	40	1.925	1.430
	0.080	14	1.844	1.374	31	1.893	1.388
	0.090	12	1.800	1.345	26	1.846	1.361
	0.100	10	1.781	1.296	29	1.695	1.415
	0.120	11	1.597	1.362	24	1.598	1.388
	0.150	6	1.647	1.152	13	1.644	1.224
	0.200	5	1.470	1.110	10	1.458	1.173
0.040	0.060	58	1.801	1.476	104	1.892	1.427
	0.070	29	1.826	1.361	63	1.869	1.369
	0.080	21	1.796	1.311	47	1.819	1.339
	0.090	17	1.754	1.279	37	1.778	1.308
	0.100	14	1.725	1.240	30	1.749	1.274
	0.110	14	1.639	1.264	26	1.704	1.254
	0.120	14	1.565	1.280	24	1.644	1.249
	0.140	10	1.546	1.191	17	1.634	1.169
	0.160	8	1.512	1.127	17	1.195	1.485
	0.18	7	1.460	1.090	12	1.521	1.096
	0.200	4	1.317	0.882	10	1.496	1.046
0.050	0.060	280	1.666	1.521	462	1.708	1.488
	0.070	66	1.723	1.373	132	1.761	1.366
	0.080	35	1.735	1.280	73	1.768	1.293
	0.090	25	1.711	1.231	53	1.730	1.260
	0.100	23	1.630	1.245	40	1.709	1.219
	0.120	14	1.619	1.134	28	1.640	1.170
	0.140	11	1.560	1.085	21	1.585	1.120
	0.160	9	1.511	1.036	16	1.560	1.060
	0.200	6	1.432	1.006	15	1.328	1.083
	0.250	5	1.324	0.860	8	1.375	0.895

From this figure, it can be easily observed that, for good quality, i.e. for smaller values of fraction nonconforming, the composite OC curve (OC curve of the variables QSS) coincides with the OC curve of the variables single sampling plan (10, 1.754). As quality deteriorates the OC curve of the composite OC curve moves toward that for the single sampling plan (10, 2.179) and comes close to it beyond the indifference quality level.

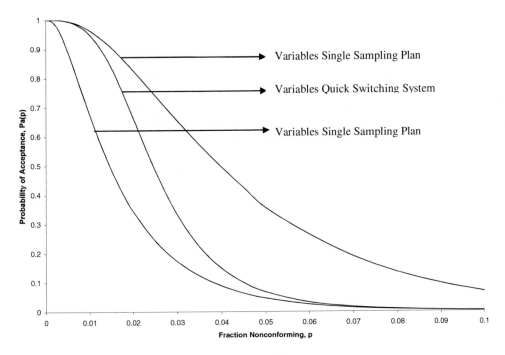

Figure 1. Operating Characteristic (OC) Curves of Single Sampling Normal Plan (10, 1.754), Quick Switching System (10; 1.754, 2.179) and Single Sampling Tightened Plan (10, 2.179).

Table 2. ASN Values of the Known Sigma Variables Single Sampling Plan, Variables Double Sampling Plan and Variables Quick Switching System

p_1	p_2	Average Sample Number			
		Variables SSP	Variables DSP	Variables* QSS	Variables ** QSS
0.001	0.002	191	154.9	191	134
0.001	0.003	74	59.4	74	45
0.005	0.010	138	112.0	138	31
0.005	0.012	85	69.5	85	23
0.03	0.04	506	434.6	506	116
0.03	0.06	81	127.7	81	22
0.04	0.07	114	180.6	114	29
0.04	0.08	72	58.4	72	21
0.05	0.07	300	246.7	300	66
0.05	0.08	149	122.3	149	35

* Average sample number given in Soundararajan and Palanivel (1997).

** Average sample number given in Table 1.

Further, it is also to be pointed that the variables QSS is economically superior to the variables double sampling plan in terms of average sample number (ASN). Obviously, a sampling plan having smaller ASN would be more desirable. The variables double or multiple sampling plans are not practically very useful. Variables sampling Standards avoid presenting such plans due to increased complexity involved in operating them.

Table 2 shows the ASN values of the variables single sampling plan and the variables double sampling plan along with the variables QSS for some arbitrarily selected combinations of AQL and LQL under known sigma case. Table 3 gives the ASN values of the above said plans when sigma is unknown. These ASN values are calculated at the producer's quality level for both known and unknown sigma plans. The sample size of the variables single sampling plan and the ASN of the variables double sampling plan can be found in Sommers (1981).

Table 3. ASN Values of the Unknown Sigma Variables Single Sampling Plan, Variables Double Sampling Plan and Variables Quick Switching System

p_1	p_2	Average Sample Number			
		Variables SSP	Variables DSP	Variables* QSS	Variables ** QSS
0.001	0.002	1032	829.1	1032	234
0.001	0.003	381	302.4	412	108
0.005	0.010	547	437.1	941	123
0.005	0.012	327	263.0	823	89
0.03	0.04	1333	1138.7	945	269
0.03	0.06	197	316.5	357	89
0.04	0.07	258	417.6	263	104
0.04	0.08	159	125.8	201	47
0.05	0.07	660	535.4	768	132
0.05	0.08	319	258.0	572	73

* Average sample number given in Soundararajan and Palanivel (1997).
** Average sample number given in Table 1.

These tables apparently show that the variables QSS will have minimum ASN when compared to the variables single and double sampling plans for both known and unknown sigma cases. Similar reduction in ASN can be achieved for any combination of AQL and LQL values. This implies that variables QSS scheme will give desired protection with minimum inspection so that the cost of inspection will greatly be reduced. Thus the variables QSS provides better protection than the variables single sampling plans and variables double sampling plans.

8. Comparison of Parameters of Variables QSS

It is to be pointed out that the ASNs of variables QSS provided in Soundararajan and Palanivel (1997) are equal or greater than the ASN of single sampling plans for some combinations of p_1 and p_2. For example, for given $p_1=0.01$ and $p_2=0.04$, ASN of single sampling variables plan is 506, but the ASN of variables QSS given in Soundararajan and Palanivel (1997) is 1856. This is a contradiction, since in the attributes case, quick switching system will always have minimum ASN than the attributes single sampling plan (see

Romboski (1969) and Soundararajan and Arumainayagam (1992)). This should be valid for variables sampling also. Hence the entire design of variables QSS provided in Soundararajan and Palanivel (1997) for both known and unknown sigma seems faulty or doubtful. Hence the parameters given in this paper are more reliable and optimum.

Table 4. Parameters of Known Sigma Variables QSS for Some Selected Combination of AQL and LQL Values

p_1	p_2	*Parameters of VQSS			**Parameters of VQSS		
		n_σ	$k_{N\sigma}$	$k_{T\sigma}$	n_σ	$k_{N\sigma}$	$k_{T\sigma}$
0.001	0.002	370	2.93	3.10	134	2.943	2.998
0.001	0.003	95	2.87	3.00	45	2.833	2.958
0.005	0.010	399	2.40	2.60	31	2.183	2.683
0.005	0.012	126	2.39	2.50	23	2.146	2.641
0.03	0.04	1856	1.73	2.00	116	1.679	1.934
0.03	0.05	515	1.73	1.90	33	1.493	1.998
0.04	0.06	965	1.62	1.78	58	1.476	1.801
0.04	0.08	121	1.55	1.68	21	1.311	1.796
0.05	0.06	1311	1.55	1.66	280	1.521	1.666
0.05	0.07	853	1.53	1.66	66	1.373	1.723

*Parameters from Soundararajan and Palanivel (1997).
**Parameters from Table 1.

Table 5. Parameters of Unknown Sigma Variables QSS for Some Selected Combination of AQL and LQL Values

p_1	p_2	*Parameters of VQSS			**Parameters of VQSS		
		n_S	k_{NS}	k_{TS}	n_S	k_{NS}	k_{TS}
0.001	0.002	2053	2.93	3.10	234	2.773	3.193
0.001	0.003	504	2.87	3.00	108	2.666	3.166
0.005	0.010	1647	2.40	2.60	123	2.205	2.705
0.005	0.012	502	2.39	2.50	89	2.169	2.664
0.03	0.04	5100	1.73	2.00	269	1.665	1.965
0.03	0.05	1365	1.73	1.90	89	1.535	1.999
0.04	0.06	2362	1.62	1.78	104	1.427	1.892
0.04	0.08	279	1.55	1.68	47	1.339	1.819
0.05	0.06	3001	1.55	1.66	462	1.488	1.708
0.05	0.07	1939	1.53	1.66	132	1.366	1.761

*Parameters from Soundararajan and Palanivel (1997).
**Parameters from Table 1.

9. Conclusions

In this paper, the problem of minimizing the average sample number is considered in variables quick switching system. In general, variables sampling plans require a smaller sample size than do attributes plans. It has also been shown that the variables QSS provided in this paper has smaller ASN than the ASN of the existing single and double sampling plans. The variables QSS provided in this paper also ensure the protection for the consumers in their point of view. This kind of variables QSS scheme will be effective and useful for compliance testing.

Acknowledgments

The authors would like to thank the reviewers and the Editor for their valuable comments which led to improve the manuscript.

References

Balamurali, S and Jun, C-H.(2006),"Repetitive Group Sampling Procedure for Variables Inspection", *Journal of Applied Statistics*, Vol.33, pp.327-338.

Dodge, H. F. (1955),"Chain Sampling Inspection Plan", *Industrial Quality Control*, Vol.11, No.4, pp. 10-13.

Dodge, H. F. (1965),"Evaluation of a Sampling System Having Rules for Switching Between Normal and Tightened Inspection", *Technical Report* No.14, Statistics Center, Rutgers University, Piscataway, NJ.

Dodge, H. F. (1967),"A Dual System of Acceptance Sampling", *Technical Report* No.16, The Statistics Center, Rutgers- The State University, New Brunswick, New Jersey.

Duncan, A. J. (1986): *Quality Control and Industrial Statistics,* 5th Ed., Richard D. Irwin, Homewood, Illinois.

Govindaraju, K and Balamurali, S. (1998),"Chain Sampling Plan for Variables Inspection", *Journal of Applied Statistics*, Vol.25, pp. 103-109.

Hald, A and Thyregod, P. (1965),"The Composite Operating Characteristic under Normal and Tightened Sampling Inspection by Attributes", *Bulletin of the International Statistical Institute*, Vol. 41, pp. 517-529.

Hamaker, H. C. (1979)," Acceptance Sampling for Percent Defective by Variables and by Attributes", *Journal of Quality Technology*, Vol.11, pp. 139-148.

Nocedal, J. and Wright, S.J. (1999): *Numerical Optimization*, Springer.

Romboski, L. D. (1969): *An Investigation of Quick Switching Acceptance Sampling System*, Doctoral Dissertation, Rutgers- The State University, New Brunswick, New Jersey.

Sommers, D. J. (1981),"Two-Point Double Variables Sampling Plans", *Journal of Quality Technology*, Vol.13, pp. 25-30.

Soundararajan, V and Arumainayagam, S. D. (1992),"Some Sampling Plans with Identical Operating Characteristics Curves", *Journal of Applied Statistics*, Vol.19, No.1, pp.141-153.

Soundararajan, V and Palanivel, M (1997),"Quick Switching Variables Single Sampling System Indexed by AQL and LQL: Acceptance Criterion Tightening", *Journal of Applied Statistical Science*, Vol.6, No.1, pp.45-57.

Stephens, K. S. and Larson, K. E. (1967),"An Evaluation of the MIL-STD 105D System of Sampling Plans", *Industrial Quality Control*, Vol.23, pp. 310-319.

In: Applied Statistical Theory and Applications
Editor: Mohammad Ahsanullah

ISBN: 978-1-63321-858-1
© 2014 Nova Science Publishers, Inc.

Chapter 7

Characteristics of BIBD and Complementary BIBD in Terms of Triplets of Treatments

S. Mandal[1], C. Zhu[1], D. K. Ghosh[2] and S. C. Bagui[3]

[1]Department of Statistics, University of Manitoba, Winnipeg, Canada
[2]Department of Statistics, Saurashtra University, Rajkot, India
[3]Department of Mathematics and Statistics,
University of West Florida, Pensacola, Florida, US

Abstract

It is well known that in a balanced incomplete block (BIB) design two treatments occur together in the same block equal number of times. Thus the restriction on triplets of treatments is the second condition for balance in the design. In this article, we establish some conditions on the occurrence of triplets of treatments in a BIB design, its complementary design and the design formed by the union of the BIB design and the complementary design. We establish the conditions in terms of the parameters of the original BIB design.

Keywords: BIB design; Characteristic matrix; Complementary design; Resolvable design; Triplets of treatments

1. Introduction

A balanced incomplete block (BIB) design, introduced by Yates (1936), is a binary and connected block design with parameters v, b, r, k and λ, where v is the number of treatments, b is the number of blocks, r is the number of times each treatment is repeated, $k(< v)$ is the block size and λ is the number of times a pair of treatments occur together in the same block. BIB design is a simple and important class of incomplete block design from the construction and analysis point of view. The characteristic matrix (C-matrix) of a BIB design is easily expressed as $C = \theta(I_v - 1/v E_{vv})$, where I_v is the identity matrix of order $v \times v$, E_{vv} is a $v \times v$ matrix with all elements 1, and θ is non-zero eigenvalue of C-matrix with multiplicity $(v-1)$ as the design is connected. The motivation of this paper is to obtain some characteristics of a BIB design, its complementary design and the union of the BIB design and its complementary design in terms of occurrence of triplets of treatments.

BIB designs have also very nice properties in terms of connectedness, non-orthogonality and balancedness. It is well known that in a BIB design two treatments occur together in the same block equal number of times. Thus the restriction on triplets of treatments is the second condition for balance in the design. Designs that are balanced for the pairs as well as for the triplets of treatments are called doubly balanced incomplete block designs (Calvin, 1954). Motivated by this fact, in the present work we establish some criteria by which we can say that, for a given BIB design, number of triplets of treatments occur together an equal number of times. However, for all BIB designs, all the triplets do not occur an equal number of times. Let d and d_1 denote a BIB design and its complementary design respectively. Given the parameters (v, b, r, k, λ) of the BIB design d, it is well known that the parameters of the complementary design d_1 are $v_1 = v, b_1 = b, r_1 = b - r, k_1 = v - k, \lambda_1 = b - 2r + \lambda$. We have shown that the incomplete block design obtained by taking the union of designs d and d_1 all triplets occur an equal number of times. We have also shown that the incomplete block design obtained by taking the union of designs d and d_1 are either another BIBD (with or without repeated blocks) or a variance balanced design with equireplicated and with unequal block sizes.

2.   Triplets of Balanced Incomplete Block Design

For any BIB design triplets of treatments occur if the block size is greater than or equal to 3. In this section we establish a condition in terms of the parameters of BIBD, by which we can express that in the existing BIBD all the triplets occur a constant number of times.

Theorem 2.1. For a BIB design d with parameters v, b, r, k, λ, and with $k \geq 3$, all the triplets occur together a constant number of times provided $\lambda(k-2)$ is divisible by $(v-2)$.

Proof. For a BIB design with parameters v, b, r, k, λ, and with $k \geq 3$, number of triplets for any block is $^kC_3$. So the total number of triplets for the b blocks is $b\,^kC_3$. These triplets will be distinct provided two blocks are distinct. However, in any two blocks, if at least three treatments are identical, then the triplets obtained from these two blocks are not distinct. Again for any BIB design with v treatments, if all triplets occur in the design, the number of distinct triplets are $^vC_3$. Hence, the triplets obtained from b blocks of the BIB design are repeated $b\,^kC_3 / {}^vC_3 = \lambda(k-2)/(v-2)$ times.

Since all the triplets being repeated is always an integer, $\lambda(k-2)$ must be divisible by $(v-2)$. Hence the theorem.

Now we will consider a series of cases.

Corollary 2.1. Any BIB design constructed using the series v, $b = {}^vC_k$, k, $r = {}^{v-1}C_{k-1}$ and $\lambda = {}^{v-2}C_{k-2}$, all triplets occur a constant number of times.

Proof. For a BIB design, all triplets occur a constant number of times if

$$\lambda(k-2) = P(v-2) \tag{1}$$

holds true, where P is an integer. For the given series, (1) becomes $^{v-2}C_{k-2}(k-2) = P(v-2)$. After simplification, we have, $P = {}^{v-3}C_{k-3}$, which is always an integer. Hence, all triplets occur a constant number of times.

Corollary 2.2. If a BIB design is resolvable satisfying $v = 2k$, all triplets occur together a constant number of times.

Proof. For a BIB design with $v = 2k$, we have from (1), $\lambda(k-2) = P(2k-2)$, that is, $P = \lambda(k-2)/2(k-1)$, which is always an integer for any possible values of λ and k of a BIB design with $v = 2k$. Hence, all triplets occur a constant number of times.

We have verified this result by taking all the BIB designs listed in Cochran and Cox (1957), Raghavarao (1971) and Das and Giri (1986). As an example, consider a BIB design with parameters $v = 8, b = 14, r = 7, k = 4, \lambda = 3$. Here P comes out as 1 so all triplets occur only once.

Remark 1.1. If a BIB design is resolvable and does not satisfy $v = 2k$, all triplets do not occur together a constant number of times.

As an example, consider a BIB design with parameters $v = 9, b = 12, r = 4, k = 3, \lambda = 1$. This is a resolvable BIB design and it does not satisfy $v = 2k$. Here, $P = \lambda(k-2)/2(k-1)$ comes out as a fraction $(1/7)$, and hence all triplets do not occur together a constant number of times.

Remark 1.2. If a BIB design is neither resolvable nor constructed using the series discussed in Corollary 2.1, but satisfies $v = 2k$, all triplets do not occur together a constant number of times. As an example consider a BIB design with parameters $v = 6, b = 10, r = 5, k = 3, \lambda = 2$.

Remark 1.3. For a BIB design, occurrence of each triplet a constant number of times implies the occurrence of each triplet another constant number of times in the corresponding complementary design provided that in both BIB design and its complementary design the block sizes are at least three.

3. Triplets of Union of BIB Design and Its Complementary BIB Design

Consider a BIB design, say d, with parameters v, b, r, k, λ. Then the parameters of the complementary design, say d_1, are $v_1 = v, b_1 = b, r_1 = b - r, k_1 = v - k, \lambda_1 = b - 2r + \lambda$. In the complementary design triplets will occur if $k_1 \geq 3$, that is, $v \geq k + 3$. Let us construct a design by taking the union of d and d_1. Call this design as d_2. This combined design is an incomplete block design with equal/unequal block sizes and equal/unequal replication numbers. In the following theorem, we establish a condition by which we can say that all triplets of treatments occur together a constant number of times.

Theorem 3.1. For design d_2, all triplets occur together a constant number of times if $b(v-1) - 3r(v-k)$ is divisible by $(v-1)$, that is, $b(v-1) - 3r(v-k) / (v-1) = P$, where P is an integer.

Proof. In each block of design d, there will be ${}^kC_3$ triplets. There are b blocks in design d. So all together we have $b\,{}^kC_3$ triplets in design d. In the complementary design d_1, we also have b blocks each of size $v - k$. So all together we have $b\,{}^{v-k}C_3$ triplets in the complementary design d_1. Thus, in design d_2, there will be $b({}^kC_3 + {}^{v-k}C_3)$ triplets. Further for design d_2 with v treatments, number of distinct triplets is ${}^vC_3$. So, number of times each triplet being repeated is obtained by

$$P = \frac{b({}^kC_3 + {}^{v-k}C_3)}{{}^vC_3} = \frac{b(v-1) - 3r(v-k)}{v-1}. \tag{2}$$

Here P must be an integer, which is only possible if $b(v-1) - 3r(v-k)$ is divisible by $(v-1)$, in which case all triplets occur together P times. Hence the theorem.

We have verified this result by taking all the BIB designs listed in Cochran and Cox (1957), Raghavarao (1971) and Das and Giri (1986).

Now we establish some nice characteristics of a BIB design along with its complementary BIB design.

Theorem 3.2. Consider a BIB design d with parameters v, $b = {}^vC_k$, $r = {}^{v-1}C_{k-1}$, k, $\lambda = {}^{v-2}C_{k-2}$ with $v = 2k$. Then the design d_2 obtained by combining the BIB design d and its complementary design d_1 is another BIB design with repeated blocks. The parameters of this resulting BIB design is given by $v_2 = v, b_2 = 2b, r_2 = b, k_2 = k, \lambda_2 = 2\lambda$.

Proof. Let N, N_1 and N_2 be the incidence matrices of design d, d_1 and d_2 respectively. As the design d_2 is the union of d and d_1, the incidence matrix N_2 can be written as $N_2 = [N : N_1]$. The concurrence matrix of d_2 can then be written as

$$N_2 N_2' = NN' + N_1 N_1' = 2[(r-\lambda)I_v + \lambda E_{vv}] \tag{3}$$

which is the concurrence matrix of a BIB design with parameters $v_2 = v, b_2 = 2b, r_2 = b, k_2 = k, \lambda_2 = 2\lambda$. Hence the theorem.

Example. Consider a BIB design d with parameters $v = 6, b = 20, r = 10, k = 3, \lambda = 4$. The parameters of the corresponding complementary design d_1 are $v_1 = 6, b_1 = 20, r_1 = 10, k_1 = 3, \lambda_1 = 4$. Using Theorem 3.2, d_2 gives a BIB design with parameters $v_2 = 6, b_2 = 40, r_2 = 20, k_2 = 3, \lambda_2 = 8$. The resulting design is also a resolvable BIB design.

Remark 3.1. BIB designs obtained by using Theorem 3.2 with $v = 2k$ are either resolvable or affine resolvable. For odd k, the design is resolvable (as $v = 2k$ implies $b = 2r$). For even k, the design is affine resolvable (as k^2/v is integer).

Corollary 3.1. Consider a BIB design that does not satisfy $v = 2k$. Then the design d_2 gives an incomplete block design that is a variance balanced design with unequal block sizes and equal replications.

Proof. The C-matrix of design d_2 is obtained by

$$C = \theta(I_v - \frac{1}{v}E_{vv})$$

where θ is the non-zero eigenvalue of the C-matrix with multiplicity $(v-1)$. So the design d_2 is variance balanced. The parameters of d_2 are easily obtained by $v_2 = v, b_2 = 2b, r_2 = b, k_2 = (k, v-k), \lambda_2 = \lambda + \lambda_1$.

As a concluding remark, in this article, our intention was not to construct a balanced incomplete block design (with or without repeated blocks) and a variance balanced design with equireplicated and unequal block sizes. Our main goal was to explain and establish conditions on the occurrences of the triplets of treatments in a BIB design, its complementary BIB design and the design formed by taking the union of a BIB design and its complementary design.

Acknowledgments

The research of S. Mandal is supported by a Discovery Grant from the Natural Sciences and Engineering Research Council (NSERC) of Canada.

References

[1] Calvin, L.D. (1954). Doubly Balanced Incomplete Block Designs for Experiments in which the Treatment Effects are Correlated. *Biometrics*, 10, 61-88.

[2] Cochran, W.G. and Cox, G.M. (1957). *Experimental Designs*. 2nd edition. John Wiley & Sons, New York.

[3] Das, M.N. and Giri, N.C. (1986). *Design and analysis of experiments*. 2nd edition. John Wiley & Sons, New York.

[4] Raghavarao, D. (1971). *Constructions and combinatorial problems in design of experiments*. John Wiley & Sons, New York.

[5] Yates, F. (1936). Incomplete randomized blocks. *Annals of Eugenics*, 7, 121-140.

In: Applied Statistical Theory and Applications
Editor: Mohammad Ahsanullah

ISBN: 978-1-63321-858-1
© 2014 Nova Science Publishers, Inc.

Chapter 8

BAYESIAN INFERENCE FOR AN IMPATIENT M|M|1 QUEUE WITH BALKING

Paul R. Savariappan[1], P. Chandrasekhar[2] and Ambily Jose[2]
[1]Department of Mathematics, Luther College, Decorah, Iowa, US
[2]Department of Statistics, Loyola College, Chennai, India

Abstract

Assuming that the stationary distribution in an M|M|1 balking situation is Negative Binomial, maximum likelihood estimator (MLE) and Bayes estimator of the parameter p based on the number of observations present at several sampled time points are obtained. Further, the minimum posterior risk associated with Bayes estimator and minimum Bayes risk of the estimator are obtained. In addition, the maximum likelihood and consistent asymptotically normal (CAN) estimators and $100(1-\alpha)\%$ asymptotic confidence interval for the expected number of customers in the system are obtained.

Keywords: Bayes estimator – maximum likelihood estimator – minimum posterior risk- M|M|1 queue with balking – multivariate central limit theorem – Slutsky theorem

AMS 2000 subject classification: Primary 60 K 25, Secondary 90 B 2.

1. Introduction

Most of the studies on queuing models are confined to only obtaining expressions for transient or stationary (steady state) solutions and do not consider the associated statistical inference problems. Parametric estimation, interval estimation and Bayesian estimation are some of the essential tools to understand any random phenomena using stochastic models. Analysis of queuing systems in all these directions has not received much attention in the past. Whenever the systems are fully observable in terms of their basic random components such as interarrival times and service times, standard parametric techniques of statistical theory are quite appropriate.

An important aspect of queuing theory is to estimate queuing parameters for which both classical and Bayesian approaches are useful. It is often the case that some information is available on the parameters of the interarrival time or service time distributions from prior experiments or prior analysis of the interarrival time or service time data. The Bayesian approach provides the methodology for formal incorporation of prior information with the current data. Table 1 indicates the present state of work of queuing systems, wherein both classical and Bayesian approaches are used for the estimation of queuing parameters.

Table 1. Confidence Limits for L_S, W_S and W_Q of queueing systems

S.No	System description	Authors	Estimators
1	M|M|1	Clarke (1957)	MLEs of λ and μ
2	M|M|1	Muddapur (1972)	Bayes estimators of λ and μ
3	M|M|1|∞ and M|M|1|N	Yadavalli et al (2004)	MLE of W_Q
4	M|M|c|∞ and M|M|c|N	Yadavalli et al (2006)	MLE of W_Q
5	Tandem queue with blocking and dependent structure for service times	Chandrasekhar et al (2006)	Moment estimators of L_S and W_S
6	Tandem queue with zero queue capacity and with blocking	Chandrasekhar et al (2008)	MLE of W_S

Thiruvaiyaru and Basawa (1992) adopted an empirical Bayesian approach to estimate the parameters of various queuing systems, where they used arrival and service times as the observed data. In all these models considered so far, it may be noted that MLE and Bayes estimator of queuing parameters are obtained by observing mainly number of arrivals and number of service completions in a discrete set up and interarrival time, service time completion, waiting time or sojourn time in the continuous setup. But in a real life situation the number of customers at different time points is easy to observe. Recently, Mukherjee and Chowdhry (2005) have obtained MLE and Bayes estimator of traffic intensity in an M\|M\|1 queuing model based on the number of customers present at several sampled time points. An attempt is made in this paper to obtain MLE of the parameter p based on the number of observations present at several sampled time points assuming that the stationary distribution in an M\|M\|1 balking situation is Negative Binomial. Further, Bayes estimator of p under the same set up, minimum Bayes risk and minimum posterior risk associated with Bayes estimator of p are obtained. In the next section, the MLE of p and its exact distribution are obtained.

2. MLE OF p and Its Exact Distribution

Assume that for an M\|M\|1 balking situation, the stationary distribution is given by

$$p_r = \binom{r + N - 1}{N - 1} p^N q^r, \qquad r = 0,1,2,3 \cdots \tag{2.1}$$

where p+q = 1.

Let $(x_1, x_2, \cdots, x_n)$ denote the number of customers present at different sampled time points $(t_1, t_2, \cdots, t_n)$. The likelihood function of the number of customers $(x_1, x_2, \cdots, x_n)$ present at $(t_1, t_2, \cdots, t_n)$ is given by

$$L(p|x_1, x_2, \cdots, x_n) = \left\{ \prod_{i=1}^{n} \binom{x_i + N - 1}{N - 1} \right\} p^{nN} (1-p)^{\sum_{i=1}^{n} x_i} \qquad (2.2)$$

Clearly,

$$\left(\frac{\partial \log L}{\partial p} \right) = 0 \Rightarrow \hat{p} = \frac{N}{(N+\bar{x})} = \frac{nN}{(nN+y)} \text{ , where } Y = \sum_{i=1}^{n} X_i \sim NB(nN, p)$$

with the probability mass function given by

$$P[Y = y] = \binom{y + nN - 1}{nN - 1} p^{nN} q^y, \qquad y = 0, 1, 2, \cdots$$

$$= f(y; p) \text{ (say)}$$

It readily follows that, $E(Y) = \frac{nNq}{p}$ and $Var(Y) = \frac{nNq}{p^2}$.

Since $\hat{p}$ is a one-to-one function of y, it is clear that $y = 0, 1, 2, 3, \cdots$ with probability mass function given by

$$P[\hat{p} = u] = P\left[\frac{nN}{nN+Y} = u \right] = P\left[Y = \frac{nN(1-u)}{u} \right]$$

$$= \binom{\frac{nN(1-u)}{u} + nN - 1}{nN - 1} p^{nN} q^{\frac{nN(1-u)}{u}} \qquad (2.3)$$

Now, for large n, $E(\hat{p}) \cong \frac{nN}{nN + E[Y]} = p$

and

$$Var(\hat{p}) \cong \left[\left(\frac{d\hat{p}}{dy} \right)^2 Var(Y) \right]_{E(Y) = \frac{nNq}{p}}$$

$$= \frac{q}{nNp^2} \frac{1}{\left(1 + \frac{E(Y)}{nN} \right)^4} = \frac{qp^2}{nN} \rightarrow 0 \text{ as } n \rightarrow \infty$$

i.e., $\hat{p}$ is a consistent estimator of p.

3. Bayes Estimator of p

In this section, Bayes estimator of p and its Bayes risk are obtained by using the same data of section 2 namely the number of customers present at several sampled time points. Beta distribution of first kind is taken as natural conjugate prior density for the parameter p. Assume that, p has a prior distribution Beta of first kind with the parameters α_1 and α_2.

$$i.e., \tau(p|\alpha_1, \alpha_2) = \frac{1}{\beta(\alpha_1, \alpha_2)} p^{\alpha_1 - 1}(1-p)^{\alpha_2 - 1}, \quad 0 < p < 1, \alpha_1, \alpha_2 > 0 \qquad (3.1)$$

The marginal pdf of Y, which is called the predictive pdf is given by

$$f^*(y) = \int_0^1 f(y; p)\, \tau(p|\alpha_1, \alpha_2) dp$$

$$= \frac{\beta(nN + \alpha_1, y + \alpha_2)}{\beta(\alpha_1, \alpha_2)} \binom{y + nN - 1}{nN - 1}$$

Hence, the posterior distribution of p is given by

$$q(p|x_1, x_2, \cdots, x_n) = \frac{f(y; p)\, \tau(p|\alpha_1, \alpha_2)}{\int_0^1 f(y; p)\, \tau(p|\alpha_1, \alpha_2)\, dp}$$

$$= \frac{1}{\beta(nN + \alpha_1, y + \alpha_2)} p^{(nN + \alpha_1) - 1}(1 - p)^{(y + \alpha_2) - 1},$$

$$0 < p < 1 \qquad (3.2)$$

It may be noted that the posterior distribution of p is also that of Beta distribution of I kind with the parameters $(nN + \alpha_1)$ and $(y + \alpha_2)$.

Thus, the Bayes estimator of p under squared error loss is given by

$$E(p|x_1, x_2, \cdots, x_n) = \int_0^1 p \cdot q(p|x_1, x_2, \cdots, x_n) dp$$

$$= \frac{(nN + \alpha_1)}{(nN + \alpha_1 + \alpha_2 + y)} \qquad (3.3)$$

Further, the minimum posterior risk associated with this Bayes estimator is given by

$$V_p(\hat{p}^B | x_1, x_2, \cdots, x_n) = E[\hat{p} - p]^2$$

$$= \int_0^1 (\hat{p} - p)^2 \cdot q(p|x_1, x_2, \cdots, x_n) dp$$

$$= \frac{n^2 N^2}{(nN + y)^2} + \frac{(nN + \alpha_1)}{(nN + \alpha_1 + \alpha_2 + y)} \left\{ \frac{y(\alpha_1 + 1) - nN(nN + \alpha_1 + 2\alpha_2 + y + 1)}{(nN + \alpha_1 + \alpha_2 + y + 1)(nN + y)} \right\} \qquad (3.4)$$

Now, the marginal distribution $h(x_1, x_2, \cdots, x_n)$ of $f(x_1, x_2, \cdots, x_n)$ is given by

$$
\begin{aligned}
h(x_1, x_2, \cdots, x_n) &= \int_0^1 L(p|x_1, x_2, \cdots, x_n) \cdot \tau(p|\alpha_1, \alpha_2) dp \\
&= \frac{\beta(nN + \alpha_1, y + \alpha_2)}{\beta(\alpha_1, \alpha_2)} \prod_{i=1}^{n} \binom{x_i + N - 1}{N - 1}
\end{aligned}
$$

Now, the minimum Bayes risk $r_{\tau, \hat{p}^B}$ of $\hat{p}^B$ is given by

$$
\begin{aligned}
r_{\tau, \hat{p}^B} &= E\left[V_p\left(\hat{p}^B | x_1, x_2, \cdots, x_n\right)\right] \\
&= \sum_{y=0}^{\infty} V_p(\hat{p}^B | x_1, x_2, \cdots, x_n) \cdot h(x_1, x_2, \cdots, x_n) \\
&= \frac{\prod_{i=1}^{n} \binom{x_i + N - 1}{N - 1}}{\beta(\alpha_1, \alpha_2)} \sum_{y=0}^{\infty} \left\{ \frac{\alpha_1(\alpha_1 + 1)y^2 + n^2 N^2 \alpha_2(\alpha_2 + 1) + nNy(nN + y - 2\alpha_1\alpha_2)}{(nN + y)^2(nN + \alpha_1 + \alpha_2 + y)(nN + \alpha_1 + \alpha_2 + y + 1)} \right\} x \\
&\qquad \beta(nN + \alpha_1, y + \alpha_2)
\end{aligned}
$$

4. Expected Number of Customers in the System

Suppose in M|M|1 balking model, the discouragement function b_n is given by

$$
b_n = e^{-\frac{\alpha n}{\mu}}, \qquad n = 1, 2, \cdots; \quad b_0 \equiv 1.
$$

Hence, the stationary distribution $\{ p_n, n \geq 0\}$ is given by

$$
p_n = p_0 \left[\frac{\lambda}{\mu}\right]^n \prod_{i=1}^{n} b_{i-1}, \qquad n = 0, 1, 2, \cdots
$$

Now, $\sum_{n=0}^{\infty} p_n = 1 \Rightarrow p_0 = \dfrac{1}{\left[1 + \sum_{j=1}^{\infty} \left(\frac{\lambda}{\mu}\right)^j \cdot e^{-\frac{j(j-1)\alpha}{2\mu}}\right]}$

In other words, $p_n = \dfrac{\left[\frac{\lambda}{\mu}\right]^n \cdot e^{-\frac{n(n-1)\alpha}{2\mu}}}{\left[1 + \sum_{j=1}^{\infty} \left[\frac{\lambda}{\mu}\right]^j \cdot e^{-\frac{j(j-1)\alpha}{2\mu}}\right]}, \qquad n = 0, 1, 2, \cdots$

Now, the expected number of customers in the system is given by

$$
L_s = \sum_{n=0}^{\infty} n p_n = \frac{1}{\left[1 + \sum_{j=1}^{\infty} \left[\frac{\lambda}{\mu}\right]^j \cdot e^{-\frac{j(j-1)\alpha}{2\mu}}\right]} \sum_{n=0}^{\infty} n \cdot \left[\frac{\lambda}{\mu}\right]^n \cdot e^{-\frac{n(n-1)\alpha}{2\mu}} \tag{4.1}
$$

5. MLE and CAN Estimator for the Expected Number of Customers in the System

5.1. ML Estimator

Let $X_1, X_2, ..., X_n$ and $Y_1, Y_2, ..., Y_n$ be two independent random samples each of size n drawn from exponential interarrival time and exponential service time populations with the parameters λ and μ respectively. It is clear that $E[\overline{X}] = \frac{1}{\lambda}$ and $E[\overline{Y}] = \frac{1}{\mu}$, where $\overline{X}$ and $\overline{Y}$ are the sample means of interarrival times and service times respectively. It can be shown that $\overline{X}$ and $\overline{Y}$ are the MLE's of $\frac{1}{\lambda}$ and $\frac{1}{\mu}$ respectively.

Let $\theta_1 = \frac{1}{\lambda}$ and $\theta_2 = \frac{1}{\mu}$. Clearly, the expected number of customers in the system given in (4.1) reduces to

$$L_s = \frac{1}{\left[1+\sum_{j=1}^{\infty}\left[\frac{\theta_2}{\theta_1}\right]^j . e^{-\frac{j(j-1)\alpha\theta_2}{2}}\right]} . \sum_{n=0}^{\infty} n . \left[\frac{\theta_2}{\theta_1}\right]^n . e^{-\frac{n(n-1)\alpha\theta_2}{2}} \tag{5.1}$$

and hence MLE of L_s is given by

$$\hat{L}_s = \frac{1}{\left[1+\sum_{j=1}^{\infty}\left[\frac{\overline{Y}}{\overline{X}}\right]^j e^{-\frac{j(j-1)\alpha\overline{Y}}{2}}\right]} . \sum_{n=0}^{\infty} n . \left[\frac{\overline{Y}}{\overline{X}}\right]^n . e^{-\frac{n(n-1)\alpha\overline{Y}}{2}}$$

It may be noted that $\hat{L}_s$ is a real valued function in $\overline{X}$ and $\overline{Y}$, which is also differentiable. Consider the following application of multivariate central limit theorem. see Rao(1974).

5.2. Application of Multivariate Central Limit Theorem

Suppose $T_1', T_2', T_3', ...$ are independent and identically distributed k- dimensional random variables such that

$$T_n' = (T_{1n}, T_{2n}, T_{3n}, ..., T_{kn}), n = 1,2,3,...$$

having the first and second order moments $E(T_n) = \mu$ and $var(T_n) = \sum$. Define the sequence of random variables

$$\overline{T}_n{}' = (\overline{T}_{1n}, \overline{T}_{2n}, ..., \overline{T}_{kn}), n = 1,2,3,...$$

where $\overline{T}_{in} = \frac{\sum_{j=1}^{n} T_{ij}}{n}$, $i = 1,2,3,...,k; j = 1,2,3,...,n$.

Then, $\sqrt{n}(\overline{T}_n - \mu) \xrightarrow{d} N_k(0, \sum)$ as $n \to \infty$.

5.3. CAN Estimator

By applying the multivariate central limit theorem given in section 5.2, it is readily seen that $\sqrt{n}[(\overline{X}, \overline{Y}) - (\theta_1, \theta_2)] \xrightarrow{d} N_2(0, \Sigma)$ as $n \to \infty$, where the dispersion matrix $\Sigma = ((\sigma_{ij}))$ is given by $\Sigma = \text{diag}(\theta_1^2, \theta_2^2)$. Again from Rao (1974), we have

$$\sqrt{n}(\hat{L}_s - L_s) \xrightarrow{d} N(0, \sigma^2(\theta)) \text{ as } n \to \infty.$$

where $\theta = (\theta_1, \theta_2)$ and

$$\sigma^2(\theta) = \sum_{i=1}^{2} \left(\frac{\partial L_s}{\partial \theta_i}\right)^2 \sigma_{ii}$$

$$= \sum_{i=1}^{2} \left(\frac{\partial L_s}{\partial \theta_i}\right)^2 \theta_i^2 \tag{5.2}$$

By substituting the partial derivatives $\left(\frac{\partial L_s}{\partial \theta_i}\right)$, $i = 1, 2$ in (5.2), we obtain an expression for $\sigma^2(\theta)$. Thus, $\hat{L}_s$ is a CAN estimator of L_s. There are several methods for generating CAN estimators and the Method of moments and the Method of Maximum likelihood are commonly used to generate such estimators. see Sinha(1986).

5.4. Confidence Limits for the Expected Number of Customers in the System

Let $\sigma^2(\hat{\theta})$ be the estimator of $\sigma^2(\theta)$ obtained by replacing θ by a consistent estimator $\hat{\theta}$ namely $\hat{\theta} = (\overline{X}, \overline{Y})$. Let $\widehat{\sigma^2} = \sigma^2(\hat{\theta})$. Since $\sigma^2(\theta)$ is a continuous function of θ, $\widehat{\sigma^2}$ is a consistent estimator of $\sigma^2(\theta)$.

$$\text{i.e., } \widehat{\sigma^2} \xrightarrow{P} \sigma^2(\theta) \text{ as } n \to \infty.$$

By Slutsky theorem

$$\left(X_n \xrightarrow{d} X, \ Y_n \xrightarrow{P} b \Rightarrow \frac{X_n}{Y_n} \xrightarrow{d} \frac{X}{b}, b \neq 0\right),$$

we have

$$\sqrt{n}\left(\frac{\hat{L}_s - L_s}{\hat{\sigma}}\right) \xrightarrow{d} N(0,1)$$

$$\text{i.e., } Pr\left[-k_{\frac{\alpha}{2}} < \frac{\sqrt{n}(\hat{L}_s - L_s)}{\hat{\sigma}} < k_{\frac{\alpha}{2}}\right] = (1 - \alpha),$$

where $k_{\frac{\alpha}{2}}$ is obtained from normal tables. Hence, a $100(1-\alpha)\%$ asymptotic confidence interval for L_s is given by

$$\hat{L}_s \pm k_{\frac{\alpha}{2}} \frac{\hat{\sigma}}{\sqrt{n}}. \tag{5.3}$$

where $\hat{\sigma}$ is obtained from (5.2).

Acknowledgment

The research of P.Chandrasekhar has been sponsored by the University Grants Commission, New Delhi.

References

[1]   Chandrasekhar, P., Chandrasekar, B. and Yadavalli, V.S.S. (2006)-Statistical Inference for a tandem queue with dependent structure for service times, *Proceedings of the Sixth IASTED International Conference on Modelling, Simulation and Optimization*, September 11-13, 2006, Gaborone, Botswana, pp 233-238.

[2]   Chandrasekhar, P., Natarajan,R. and Yadavalli, V.S.S.(2008)-Statistical analysis for a tandem queue with blocking, *Proceedings of the second National Conference on Management Science and Practice* (N. Ravichandran, Ed), Allied Publishers Pvt. Ltd, March 9-11, 2007, Chennai, India, pp 65-72.

[3]   Clarke, A. B. (1957)- Maximum Likelihood estimates in a simple queue, *Ann. Math Stat.*, 28, pp 1036-1040.

[4]   Muddapur, M. V. (1972)-Bayesian estimates of parameters in some queuing models, *Ann. Inst. Stat. Math.*, 24, pp 327-331.

[5]   Mukherjee, S. P. and Shovan Chowdhury (2005)-Maximum Likelihood and Bayes estimators in M|M|1 queue, *Stochastic Modelling and Applications*, Vol 8, No 2, pp 47-55.

[6]   Radhakrishna Rao, C. (1974)-*Linear Statistical Inference and its applications*, Wiley Eastern Pvt. Ltd., New Delhi.

[7]   Sinha, S. K. (1986)-*Reliability and Life Testing*, Wiley Eastern Pvt. Ltd., New Delhi.

[8]   Thiruvaiyaru, D. and Basawa, I. V. (1992)-Empirical Bayes estimation for queuing systems and networks, *Queuing Sys.*, 11, pp 179-202.

[9]   Yadavalli, V. S. S., Adendorff, K., Erasmus, G., Chandrasekhar, P. and Deepa, S. P. (2004)-Confidence limits for expected waiting time of two queuing models, *OriON* (South Africa), Vol. 20, No 1, pp 1-6.

[10] Yadavalli, V.S.S., Natarajan, R., and Chandrasekhar, P. (2006)-Confidence limits for expected waiting time of M|M|c|∞ and M|M|c|N queuing models, *Pak. J. Statist*, Vol. 22(2), pp 171-178.

In: Applied Statistical Theory and Applications
Editor: Mohammad Ahsanullah

ISBN: 978-1-63321-858-1
© 2014 Nova Science Publishers, Inc.

Chapter 9

INTERVAL ESTIMATION FOR WEIBULL DISTRIBUTION BASED ON A SAMPLE OF SIZE ONE

S. V. Sabnis[1] and A. D. Dharmadhikari[2]
[1]Dept. of Mathematics, IIT Bombay, Powai, Mumbai, India
[2]Quality & Reliability Division, Tata Motors, Pune, India

Abstract

In this paper, we demonstrate the method of construction of $100(1-\delta)\%$ confidence interval for parameter λ (scale parameter) of a Weibull distribution based on a sample of size one. We take a cue from this method to construct a similar $100(1-\delta)\%$ confidence intervals for these parameters based on $X_{1:n} = \min\{X_1, X_2, \ldots, X_n\}$ where $X_1, X_2, \ldots, X_n$ are $n(\geq 2)$ independent random variables from a Weibull distribution having parameters λ and β. For $\beta = 1$, i.e. for exponential distribution, although the proposed confidence interval for the mean λ overlaps with the confidence interval based on chi-square distribution, the former one is significantly narrower than the latter one. For $n \geq 2$ additional numerical results that compare proposed $100(1-\delta)\%$ confidence intervals for λ with the ones that are given in Bain and Engelhardt (1991) are provided. It is interesting to note that the former ones turn out to be significantly narrower than the latter ones for samples of sizes 1 through 5 for $\delta = 0.02, 0.05$ and 0.10.

1. Introduction

In many industrial situations, development of a product involves use of extremely expensive prototypes. Even the accelerated life testing requires large amount of time to yield complete life. In such situations the user is required to make inferences about the product as and when the first observation becomes available. Such inferential work based on sample size one is available for random variables having normal distribution. Machol and Rosenblatt (1966) provided $100(1-\delta)\%$ confidence interval (CI) of finite length for the mean (μ) for the given standard deviation, σ, when $X \sim N(\mu, \sigma^2)$. For this case, Balchman and Machol (1987) obtained σ-free bounds for μ. Edelman (1990) showed that for every value of δ, $100(1-\delta)\%$ confidence interval can be constructed for the mean of any unimodal distribution. Recently, Wall, Boen and Tweedie (2001) produced σ-free bounds for μ based on samples of size n=2 that are better than traditional bounds based on t-distribution.

In the context of reliability theory parametric distributions such as exponential, Gamma and Weibull distributions play very vital role. In this paper some inferential work based on sample of size one as well as sample of size $n \geq 2$ for Weibull distribution is presented. To be specific we consider the problem of providing $100(1-\delta)\%$ confidence interval for the scale parameter λ of a Weibull distribution on the basis of sample sizes n=1 and $n \geq 2$ when the shape parameter β is unknown. The only information required about β is whether $\beta < 1$ or $\beta > 1$, i.e., essentially the information in terms of the aging properties of the component. It should be emphasized that when n=1 and $\beta = 1$ (exponential distribution), although the proposed confidence interval overlaps with the traditional confidence interval based on chi-square distribution, it is significantly narrower than the latter one. It is interesting to note that for $n \geq 2$, the pivot for the confidence interval is taken to be the first order statistics $X_{1:n}$ which represents the lifetime of a series system of n independent components. For $n \geq 2$ additional numerical results that compare proposed $100(1-\delta)\%$ confidence intervals for λ with the ones that are given in Bain and Engelhardt (1991) are provided. It should be highlighted that the former ones turn out to be significantly narrower than the latter ones for samples of sizes 1 through 5 for $\delta = 0.02, 0.05$ and 0.10.

The organization of this paper is as follows. Section 1 contains introduction. Various subsections of Section 2 contain discussion on $100(1-\delta)\%$ confidence intervals for various ranges of β. Specifically, Subsections 2.1, 2.2 and 2.3 deal with construction of $100(1-\delta)\%$ confidence intervals for the scale parameter of Weibull distribution based on a single observation and when $\beta = 1$, $\beta > 1$ and $\beta < 1$ respectively. Subsection 2.4 discusses numerical results corresponding to theoretical results presented in Subsections 2.2 and 2.3. Section 3 gives similar results when the sample size n is at least 2.

2. Confidence Interval for λ Based on Sample of Size One

It is known that the cumulative distribution function (CDF) of a Weibull random variable X with parameters λ and β is given by

$$F(x) = 1 - \exp\left(-\left(\frac{x}{\lambda}\right)^{\beta}\right), \quad x > 0; \ \lambda > 0, \ \beta > 0. \tag{2.1}$$

To decide the nature of the confidence interval, we use the fact that $F(X)$ is $U[0,1]$ random variable. Now for given $\delta \in (0,1)$ there exist a and b $(0 < a < b < 1)$ such that

$$P[a < F(X) < b] = 1 - \delta. \tag{2.2}$$

Using $F(x)$ as given in Equation 2.1, one can simplify Equation 2.2 as

$$P[k_1 X \leq \lambda \leq k_2 X] = 1 - \delta \tag{2.3}$$

where k_1 and k_2 depend upon shape parameter β. Further k_2 may be infinite and k_1 may be zero for a given value of δ. The question is - can one get β-free bounds for λ? We answer this question in affirmative. We in fact show that if limited information about β, say $\beta < 1$ or $\beta > 1$, is available then for δ in disjoint subintervals of (0,1) it is possible to provide β-free bounds for λ. It is worthwhile to note that $\beta > 1$ ($\beta < 1$) is a well known case of IFR

(DFR) distribution. If the problem is related to the life of a mechanical component whose lifetime has adverse effect on aging then assuming $\beta > 1$ is natural, where as, if the problem is related to repair (replacement) times then assuming $\beta < 1$ may be more adequate. Below, we attempt to provide CI for both these situations.

Note that when $k_1 > 0$ and $k_2 > 0$, in view of Equation 2.1, Equation 2.3 simplifies to

$$e^{-(\frac{1}{k_2})^\beta} - e^{-(\frac{1}{k_1})^\beta} = 1 - \delta. \tag{2.4}$$

This, in turn, yields

$$k_2(\beta) = [-\ln\{(1-\delta) + e^{-(\frac{1}{k_1})^\beta}\}]^{-1/\beta}. \tag{2.5}$$

Note that $k_2(\beta)$ in the above equation is defined if and only if

$$k_1 < q_1^{1/\beta} \tag{2.6}$$

where $q_1 = (-\ln\delta)^{-1}$. Hence for a known β, one may select $k_1 = q_1^{1/\beta}$ and the corresponding $100(1-\delta)\%$ confidence interval will become $(k_1 X, k_2 X)$. Observe that $q_1 < 1 \Leftrightarrow \delta < e^{-1}$ and $q_1 \geq 1 \Leftrightarrow \delta \geq e^{-1}$. However for this choice of k_1, $k_2(\beta) = \infty$ for all values of β. This suggests that we need to consider values of $k_1 \in (0, q_1^{1/\beta})$ for which k_2 is finite. As mentioned earlier, our aim is to construct β-free confidence interval when the value of β is unknown. We, first begin with the case $\beta = 1$ which corresponds to exponential distribution having mean λ.

2.1.   Confidence Interval for λ when $\beta = 1$

As noted above, $k_2(1)$ is defined if and only if $k_1 \leq q_1^1$ where $q_1 = (-\ln\delta)^{-1}$. Therefore $100(1-\delta)\%$ CI exists and is given by $(k_1 X, k_2(1)X)$ where $k_1 = a(-\ln\delta)^{-1}$ for $a \in (0, 1)$ and $k_2(1)$ is as defined in Equation 2.5. The comparison of this CI with the CI based on chi-square distribution is made in the following table by taking $a = 1/2$ and it reveals that although the former CI is not completely contained in the latter CI, it is significantly narrower than the CI's based on chi-square distribution. Moreover, it turns out to be narrower irrespective of the value of a. As the value of a increases, the confidence interval becomes more and more narrower, and eventually it gets completely contained in the confidence interval based on chi-square distribution. X appearing in the following table represents a single observation from exponential distribution with mean λ.

Remark 2.1. *It is true that the CI based on chi-square distribution can be made shorter by moving the cut-off points to the left. However, note that in the methodology given above k_1 depends on $a \in (0, 1)$ and thus the choice of a can be made so as to ensure that the proposed CI is shorter than the former one.*

Remark 2.2. *It may be noted that, unlike the traditional CI, the proposed CI is not constructed using maximum likelihood estimator.*

Next, we consider the case $\beta > 1$.

Table 2.1.

	CI based on chi-square distribution	New proposed CI
$\delta = .01$	(0.1887X, 199.4992X)	(0.1086X, 100.5092X)
$\delta = .05$	(0.2711X, 39.5257X)	(0.1669X, 20.5488X)
$\delta = 0.1$	(0.3338X, 19.4956X)	(0.2171X, 10.6032X)

2.2. Confidence Interval for λ when $\beta > 1$

It follows from Inequality (2.6) that $100(1-\delta)\%$ CI $(k_1 X, k_2 X)$ has an infinite length when $k_1 = q_1^{1/\beta}$. Thus it is of interest to determine values of k_1 in $(0, q_1^{1/\beta})$ for which $0 < k_1 < k_2 < \infty$. The natural β-free choice for k_1 is $\inf\limits_{\beta > 1} q_1^{1/\beta}$. Thus

$$\inf_{\beta > 1} q_1^{1/\beta} = \begin{cases} q_1 & \text{if } \delta < e^{-1} \quad (i.e. \ q_1 < 1) \\ 1 & \text{if } \delta \geq e^{-1} \quad (i.e. \ q_1 \geq 1). \end{cases}$$

We need to consider two cases.

Case I. $\delta < e^{-1}$ (i.e. $q_1 < 1$)

In this case $\inf\limits_{\beta > 1} q_1^{1/\beta} = q_1$, and if we take $k_1 = q_1$ then

$$\begin{aligned} k_2(\beta) &= [-\ln(1 - \delta + e^{-(\frac{1}{q_1})^\beta})]^{-1/\beta} \\ &< q_3^{1/\beta} \end{aligned} \tag{2.7}$$

where $q_3 = [-\ln(1 - \delta + e^{-(\frac{1}{k_1})})]^{-1}$ for $k_1 \in (0, q_1)$. Hence any value in the interval $(k_2(\beta), \infty)$ is a candidate for the coefficient of an upper bound. In order to have a β-free choice of the coefficient of an upper bound, one needs to consider $\bigcap\limits_{\beta > 1} (k_2(\beta), \infty)$ which is equal to $(\sup\limits_{\beta > 1} k_2(\beta), \infty)$. However, $\sup\limits_{\beta > 1} k_2(\beta) = \infty$ for $q_1 < 1$. This shows that there is no finite upper bound when $q_1 < 1$. Further, it is worthwhile to add that for any value of $k_1 \in (0, q_1)$, the corresponding β-free upperbound is ∞.

Thus, in this case, CI is of the type $(aq_1 X, \infty)$, $a \in (0, 1)$, having at least $(1 - \delta)$ confidence coefficient. Note that $(q_1 X, \infty)$ is the optimal CI having $(1 - \delta)$ confidence coefficient.

Next we consider the case $\delta > e^{-1}$.

Case II. $\delta \geq e^{-1}$ (i.e. $q_1 \geq 1$)

In this case $\inf\limits_{\beta > 1} q_1^{1/\beta} = 1$ and, therefore, the coefficient, k_1, of lower bound is a number between $(0,1]$. When $k_1 = 1$, $k_2(\beta) = q_2^{1/\beta}$ where

$$q_2 = [-\ln(1 - \delta + e^{-1})]^{-1}.$$

The following observations, namely,

$$q_2 > 1 \Leftrightarrow \delta < 1,$$

and

$$\delta \geq e^{-1} \Leftrightarrow q_2 \geq 0$$

ensure that an upper bound $q_2^{1/\beta}X$ is finite provided $\delta \in [e^{-1}, 1)$. Now, using arguments similar to Case I, it follows that for β-free CI the coefficient k_2 must belong to $\bigcap_{\beta>1} (q_2^{1/\beta}, \infty)$ and this intersection is equal to $[\sup_{q_2>1,\beta>1} q_2^{1/\beta}, \infty)$. In otherwords, the coefficient $k_2 \in [q_2, \infty)$. When $k_2 = q_2$, the CI with at least $(1-\delta)$ confidence coefficient is given by (X, q_2X).

Results obtained in Case I and Case II are summarized below in the form of a theorem.

Theorem 2.1. *If $X \sim W(\lambda, \beta)$, $\beta > 1$ with $F_X(x) = 1 - \exp(-(\frac{x}{\lambda})^\beta)$, then β-free confidence interval with at least $(1-\delta)$ confidence coefficient for the scale parameter λ is (i) (q_1X, ∞) for $\delta \in (0, e^{-1})$ with $q_1 = (-\ln\delta)^{-1}$ and (ii) (X, q_2X) for $\delta \in (e^{-1}, 1)$ with $q_2 = [-\ln(1 - \delta + e^{-1})]^{-1}$.*

We note that the above theorem provides a finite length CI for $\delta \in (e^{-1}, 1)$, while for $\delta \in (0, e^{-1})$ it does not have a finite upper bound. We address the latter issue in Theorems 2.3 and 2.4. Prior to that, below, we examine the case for $\beta < 1$.

2.3. Confidence Interval for λ when $\beta < 1$

The rationale employed in Section 2.2 to obtain β-free upper and lower bounds, wherever possible, is used in this section also. To avoid repetition, it is not stated explicitly below. In this case

$$\inf_{\beta<1} k_1 = \begin{cases} 0 & \text{if } \delta < e^{-1} \\ q_1 & \text{if } \delta \geq e^{-1}. \end{cases}$$

When $\delta < e^{-1}$, using $k_1 = 0$, Equation 2.5 yields,

$$k_2(\beta) = [-\ln(1-\delta)]^{-1/\beta}.$$

For $0 < \delta < e^{-1}$, $[-\ln(1-\delta)]^{-1} > 1$ we have $\sup k_2(\beta) = \infty$. Hence $100(1-\delta)\%$ confidence interval for $\delta < e^{-1}$ and $\beta < 1$ is $(0, \infty)$.

For $\delta > e^{-1}$, we have $\inf q_1^{1/\beta} = q_1$ which is greater than or equal to one. Hence any number aq_1 with $0 < a < 1$ is a candidate for k_1. One may verify that β-free bound for $k_2(aq_1)$ turns out to be ∞ when supremum is taken over entire range $(0,1)$ of β. Hence in this case, the result can be summarized as given below.

Theorem 2.2. *If $X \sim W(\lambda, \beta)$, $\beta < 1$ with $F_X(x) = 1 - e^{(-(\frac{x}{\lambda})^\beta)}$, then β-free confidence interval with at least $(1-\delta)$ confidence coefficient for the scale parameter λ is (i) $(0, \infty)$ for $\delta \in (0, e^{-1})$ and (ii) (q_1X, ∞) for $\delta \in (e^{-1}, 1)$ with $q_1 = (-\ln\delta)^{-1}$.*

Note that Theorem 2.2 states that with minimal information, one can not provide a finite length β-free confidence interval for the scale parameter λ of a Weibull distribution having β as its shape parameter.

Table 2.2.

	$\delta \in (0, e^{-1})$	$\delta \in (e^{-1}, 1)$
$\beta \in (0,1)$	$(0, \infty)$	$(q_1 X, \infty)$
$\beta \in (1, \infty)$	$(q_1 X, \infty)$	$(X, q_2 X)$

These several $100(1-\delta)\%$ CIs obtained in Theorems 2.1 and 2.2 can be summarized in the following table.

where q_1 and q_2 are as defined in Theorems 2.1 and 2.2. Next we give below a theorem which shows that if an additional information about β such as $1 < \beta_0 \leq \beta$ or $0 < \beta_0 < \beta < 1$ for known β_0 is available then it is possible to provide finite length CI for λ.

Theorem 2.3. *For $\beta \in [\beta_0, \infty)$, $\beta_0 > 1$, $100(1-\delta)\%$ CI is given by (i) $(aq_1 X, q_4^{1/\beta_0} X)$ if $\delta \in (0, e^{-1})$, (ii) $(X, q_2 X)$ if $\delta \in (e^{-1}, 1 - e^{-1})$, and, (iii) $(\max\{aq_1 X, X\}, \min\{q_2 X, X\})$ if $\delta \in (1 - e^{-1}, 1)$ where $q_1 = (-\ln \delta)$, $q_2 = [-\ln(1 - \delta + e^{-1})]^{-1}$, and $q_4 = [-\ln(1 - \delta + e^{-n})]^{-1}$. Here $a \in (0,1)$, and $n > 1$ are such that $\left(\dfrac{1}{aq_1}\right)^{\beta_0} > n$.*

Proof. Recall that

$$k_2 = \left[-\ln \left(1 - \delta + e^{-\left(\frac{1}{k_1}\right)^\beta} \right)^{-1} \right]^{1/\beta}$$

is defined only if $k_1 \leq q_1^{1/\beta}$ where $q_1 = (-\ln \delta)^{-1}$. Now,

$$\inf_{\beta \in [\beta_0, \infty)} k_1 = \begin{cases} q_1 & \text{if } q_1 < 1 \\ 1 & \text{if } q_1 \geq 1. \end{cases}$$

Here again two cases arise.

Case 1. If $q_1 \geq 1$ let $k_1 = 1$. Then $k_2 = q_2^{1/\beta}$ where $q_2 = [-\ln(1 - \delta + e^{-1})]^{-1}$, and,

$$\sup_{\beta \in [\beta_0, \infty)} q_2^{1/\beta} = \begin{cases} 1 & \text{if } q_2 \leq 1 \\ q_2 & \text{if } q_2 \geq 1 \end{cases}$$

Hence for $\delta \in (e^{-1}, 1)$, $100(1-\delta)\%$ CI for λ is $(X, q_2 X)$.

Case 2. If $q_1 < 1$ then $k_1 = q_1$. This yields the following inequality, namely,

$$\left[-\ln(1 - \delta + e^{-\left(\frac{1}{q_1}\right)^\beta})^{-1} \right]^{1/\beta} = k_2(q_1)$$

$$< q_3^{1/\beta} \qquad (2.8)$$

where $q_3 = [-\ln(1 - \delta + e^{-(\frac{1}{q_1})})]^{-1}$. But $k_1 = q_1$ implies that $q_3 = \infty$. Hence $k_1 = q_1$ does not provide finite upper bound. To get a finite upper bound, we find a, n such that

$$\frac{1}{q_1}\left(\frac{1}{n+1}\right)^{1/\beta} < a < \frac{1}{q_1}\left(\frac{1}{n}\right)^{1/\beta}$$

and this, in turn, leads to

$$[-\ln(1 - \delta + e^{-(n+1)})^{-1}]^{1/\beta} < [-\ln(1 - \delta + e^{-\frac{1}{aq_1}})^{-1}]^{1/\beta} < [-\ln(1 - \delta + e^{-(n)})^{-1}]^{1/\beta}.$$

Therefore, $k_2(aq_1) \le q_4^{1/\beta}$ where $q_4 = [-\ln(1 - \delta + e^{-n})]^{-1}$. Therefore,

$$\sup_{\beta \in [\beta_0, \infty)} q_4^{1/\beta} = \begin{cases} 1 & \text{if } q_4 \le 1 \\ q_4^{1/\beta_0} & \text{if } q_4 \ge 1. \end{cases}$$

Therefore, for $\delta \in (0, e^{-1})$ $100(1 - \delta)\%$ CI for λ is given by $(aq_1 X, q_4^{1/\beta_0} X)$. If $q_4 < 1$ then $100(1 - \delta)\%$ CI for λ is given by $(aq_1 X, X)$.

Theorem 2.4. *For* $\beta \in (\beta_0, 1)$, $\beta_0 > 0$, $100(1 - \delta)\%$ *CI for* λ *is (i)* $(aq_1 X, q^{1/\beta_0} X)$ *if* $\delta \in (e^{-1}, 1 - e^{-1})$, *(ii)* $(aq_1 X, qX)$ *if* $\delta > 1 - e^{-1}$ *where* $q = [-\ln(1 - \delta + e^{-m})]^{-1}$, $0 < a < \frac{1}{q_1}$ *and* $m > 1$ *are numbers such that* $a < \dfrac{1}{m^{\frac{1}{\beta_0}} q_1}$.

Proof. Let $\beta \in (\beta_0, 1)$. Note that for $a \in (0, \frac{1}{q_1})$, there exists $m(\beta_0, \delta)$ such that $a < \dfrac{1}{m^{\frac{1}{\beta_0}} q_1}$. This leads to

$$[-\ln(1 - \delta + e^{-\left(\frac{1}{aq_1}\right)^{\beta}})]^{-1/\beta} < [-\ln(1 - \delta + e^{-m})]^{-1/\beta} = q^{1/\beta}$$

where $q = [-\ln(1 - \delta + e^{-m})]^{-1}$. Therefore,

$$\sup_{\beta \in (\beta_0, 1)} q^{\frac{1}{\beta}} = \begin{cases} q & \text{if } q \le 1 \\ q^{1/\beta_0} & \text{if } q \ge 1. \end{cases}$$

Therefore, for $\delta > 1 - e^{-1}$, $100(1 - \delta)\%$ CI for λ is given by $(aq_1 X, qX)$ whereas the same for $\delta \in (e^{-1}, 1 - e^{-1})$ is equal to $(aq_1 X, q^{1/\beta_0} X)$. In view of Theorems 2.3 and 2.4, Table 2.2 is modified accordingly to contain more precise information on bounds on λ and is given below in the form of Table 2.3.

Here q, q_1, q_2 and q_4 are as defined in Theorems 2.3 and 2.4.

Remark 2.3. *For completeness sake, confidence intervals are provided for various values of* $\delta \in (0, 1)$. *For* $\beta < 1$ *and for smaller values of* δ, *finite intervals do not exit and hence are not available. However for* $\beta > 1$, *finite confidence intervals having confidence coefficient to be at least 0.63 can be obtained. It may, further, be noted that in practice there are instances in which actual coverage probabilities are as low as 30% for 95% or 99% confidence intervals for parameters of interest. Thus with confidence intervals having at least 0.63 confidence coefficient, it should be considered quite reasonable even if the coverage probability is about 50%.*

Table 2.3.

	$\delta \in (0, e^{-1})$	$\delta \in (e^{-1}, 1 - e^{-1})$	$\delta \in (1 - e^{-1}, 1)$
$0 < \beta_0 < \beta < 1$	$(0, \infty)$	$\left(aq_1 X, q^{\frac{1}{\beta_0}} X \right)$	$(aq_1 X, qX)$
$\beta > \beta_0 > 1$	$\left(aq_1 X, q_4^{\frac{1}{\beta_0}} X \right)$	$(X, q_2 X)$	$(X, q_2 X)$

Remark 2.4. *As mentioned earlier, it may be noted that the issue of optimality of CIs has not been considered in this paper.*

Remark 2.5. *Edelman (1990) showed that if X is a continuous random variable with unimodal density that has mode θ, then for any fixed a and $t > 1$,*

$$P[X - t|X - a| \leq \theta \leq X + t|X - a|] \geq 1 - \frac{2}{t+1}.$$

Note that for Weibull distribution with parameters λ and β,

$$\theta = \begin{cases} 0 & \text{if } \beta \leq 1 \\ \lambda(\frac{\beta-1}{\beta})^{1/\beta} & \text{if } \beta > 1. \end{cases}$$

Thus if $\beta > 1$, then Edelman's bounds with $a = 0$ acquire the following form, namely,

$$X - t|X| \leq \lambda(\frac{\beta-1}{\beta})^{1/\beta} \leq X + t|X|.$$

This implies that

$$(X - t|X|)(\frac{\beta}{\beta-1})^{1/\beta} \leq \lambda \leq (X + t|X|)(\frac{\beta}{\beta-1})^{1/\beta}.$$

Therefore, β-free bounds on λ can be obtained by taking the infimum and supremum w.r.t. $\beta(> 1)$ of the lower and upper bounds, respectively, of the above inequality. On comparing, it is found that β-free CI of λ obtained using Edelman's result is of infinite length while CIs obtained using Theorems 2.3, 2.4 all have finite lengths.

2.4. Numerical Results

From Table 2.3 it is clear that the meaningful numerical results are possible only for $\beta > \beta_0 > 1$ and $(1 - \delta) \in (0.63212, 1)$ and the same are reported below for $\beta_0 = 2$ and $(1 - \delta) = 0.95$. It may, further, be noted that the meaningful confidence intervals are possible only when a is smaller than the value shown against each confidence interval.

Table 2.4.

m	confidence interval
3	$(a(0.3338)X,\ 68.4981X),\ a < 1.7296$
4	$(a(0.3338)X,\ 5.5730X),\ a < 1.4979$
5	$(a(0.3338)X,\ 4.7551X),\ a < 1.3398$
6	$(a(0.3338)X,\ 4.5300X),\ a < 1.2230$

3. Bounds for λ Based on $n(\geq 2)$

Here, unlike in Section 2, we assume that $n(\geq 2)$ independent observations $X_1, X_2, \ldots, X_n$ are available. Further assume that X_i observation follows Weibull distribution with λ_i as its scale parameter, and β as its shape parameter for $i = 1, 2, \ldots, n$. We see in this section that a closure property of Weibull distribution together with results in Subsections 2.1, 2.2 and 2.3 yields a number of very useful confidence intervals for various functions of the original scale parameter λ_i. These, in turn, provide several important results in the context of reliability studies. We first state below a closure property of a Weibull distribution in the form of a theorem.

Theorem 3.1. *If $X_1, X_2, \ldots, X_n$ are independent random variables such that X_i has Weibull distribution with parameters λ_i & β, $i = 1, 2, \ldots, n$ then $X_{1:n} = \min(X_1, \ldots, X_n)$ follows $W(\lambda_0, \beta)$ where $\lambda_0 = \left(\sum_1^n \lambda_i^\beta \right)^{1/\beta}$.*

In view of this result (and the results in Subsections 2.2-2.3) it is quite clear that $100(1 - \delta)\%$ CIs for λ_0 can easily be constructed along the lines of the ones in these two sections. We emphasize that these are $100(1 - \delta)\%$ CIs based on n independent observations from Weibull distribution and are in terms of the minimum of n observations.

Remark 3.1. *Note that $X_{1:n} = \min(X_1, X_2, \ldots, X_n)$ can be viewed as the lifetime of a series system comprising of components having independent Weibull lifetimes. As the confidence bounds for λ_0 are based on $X_{1:n}$, they, in turn, can be used to yield confidence bounds for reliability of the corresponding system. This observation has significant practical value as these bounds on reliability of the system are available for any life distribution which is a member of the Weibull family of distribution functions and not necessarily that of only exponential family of distribution functions.*

Remark 3.2. *Let $\lambda_{\min} = \min\{\lambda_1, \lambda_2, \ldots, \lambda_n\}$ and $\lambda_{\max} = \max\{\lambda_1, \lambda_2, \ldots, \lambda_n\}$. As $n^{1/\beta}(\lambda_{\min}) \leq \lambda_0 \leq n^{1/\beta}(\lambda_{\max})$, suitable confidence intervals for $\lambda_{\min}, \lambda_{\max}$ can be determined. However, it should be noted that these confidence intervals are one-sided and have confidence coefficient greater than or equal to $(1 - \delta)$. Further, the above remark regarding confidence intervals on the reliability of the system is applicable when component lifetimes are independent, Weibully distributed random variables having $\lambda_{\min}$ or $\lambda_{\max}$ and β as parameters.*

Remark 3.3. *If in addition $X_1, X_2, \ldots, X_n$ are also identically distributed then $\lambda_0 = n^{1/\beta}\lambda$. Therefore using results of Section 2, CIs for λ would become available for different ranges of β and δ.*

Remark 3.4. *The dependence of λ_0 on β, in general, does not pose any problem because metallurgical properties suggest that β can be determined using Hooke's law (Barlow (1998)) and thus, in principle, it can be assumed to be known.*

3.1. Numerical Results

Let $\beta = 1$. A two-sided $100(1-\delta)\%$ confidence interval for λ based on the ith order statistic is given by

$$\left[\frac{X_{i:n}}{-\ln[B_{\delta/2}(n-i+1,i)]}, \frac{X_{i:n}}{-\ln[B_{1-\delta/2}(n-i+1,i)]} \right]$$

where $B_r(p,q) = \dfrac{pF_r(2p,2q)}{q + pF_r(2p,2q)}$. $B_r(p,q)$ and $F_r(2p,2q)$ are the percentage points of the beta and F distributions respectively. This result is available in Bain and Engelhardt (1991, page 185). For $i = 1$, this two-sided $100(1-\delta)\%$ confidence interval for λ becomes

Table 3.1.

n	δ	Value of $X_{1:n}$ in a sample of size n drawn from Exp(1) distribution	100(1−δ)% confidence interval given in Bain & Engelhardt	interval proposed in this paper
1	0.02	1.9229	[0.4174, 191.3241]	(0.2457, 96.4481)
	0.05		[0.5213, 75.9495]	(0.3209, 39.5128)
	0.10		[0.6419, 37.4960]	(0.4175, 20.3886)
2	0.02	1.3196	[0.5731, 262.5657]	(0.0843, 33.3308)
	0.05		[0.7154, 104.0652]	(0.1101, 13.5576)
	0.10		[0.8812, 51.4936]	(0.1432, 6.9957)
3	0.02	1.0184	[0.6636, 308.1093]	(0.0434, 17.1500)
	0.05		[0.8282, 120.6740]	(0.0567, 6.9759)
	0.10		[1.0204, 59.3955]	(0.0737, 3.5996)
4	0.02	0.4055	[0.3521, 166.9972]	(0.0130, 5.1203)
	0.05		[0.4397, 64.1621]	(0.0169, 2.0831)
	0.01		[0.5413, 31.7260]	(0.0220, 1.0750)
5	0.02	1.4198	[1.5415, 706.0310]	(0.0363, 14.3456)
	0.05		[1.9235, 277.6901]	(0.04739, 5.8352)
	0.10		[2.3710, 138.4346]	(0.0617, 3.0110)
6	0.02	0.3865	[0.5033, 227.1625]	(0.0082, 3.2542)
7	0.02	0.2339	[0.3557, 166.9687]	(0.00427, 1.6882)

$$\left[\frac{X_{1:n}}{-\ln[B_{\delta/2}(n,1)]}, \frac{X_{1:n}}{-\ln[B_{1-\delta/2}(n,1)]} \right].$$

(3.1)

In view of Theorem 3.1 and Remarks 3.3 and 3.4, confidence intervals indicated in Table 2.3 would become applicable for $n > 1$ with X being replaced with $X_{1:n}$. The comparison of these resulting confidence intervals with those given in (3.1) is carried out here for various values of δ by drawing random samples of sizes ranging from 1 to 10 from the exponential distribution with mean 1. These results are presented below in Table 3.1.

It is quite evident from this table that for samples having sizes 1 through 5 and for $\delta = 0.02, 0.05, 0.1$, the newly proposed confidence intervals are significantly narrower than those given in Bain and Engelhardt (1991, page 185) inspite of the fact that the latter ones are obtained using maximum likelihood approach. However, for samples of sizes 6 through 8, similar observation is available only for delta $\delta = 0.02$. This is because for other values of $\delta = 0.05$ and 0.1, and for $n = 6, 7, 8$, the confidence intervals proposed in this paper do not include the value of the parameter $\lambda = 1$.

Acknowledgment

The 1st and 2nd authors would like to thank Department of Science and Technology, and CSIR, Government of India, New Delhi, respectively, for providing grant to carry out this research work.

References

Abbot, J.H., and Rosenblatt, J. (1963). Two Stage Estimation With One Observation on the First Stage. *Annals of the Institute of Statistical Mathematics*. 14, 229-235.

Bain, L.J., and Engelhardt M. (1991). *Statistical Analysis of Reliability And Life-Testing Models*, 2nd Ed, Marel Dekker, New York.

Barlow, R.E. (1998). Engineering Reliability. *ASA-SIAM Series on Statistics and Applied Probability*.

Blachman, N.M., and Machol, R.E. (1987). Confidence Intervals Based on One or More Observations. *IEEE Transactions on Information Theory*. IT-33, No.3, 373-382.

Edelman, D. (1990). A Confidence Interval for the Center of an Unknown Unimodal Distribution Based on a Sample Size 1. *The American Statistician*. 44, 285-287.

Machol, R.E., and Rosenblatt, J. (1966). Confidence Interval Based on Single Observation. *Proceedings of IEEE*. 54, 1087-1088.

Wall, M.M., Boen J. and Tweedie R. (2001). An Effective Confidence Interval for the Mean With Samples of Size One and Two. *The American Statistician*. 55, 102-105.

In: Applied Statistical Theory and Applications
Editor: Mohammad Ahsanullah
ISBN: 978-1-63321-858-1
© 2014 Nova Science Publishers, Inc.

Chapter 10

INFERENCES UNDER TRUNCATED GENERALIZED CAUCHY DISTRIBUTION

Saieed F. Ateya[1,2,*] ***and Essam K. AL-Hussaini***[3,†]

[1]Mathematics & Statistics Department, Taif University,
Hawia, Taif, Saudi Arabia
[2]Mathematics Department, Faculty of Science, Assiut University, Egypt
[3]Faculty of Science, Alexandria University, Alexandria, Egypt

Abstract

In this paper, we propose a truncated version of *generalized Cauchy* distribution suggested by Rider[18] in a special setting. One possible use for the proposed model is in life-testing where the domain of definition is not only non-negative but also guarantees no failure before a given time (truncated parameter). The parameters, reliability (RF) and hazard rate (HRF) functions are estimated using the maximum likelihood and Bayes methods. The Bayes estimates $(BE's)$ are obtained under the squared-error and liner exponential $(LINEX)$ loss functions. The computations have been carried out using the Markov Chain Monte Carlo (MCMC) algorithm. Also, the Bayesian prediction intervals $(BPI's)$ of future observation from the proposed distribution are constructed.

Keywords: Guarantee time, maximum likelihood and Bayes estimation, MCMC algorithm, squared error and $LINEX$ loss functions' Bayesian prediction intervals

Mathematics Subject Classification (2010): 62F10; 62F15; 62N01; 62N02

1. Introduction

The Cauchy distribution is a symmetric distribution with bell-shaped density function as the normal distribution but with a greater probability mass in the tails. The distribution is often used in the cases which arise in outlier analysis.

---

*E-mail address: said_f_atya@yahoo.com
†E-mail address: ekalh2011@yahoo.com

It is well-known that the Cauchy distribution can arise as the ratio of two independent normal variates. The probability density function (*PDF*) with location parameter β (representing the population median) and scale parameter γ (representing the semi-quartile range) is given by

$$f_X(x) = \frac{1}{\pi\gamma}\left[1 + \left(\frac{x-\beta}{\gamma}\right)^2\right]^{-1}, -\infty < x < \infty, -\infty < \beta < \infty, \gamma > 0. \qquad (1.1)$$

Chan [5], Cane [4], Balmer et al.[2] and Howlader and Weiss [13-14] found the maximum likelihood and Bayes estimates of β, γ and the reliability function. Copas [6] and Gabrielsen [10] have established that the joint maximum is unique. Also, Hinkley [11] has carried out large-scale computer simulation of samples of sizes 20 and 40 and found that Newton-Raphson iteration method rarely failed to converge rapidly.

Ferguson [8] gave closed-form solutions for the maximum likelihood estimators of β and γ when $n < 5$.

Frank [9] studied the problem of testing the normal versus Cauchy distributions and Spiegel-halter [19] used Frank's results to obtain exact Bayes estimators for β and γ using a non-informative prior. Howlader and Weiss [12] used Lindley's approximation form to obtain the *BE's* of β and γ. The book by Johnson, Kotz et al. [15] covers the Cauchy distribution in many of its aspects starting from the history, properties, developments and applications up to the most recent research done in the subject matter, to the date of the book's publication.

A random variable X is said to have a generalized Cauchy distribution (*GCD*) according to Rider [18], if its *PDF*, takes the form

$$f_X(x) = \frac{\delta\,\Gamma(\omega)}{2\,\Gamma(1/\delta)\,\Gamma(\omega - 1/\delta)}\left[1 + |x-\beta|^\delta\right]^{-\omega},$$

where

$$-\infty < x < \infty, -\infty < \beta < \infty,\ \delta,\ \omega > 0\ \text{and}\ \delta\,\omega > 1.$$

The Cauchy distribution has received applications in many areas, including biological analysis, clinical trials, stochastic modeling of decreasing failure rate life components, queueing theory, and reliability. For data from these areas, there is no reason to believe that empirical moments of any order should be infinite. Thus, the choice of the Cauchy distribution as a model is unrealistic since its moments of all orders are not finite.

The introduced truncated generalized Cauchy distribution can be a more appropriate model for the kind of data mentioned.

We suggest a left truncated version of Rider's *GCD* at β when $\delta = 2$, $\omega = \alpha + 1/2$ and introduce a scale parameter γ so that the *PDF* takes the form

$$f_X(x) = \frac{2}{\sqrt{\pi}}\ \frac{\Gamma(\alpha + 1/2)}{\gamma\,\Gamma(\alpha)}\left[1 + \left(\frac{x-\beta}{\gamma}\right)^2\right]^{-\alpha - 1/2}, x \geq \beta, (\beta, \gamma, \alpha > 0), \qquad (1.2)$$

and the corresponding cumulative distribution function (*CDF*) and reliability function (*RF*) can be written in the forms

$$F_X(x) = \frac{1}{B(\alpha, 1/2)}\int_\beta^x \left[1 + \left(\frac{u-\beta}{\gamma}\right)^2\right]^{-\alpha - 1/2} du, x \geq \beta, (\beta, \gamma, \alpha > 0), \qquad (1.3)$$

$$R_X(x) = \frac{1}{B(\alpha,1/2)} \int_x^\infty \left[1 + \left(\frac{u-\beta}{\gamma}\right)^2 \right]^{-\alpha-1/2} du, x \geq \beta, (\beta,\gamma,\alpha > 0), \qquad (1.4)$$

where $B(a,b) = \int_0^1 x^{a-1}(1-x)^{b-1}dx$ is the complete beta function.

We shall write $X \sim TGCD(\beta,\gamma,\alpha)$ to denote that the random variable X has $PDF(1.2)$.

Ateya and Madhagi[1] introduced a multivariate version of $TGCD$, $MVTGCD$, and derived its moment generating function, conditional density functions, mixed moments and estimate its parameters using the maximum likelihood and Bayes methods.

One reason for truncation at β is that, in industry, we sometimes require a minimum time β before which no failure occurs. This minimum time β is known as the *guarantee time*. Another use for truncation at $\beta > 0$ is in epidemiological or biomedical applications where β may represent the latent period of some disease. For example, in cancer research problems, β is regarded as the time elapsed between first exposure to carcinogen and the appearance of tumer.

A special case of (1.2) may be obtained when $\alpha = k - 1/2$, $k = 1,2,\ldots$ in this case, the *PDF* becomes

$$f_X(x) = \frac{2\,\Gamma(k)}{\sqrt{\pi}\,\gamma\,\Gamma(k-1/2)} \left[1 + \left(\frac{x-\beta}{\gamma}\right)^2 \right]^{-k}, x \geq \beta. \qquad (1.5)$$

If $k = 1$, $f_X(x)$ is then the left truncated version of the Cauchy $PDF(1.1)$ that takes the form

$$f_X(x) = \frac{2}{\pi\gamma} \left[1 + \left(\frac{x-\beta}{\gamma}\right)^2 \right]^{-1}, x \geq \beta. \qquad (1.6)$$

Dahiya et al [7] studied the maximum likelihood estimates $(MLE's)$ of the parameters of a doubly truncated Cauchy distribution.

If $k \geq 2$ we then have

$$f_X(x) = \frac{2^k\,(k-1)!}{\gamma\,\pi[1.3.5\ldots(2k-3)]} \left[1 + \left(\frac{x-\beta}{\gamma}\right)^2 \right]^{-k}, x \geq \beta. \qquad (1.7)$$

Another special case of (1.2) is when $\gamma^2 = 2\alpha = k$ and so that

$$f_X(x) = \frac{2\,\Gamma(\frac{k+1}{2})}{\Gamma(k/2)\,\sqrt{k\pi}} \left[1 + \frac{(x-\beta)^2}{k} \right]^{-\frac{k+1}{2}}, x \geq \beta. \qquad (1.8)$$

This is the *PDF* of a left truncated t-distribution with k degrees of freedom.

1.1. Properties of the $TGCD$

The *PDF* (1.2) of the $TGCD$ is monotone decreasing on the interval $[\beta,\infty)$. The maximum value of f is attained at $x = \beta$ and $f(\beta) = 2\Gamma(\alpha+1/2)/[\sqrt{\pi}\gamma\Gamma(\alpha)]$.

While the moment generating function (MGF) of the Cauchy PDF (1.1)(and the moments of any order) do not exist, the MGF of the $TGCD$ and moments of all orders do exist. In fact, it can be shown that if $X \sim TGCD(\beta, \gamma, \alpha)$, then

$$M_X(t) = \frac{2}{\sqrt{\pi}} \frac{\Gamma(\alpha+1/2)}{\Gamma(\alpha)} \int_0^{\pi/2} \exp[(\beta+\gamma\tan\phi)t] \, (\cos\phi)^{2\alpha-1} \, d\phi.$$

For $r = 1, 2, \dots$ such that $r < 2\alpha$,

$$E(X^r) = \frac{1}{\sqrt{\pi}} \frac{\Gamma(\alpha+1/2)}{\Gamma(\alpha)} \sum_{i=0}^r \binom{r}{i} \gamma^i \beta^{r-i} \, \text{Beta}(\alpha - \frac{i}{2}, \frac{i+1}{2}),$$

where $B(a,b) = \int_0^1 z^{a-1} (1-z)^{b-1} \, dz$, is the standard beta integral.
Furthermore, the cumulative distribution function (CDF) takes the form

$$F_X(x) = \frac{2}{\sqrt{\pi}} \frac{\Gamma(\alpha+1/2)}{\Gamma(\alpha)} \int_0^{\tan^{-1}(\frac{x-\beta}{\gamma})} (\cos\phi)^{2\alpha-1} \, d\phi.$$

The reliability function (RF) and hazard rate function (HRF), are defined, respectively, at time x, by

$$R_X(x) = 1 - F_X(x) \quad \text{and} \quad h_X(x) = f_X(x)/R_X(x). \tag{1.9}$$

Graphs of $f_X(x)$, $R_X(x)$ and $h_X(x)$ are shown in Figures 1, 2 and 3 for different choices of (β, γ, α)

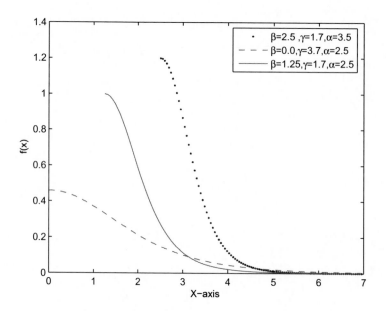

Figure 1.

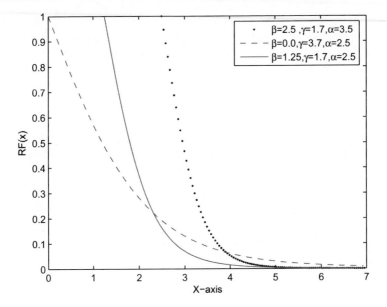

Figure 2.

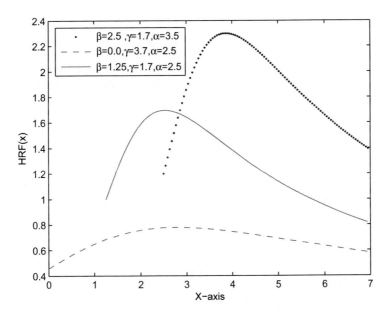

Figure 3.

2. Maximum Likelihood Estimation

Let $X_1, ..., X_n$ be a random sample drawn from a population having a *PDF* given by (1.2). The likelihood function (LF) is then given, for $x_i \geq \beta$, $i = 1, 2, ..., n$, by

$$L(\beta, \gamma, \alpha | x) = \prod_{i=1}^{n} \left[\frac{2}{\sqrt{\pi}} \frac{\Gamma(\alpha + 1/2)}{\gamma \Gamma(\alpha)} \left[1 + \left(\frac{x_i - \beta}{\gamma} \right)^2 \right]^{-\alpha - 1/2} \right]. \qquad (2.1)$$

where $x = (x_1,...,x_n)$ is the vector of observations (realization of $X_1,...,X_n$).
The *LF* (2.1) is a monotone increasing function of the parameter β on the interval
$(0, \min\{x_i\})$, so that, the maximum likelihood estimate of the parameter β, denoted by $\hat{\beta}$, is
given by

$$\hat{\beta} = \min\{X_i\}. \tag{2.2}$$

The logarithm of (2.1) is given by

$$\ell(\beta,\gamma,\alpha|x) = n\ln(2) - \frac{n}{2}\ln(\pi) - n\ln(\gamma) - n\ln(\Gamma(\alpha)) + n\ln(\Gamma(\alpha+1/2))$$
$$- (\alpha+1/2)\sum_{i=1}^{n}\ln\left[1+\left(\frac{x_i-\beta}{\gamma}\right)^2\right]. \tag{2.3}$$

Replacing the parameter β by $\hat{\beta}$ in (2.3), differentiating with respect to γ and α and then
setting to zero, we obtain the two likelihood equations $(LE's)$

$$\begin{cases} \frac{\partial\ell}{\partial\gamma} = 0 = -n/\hat{\gamma} + (2\hat{\alpha}+1)\sum_{i=1}^{n}(x_i-\hat{\beta})^2/\{\hat{\gamma}[\hat{\gamma}^2+(x_i-\hat{\beta})^2]\}, \\ \frac{\partial\ell}{\partial\alpha} = 0 = -n\,\psi(\hat{\alpha}) + n\,\psi(\hat{\alpha}+1/2) - \sum_{i=1}^{n}\ln\left[1+\left([x_i-\hat{\beta}]/\hat{\gamma}\right)^2\right]. \end{cases} \tag{2.4}$$

where
$\psi(z) = \frac{d}{dz}\ln\Gamma(z)$, is the digamma function.
Equations (2.4) represent two nonlinear equations which can be solved using some iteration
scheme, such as Newton-Raphson, to obtain the *MLE's* of γ and α, denoted by $\hat{\gamma}$ and $\hat{\alpha}$. The
invariance property of *MLE's* can be applied to obtain *MLE's* for the *RF* and *HRF*, $R_X(x^*)$
and $h_X(x^*)$, at some x^*.

3. Bayes Estimation

Let $u(\theta)$ be a general continuous function of the vector of parameters $\theta = (\theta_1,\theta_2,...,\theta_m)$.
Under the **squared error loss** function (SEL), $L^* = [\hat{u}(\theta) - u(\theta)]^2$, the Bayes estimate of
$u(\theta)$ is given by

$$\hat{u}_S(\theta) = E(u(\theta)|x) = \int ... \int u(\theta)\pi^*(\theta|x)\,d\theta_1...d\theta_m. \tag{3.1}$$

The integrals are taken over the m-dimensional space.

The *SEL* function has probably been the most popular loss function used in literature.
The symmetric nature of *SEL* function gives equal weight to over- and underestimation of
the parameter(s) under consideration. However, in life testing, overestimation may be more
serious than underestimation or vice-versa. Research has then been directed towards asymmetric loss functions and Varian [21] suggested the use of the linear-exponential($LINEX$)
loss function to be of the form

$$L^*(\Delta) = b\left[e^{a\Delta} - a\Delta - 1\right],$$

where $|a| \neq 0, b \geq 0, \Delta = \hat{u}(\theta) - u(\theta)$.

Thompson and Basu [20] generalized the *LINEX* loss function to the squared-exponential (*SQUAREX*) loss function to be in the form

$$L^*(\Delta) = b\left[e^{a\Delta} - d\Delta^2 - a\Delta - 1\right],$$

where $d \neq 0$, a, b and Δ are as before.

Indeed, the *SQUAREX* loss function reduces to the *LINEX* loss function if $d = 0$. If $a = 0$, the *SQUAREX* loss function reduces to *SEL* function.

We shall use the *LINEX* loss function since it is simpler to use than the *SQUAREX* loss function. Notice that in *LINEX* loss function, for $\hat{u}(\theta) - u(\theta) = 0, L^*(\Delta) = 0$. For $a > 0$, the loss declines almost exponentially for $\hat{u}(\theta) - u(\theta) > 0$ and rises approximately linearly when $\hat{u}(\theta) - u(\theta) < 0$. For $a < 0$, the reverse is true. By expanding $e^{a\Delta}$, $L^*(\Delta)$ can be approximated to the *SEL* function when $\hat{u}(\theta) - u(\theta)$ is small. Without loss of generality we shall take $b = 1$.

Using the *LINEX* loss function, the Bayes estimate of $u(\theta)$ is given by

$$\hat{u}_L(\theta) = \frac{-1}{a}\ln[E(e^{-au(\theta)}|x)] = \frac{-1}{a}\ln\left[\int \ldots \int e^{-au(\theta)}\pi^*(\theta|x)\,d\theta_1\ldots d\theta_m\right], \qquad (3.2)$$

where $\pi^*(\theta|x) \propto \pi(\theta)L(\theta|x)$ is the posterior *PDF* of the vector of parameters θ given the vector of observations x, $\pi(\theta)$ is a prior density function of θ and $L(\theta|x)$ is the likelihood function of θ given x. The integrals are taken over the m-dimensional space R^m. To compute the integrals, we use *Markov Chain Monte Carlo* (*MCMC*), method to generate a random sample $[\theta^i = (\theta_1^i, \ldots, \theta_m^i), i = 1, 2, \ldots, k]$ from the posterior density function $\pi^*(\theta|x)$ and then write (3.1) and (3.2), respectively in the forms,

$$\hat{u}_S(\theta) = \frac{\sum_{i=1}^k u(\theta^i)}{k} \qquad (3.3)$$

and

$$\hat{u}_L(\theta) = (-1/a)\ln\left[\frac{1}{k}\sum_{i=1}^k e^{-au(\theta^i)}\right]. \qquad (3.4)$$

The *MCMC* method is described in Press [17].

3.1. Bayes Estimation of $\beta, \gamma, \alpha, R_X(x^*)$ and $h_X(x^*)$ Under Squared Error Loss Function

In this subsection the *BE's* of $\beta, \gamma, \alpha, R_X(x^*)$ and $h_X(x^*)$ are obtained under squared error loss function in case of informative and non-informative priors. To estimate these parameters and functions we define a function $u(\beta, \gamma, \alpha)$ as

$$u(\beta, \gamma, \alpha) = \beta^{\delta_1}\gamma^{\delta_2}\alpha^{\delta_3}\left(f(x^*)\right)^{\delta_4}\left(R_X(x^*)\right)^{\delta_5}. \qquad (3.5)$$

The Bayes estimate of $u(\beta, \gamma, \alpha)$ is obtained in five cases:

1. when $\delta_1 = 1, \delta_2 = \delta_3 = \delta_4 = \delta_5 = 0$, which is equivalent to estimating β,

2. when $\delta_2 = 1, \delta_1 = \delta_3 = \delta_4 = \delta_5 = 0$, which is equivalent to estimating γ,

3. when $\delta_3 = 1, \delta_1 = \delta_2 = \delta_4 = \delta_5 = 0$, which is equivalent to estimating α.

4. when $\delta_5 = 1, \delta_1 = \delta_2 = \delta_3 = \delta_4 = 0$, which is equivalent to estimating $R_X(x^*)$.

5. when $\delta_4 = 1, \delta_5 = -1, \delta_1 = \delta_2 = \delta_3 = 0$, which is equivalent to estimating $h_X(x^*)$.

3.1.1. Bayes Estimation in Case of Informative Prior

Suppose that the prior belief of the experimenter is measured by a function $\pi(\beta, \gamma, \alpha)$, where α is assumed to be independent of β and γ, so that the prior density function is given by

$$\begin{aligned}
\pi(\beta, \gamma, \alpha) &= \pi_1(\beta, \gamma)\, \pi_2(\alpha) \\
&= \pi_{11}(\beta \mid \gamma)\, \pi_{12}(\gamma)\, \pi_2(\alpha).
\end{aligned} \tag{3.6}$$

Suppose that $\pi_{11}(\beta \mid \gamma)$ is Gamma (c_1, γ), $\pi_{12}(\gamma)$ is Gamma (c_2, c_3) and $\pi_2(\alpha)$ is Gamma (c_4, c_5), with respective densities

$$\pi_{11}(\beta|\gamma) \propto \gamma^{c_1}\, \beta^{c_1-1} \exp(-\gamma\beta), \ \beta, \ \gamma > 0, \ (c_1 > 0),$$

$$\pi_{12}(\gamma) \propto \gamma^{c_2-1} \exp(-c_3\, \gamma), \ \gamma > 0, \ (c_2, \ c_3 > 0),$$

$$\pi_2(\alpha) \propto \alpha^{c_4-1} \exp(-c_5\, \alpha), \ \alpha > 0, \ (c_4, \ c_5 > 0),$$

It then follows that the prior density of β, γ and α is given by

$$\begin{aligned}
\pi(\beta, \gamma, \alpha) &\propto \alpha^{c_4-1}\, \beta^{c_1-1}\, \gamma^{c_1+c_2-1} \exp(-\gamma\beta - c_3\,\gamma - c_5\,\alpha), \\
&\alpha, \ \beta, \ \gamma > 0, \ (c_1, c_2, c_3, c_4, c_5 > 0),
\end{aligned} \tag{3.7}$$

where, c_1, c_2, c_3, c_4 and c_5 are the prior parameters (also known as hyperparameters). From (2.1) and (3.7), the posterior density function can be written in the form

$$\begin{aligned}
\pi^*(\beta, \gamma, \alpha \mid x) &= A\, \alpha^{c_4-1}\, \beta^{c_1-1}\, \gamma^{c_1+c_2-1} \exp(-\gamma\beta - c_3\,\gamma - c_5\,\alpha). \\
&\prod_{i=1}^{n} \left[\frac{2}{\sqrt{\pi}}\, \frac{\Gamma(\alpha+1/2)}{\gamma\,\Gamma(\alpha)} \left[1 + \left(\frac{x_i - \beta}{\gamma} \right)^2 \right]^{-\alpha-1/2} \right], \\
&\alpha, \ \beta, \ \gamma > 0, \ (c_1, c_2, c_3, c_4, c_5 > 0),
\end{aligned} \tag{3.8}$$

where A is a normalizing constant. Using *MCMC* method, we get the *BE's* of the considered parameters and functions.

3.1.2. Bayes Estimation in Case of Non-informative Prior

In this case, we consider independent non-informative priors of the parameters β, γ and α in the forms

$$\pi_1(\beta) \propto 1/\beta, \beta > 0,$$

$$\pi_2(\gamma) \propto 1/\gamma, \gamma > 0,$$

$$\pi_3(\alpha) \propto 1/\alpha, \alpha > 0.$$

so that

$$\pi(\beta, \gamma, \alpha) \propto (\alpha \beta \gamma)^{-1}. \tag{3.9}$$

Using this prior and the likelihood function (2.1), the posterior density function of β, γ and α can be written in the form

$$\pi^*(\beta,\gamma,\alpha|x) = A_1\, \alpha^{-1}\, \beta^{-1}\, \gamma^{-1} \prod_{i=1}^{n}\left[\frac{2}{\sqrt{\pi}}\, \frac{\Gamma(\alpha+1/2)}{\gamma\,\Gamma(\alpha)}\left[1+\left(\frac{x_i-\beta}{\gamma}\right)^2 \right]^{-\alpha-1/2} \right], \tag{3.10}$$

$$\alpha, \beta, \gamma > 0,$$

where A_1 is a normalizing constant.

Using *MCMC* method, we can obtain the *BE's* of $\beta, \gamma, \alpha, R_X(x^*)$ and $h_X(x^*)$.

3.2. Bayes Estimation of $\beta, \gamma, \alpha, R_X(x^*)$ and $h_X(x^*)$ Under *LINEX* Loss Function

The *MCMC* method is used to generate a random sample of size k, $[\theta^i = (\theta_1^i, ..., \theta_m^i), i = 1, 2, ..., k]$ by using the posteriors (3.8) and (3.10). Equation (3.4),(a=1, 7), is then used to compute the *BE's* of the parameters and functions of such parameters under *LINEX* loss function.

4. BPI's of Future Observation Based on One-Sample Scheme

Suppose that $X_1 < X_2 < ... < X_r$ is the informative sample, representing the first r ordered lifetimes of a random sample of size n drawn from a population with probability density function (*PDF*) $f_X(x)$, cumulative distribution function (*CDF*) $F_X(x)$ and reliability function (*RF*) $R_X(x)$. In one-sample scheme the Bayesian prediction intervals (*BPI's*) for the remaining unobserved future $(n-r)$ lifetimes are sought based on the first r observed ordered lifetimes.

For the remaining $(n-r)$ components, let $X_s^* = X_{r+s}$ denote the future lifetime of the sth component to fail, $1 \leq s \leq (n-r)$. The conditional density function of X_s^* given that the r components had already failed is

$$g_1(x_s^*|\theta) \propto [R_X(x_r) - R_X(x_s^*)]^{(s-1)}[R_X(x_s^*)]^{n-r-s}[R_X(x_r)]^{-(n-r)}f_X(x_s^*|\theta), x_s^* > x_r, \tag{4.1}$$

θ is the vector of parameters.

The predictive density function is given by

$$g_1^*(x_s^*|x) = \int_\Theta g_1(x_s^*|\theta)\pi^*(\theta|x)d\theta, x_s^* > x_r, \tag{4.2}$$

$\pi^*(\theta|x)$ is the posterior density function of θ given x and $x = (x_1,...,x_r)$.

In our study, we will assume that $\beta = 0$ and $\gamma = 1$, so that the reliability function in (1.4) can be written in the form(after some simple mathematical steps),

$$R_X(x) = \int_x^\infty \left(\frac{4}{\pi}\right)^{1/2} \frac{\Gamma(\alpha+1/2)}{\Gamma(\alpha)} \left[1+u^2\right]^{-\alpha-1/2} du$$

$$= \frac{1}{B(\alpha,1/2)} \int_x^\infty \left[1+u^2\right]^{-\alpha-1/2} du = \zeta_x(\alpha,1/2). \tag{4.3}$$

Suppose that the prior belief of the experimenter is given by the *PDF*, $\pi(\alpha) \propto \alpha^{c_1-1} e^{-c_2\alpha}$. **The likelihood function** of α given $x_1,...,x_r$ is given by

$$L(\alpha|x_1,...,x_r) \propto [R_X(x_r)]^{n-r}\prod_{i=1}^{r} f_X(x_i). \tag{4.4}$$

Using the prior and the likelihood functions, the posterior *PDF* can be written as

$$\pi^*(\alpha|x_1,...,x_r) \propto \alpha^{c_1-1}\exp[-c_2\alpha][\zeta_{x_r}(\alpha,1/2)]^{n-r}\left[\frac{1}{B(\alpha,1/2)}\right]^r\prod_{i=1}^{r}\left[1+x_i^2\right]^{(-\alpha-1/2)}, \alpha > 0. \tag{4.5}$$

From (4.5) and (4.1), the predictive density function of X_s^* can be written as follows

$$g_1^*(x_s^*|x_1,...,x_r) = \int_0^\infty g_1(x_s^*|\alpha)\pi^*(\alpha|x_1,...,x_r)d\alpha, \tag{4.6}$$

where

$$g_1(x_s^*|\alpha)\pi^*(\alpha|x_1,...,x_r) = A_1\alpha^{c_1-1}\exp[-c_2\alpha]\sum_{i=0}^{s-1}(-1)^i\binom{s-1}{i}[\zeta_{x_s^*}(\alpha,1/2)]^{n-r-s+i}$$

$$[\zeta_{x_r}(\alpha,1/2)]^{s-i-1}\left[\frac{1}{B(\alpha,1/2)}\right]^{r+1}\left[1+x_s^{*2}\right]^{(-\alpha-1/2)}\prod_{i=1}^{r}\left[1+x_i^2\right]^{(-\alpha-1/2)}, x_s^* > x_r \tag{4.7}$$

where A_1 is a normalizing constant which can be computed from the relation

$$A_1^{-1} = \int_{x_r}^\infty\int_0^\infty \alpha^{c_1-1}\exp[-c_2\alpha]\sum_{i=0}^{s-1}(-1)^i\binom{s-1}{i}[\zeta_{x_s^*}(\alpha,1/2)]^{n-r-s+i}$$

$$[\zeta_{x_r}(\alpha,1/2)]^{s-i-1}\left[\frac{1}{B(\alpha,1/2)}\right]^{r+1}\left[1+x_s^{*2}\right]^{(-\alpha-1/2)}\prod_{i=1}^{r}\left[1+x_i^2\right]^{(-\alpha-1/2)} d\alpha\, dx_s^*. \tag{4.8}$$

To obtain $(1-\tau)\% \ BPI$ for X_s^*, say (L,U), we solve the following two nonlinear equations,

$$P(X_s^* > L|x_1,...,x_r) = \int_L^\infty g_1^*(x_s^*|x_1,...,x_r)dx_s^* = 1 - \frac{\tau}{2}, L > x_r, \tag{4.9}$$

$$P(X_s^* > U|x_1,...,x_r) = \int_U^\infty g_1^*(x_s^*|x_1,...,x_r)dx_s^* = \frac{\tau}{2}, U > x_r. \tag{4.10}$$

The interval (L,U) can be obtained by solving equations (4.9) and (4.10), using Newton-Raphson iteration form as follows

$$L_{j+1} = L_j - \frac{\int_{L_j}^\infty g_1^*(x_s^*|x)dx_s^* - (1 - \frac{\tau}{2})}{-g_1^*(L_j|x)}, \tag{4.11}$$

$$U_{j+1} = U_j - \frac{\int_{U_j}^\infty g_1^*(x_s^*|x)dx_s^* - \frac{\tau}{2}}{-g_1^*(U_j|x)}, \tag{4.12}$$

where the initial values L_0, U_0 can be taken equal to x_r.
The integrals in (4.11) and (4.12) can be obtained using the routine *QDAGI* in *IMSL* library.

5. BPI's of Future Observation Based on Two-Sample Scheme

Let $X_1 < X_2 < ... < X_r$ and $Z_1 < Z_2 < ... < Z_m$ represent informative (type II censored) sample from a random sample of size n and a future ordered sample of size m, respectively. It is assumed that the two samples are independent and drawn from a population with $(PDF)f_X(x)$, $(CDF)F_X(x)$ and $(RF)R_X(x)$.

Our aim is to obtain the $BPI's$ for $Z_s, s = 1, 2, ..., m$. The conditional density function of Z_s, given the vector of parameters θ, is

$$g_2(z_s|\theta) \propto [1 - R_X(z_s)]^{(s-1)}[R_X(z_s)]^{m-s}f_X(z_s|\theta), z_s > 0, \tag{5.1}$$

θ is the vector of parameters.
The predictive density function is given by

$$g_2^*(z_s|x) = \int_\Theta g_2(z_s|\theta)\pi^*(\theta|x)d\theta, z_s > 0, \tag{5.2}$$

$\pi^*(\theta|x)$ is the posterior density function of θ given x and $x = (x_1, ..., x_r)$.
Using the posterior in (4.5) and the conditional density function in (5.1), the predictive density function of Z_s is given by

$$g_2^*(z_s|x_1,...,x_r) = \int_0^\infty g_2(z_s|\alpha)\pi^*(\alpha|x_1,...,x_r)d\alpha, z_s > 0, \tag{5.3}$$

where

$$g_2(z_s|\alpha)\pi^*(\alpha|x_1,...,x_r) = A_2\alpha^{c_1-1}\exp[-c_2\alpha][\zeta_{x_r}(\alpha,1/2)]^{n-r}\sum_{i=0}^{s-1}(-1)^i\binom{s-1}{i}$$

$$\times [\zeta_{z_s}(\alpha,1/2)]^{m+i-s}\left[\frac{1}{B(\alpha,1/2)}\right]^{r+1}\left[1+z_s^2\right]^{(-\alpha-1/2)}\prod_{i=0}^r\left[1+x_i^2\right]^{(-\alpha-1/2)}, z_s > 0 \tag{5.4}$$

By choosing A_2 such that

$$A_2^{-1} = \int_0^\infty \int_0^\infty \alpha^{c_1-1} \exp[-c_2\alpha][\zeta_{x_r}(\alpha, 1/2)]^{n-r} \sum_{i=0}^{s-1} (-1)^i \binom{s-1}{i}$$

$$\times [\zeta_{z_s}(\alpha, 1/2)]^{m+i-s} \left[\frac{1}{B(\alpha, 1/2)}\right]^{r+1} \left[1+z_s^2\right]^{(-\alpha-1/2)} \prod_{i=0}^r \left[1+x_i^2\right]^{(-\alpha-1/2)} d\alpha dz_s. \tag{5.5}$$

To obtain $(1-\tau)$ % BPI for Z_s, say (L,U), we solve the following two nonlinear equations,

$$P(Z_s > L|x_1,...,x_r) = \int_L^\infty g_2^*(z_s|x_1,...,x_r)dz_s = 1 - \frac{\tau}{2}, L > 0, \tag{5.6}$$

$$P(Z_s > U|x_1,...,x_r) = \int_U^\infty g_2^*(z_s|x_1,...,x_r)dz_s = \frac{\tau}{2}, U > 0. \tag{5.7}$$

The interval (L,U) can be also obtained by solving equations (5.6) and (5.7), using Newton-Raphson iteration form as follows

$$L_{j+1} = L_j - \frac{\int_{L_j}^\infty g_2^*(z_s|x)dz_s - (1-\frac{\tau}{2})}{-g_2^*(L_j|x)}, \tag{5.8}$$

$$U_{j+1} = U_j - \frac{\int_{U_j}^\infty g_2^*(z_s|x)dz_s - \frac{\tau}{2}}{-g_2^*(U_j|x)}, \tag{5.9}$$

where the initial values L_0, U_0 can be taken equal to x_1.
The integrals in (5.8) and (5.9) can be obtained using the routine $QDAGI$ in $IMSL$ library. we get the interval (L,U).

6. Simulation Study

In this section the maximum likelihood, Bayes estimates of β, γ, α, $R_X(x^*)$ and $h_X(x^*)$ and the $BPI's$ of future observation are obtained as follows :

Estimation problem

1. For a given set of prior parameters, generate the population parameters β, γ, α.

2. Making use of the generated population parameters, generate random samples of different sizes $(30, 40, 50)$ from the population distribution under study.

3. The maximum likelihood estimate $(MLE)$of the parameter β is the minimum value of the random sample.

4. The MLE $\hat\beta$ of β, given by (2.2), on the basis of the samples of sizes 30, 40, 50, obtained in step 2. The estimate $\hat\beta$ is then substituted in the nonlinear equations (2.4). Solving these equations we get the maximum likelihood estimates $\hat\gamma$ of γ and $\hat\alpha$ of α.
   The use of the invariance property of the $MLE's$ yields $MLE's$ of RF and HRF, given by (1.9).

5. The $BE's$ of $\beta, \gamma, \alpha, R_X(x^*)$ and $h_X(x^*)$ are computed under the SEL and $LINEX$ loss functions using the function u, defined in (3.5), for different values of δ_i, $i = 1, 2, ..., 5$. the $MCMC$ technique is used in the computations.

6. Steps $2 - 5$ are repeated $m = 1000$ times.

7. If $\hat{\theta}_j$ is an estimate of θ, based on sample j, $j = 1, 2, ..., m$, then the average estimate over the m samples is given by
$\bar{\hat{\theta}} = \frac{1}{m} \sum_{j=1}^{m} \hat{\theta}_j.$

8. The variance of $\hat{\theta}$, $V(\hat{\theta})$, over the m samples is given by
$V(\hat{\theta}) = \frac{1}{m} \sum_{j=1}^{m} (\hat{\theta}_j - \bar{\hat{\theta}})^2.$

9. Using steps (7) and (8), compute $\bar{\hat{\beta}}, \bar{\hat{\gamma}}, \bar{\hat{\alpha}}, \bar{\hat{R}}(x^*), \bar{\hat{h}}(x^*), V(\hat{\beta}), V(\hat{\gamma}), V(\hat{\alpha}), V(\hat{R}(x^*))$ and $V(\hat{h}(x^*))$.

Prediction problem

1. Using $\beta = 0$ and $\gamma = 1$ and for a given prior parameter, c, generate the population parameter α.

2. Making use of the generated population parameter, generate type II random samples of size $n = 50$ and different censoring values, $r, (10, 20, 45)$ from the population distribution under study.

3. Based on the previous type II censored sample, the $BPI's$ of the first, the second and the third future observations are obtained in case of type one- and two-sample schemes.

In our study, Table(1) displays the average estimates and variances of the $MLE's$ and $BE's$, using informative and non-informative priors, under squared error loss function, based on samples of different sizes n and for $m = 1000$ repetitions. Tables(2) and (3) display the same data as Table(1) under $LINEX$ loss function in case of $a = 1$ and $a = 7$.
The given vector of hyperparamters is $(c_1 = 1.7, c_2 = 1.0, c_3 = 1.8, c_4 = 2.0, c_5 = 2.7)$ and the generated population parameters are $(\beta = 2.5, \gamma = 1.7, \alpha = 3.5)$. The population reliability and hazard rate functions are computed at $x^* = 3.5$, using (1.9) and the population parameters. Their values are $R_X(x^*) = 0.1636$ and $h_X(x^*) = 2.2317$.
In Tables (4) and (5) 95%$BPI's$ are computed in case of the one- and two-sample predictions, respectively, using informative samples of different sizes, r.

Table 1. Maximum Likelihood and Bayes Estimation Under SEL Function

n		Method	$\hat{\beta}$ $V(\hat{\beta})$	$\hat{\gamma}$ $V(\hat{\gamma})$	$\hat{\alpha}$ $V(\hat{\alpha})$	$\hat{R}(x^*)$ $V(\hat{R}(x^*))$	$\hat{h}(x^*)$ $V(\hat{h}(x^*))$
30	B	Informative Prior	2.6805 0.1998	1.7941 0.0917	3.4027 0.2186	0.2351 0.0516	1.9703 0.8215
		Non-Informative Prior	2.6947 0.2018	1.8013 0.0994	3.3901 0.2397	0.2607 0.0651	1.9133 0.8913
		ML	2.7132 0.2230	1.8215 0.1084	3.3156 0.2447	0.2939 0.0733	1.8925 0.9761
40	B	Informative Prior	2.5311 0.0878	1.7508 0.0685	3.4713 0.1366	0.2183 0.0492	2.1625 0.5917
		Non-Informative Prior	2.5303 0.1251	1.7759 0.0692	3.4435 0.1514	0.2206 0.0588	2.1316 0.6351
		ML	2.6105 0.1423	1.7936 0.0790	3.4236 0.1678	0.2364 0.0633	2.005 0.7009
50	B	Informative Prior	2.5093 0.0735	1.72110 0.04719	3.5116 0.0925	0.1701 0.0297	2.2013 0.4902
		Non-Informative Prior	2.5108 0.0882	1.7194 0.05032	3.4911 0.1051	0.1739 0.0381	2.1933 0.5922
		ML	2.5210 0.0990	1.7131 0.0534	3.4871 0.1303	0.1751 0.0433	2.1655 0.6313

Table 2. Maximum Likelihood and Bayes Estimation Under $LINEX$ Loss Function
$(a = 1)$

n		Method	$\hat{\beta}$ $V(\hat{\beta})$	$\hat{\gamma}$ $V(\hat{\gamma})$	$\hat{\alpha}$ $V(\hat{\alpha})$	$\hat{R}(x^*)$ $V(\hat{R}(x^*))$	$\hat{h}(x^*)$ $V(\hat{h}(x^*))$
30	B	Informative Prior	2.6908 0.2001	1.8061 0.0977	3.4011 0.2285	0.1905 0.0531	2.0132 0.8735
		Non-Informative Prior	2.7023 0.2199	1.8090 0.1015	3.3170 0.2502	0.2103 0.0691	1.9074 0.9105
		ML	2.7132 0.2230	1.8215 0.1084	3.3156 0.2447	0.2939 0.0733	1.8925 0.9761
40	B	Informative Prior	2.5516 0.0920	1.7861 0.0714	3.4605 0.1509	0.1822 0.0516	2.1930 0.6220
		Non-Informative Prior	2.5702 0.1413	1.7905 0.0721	3.4310 0.1622	0.1952 0.0611	2.1441 0.6616
		ML	2.6105 0.1423	1.7936 0.0790	3.4236 0.1678	0.2364 0.0633	2.0056 0.7009
50	B	Informative Prior	2.5116 0.0792	1.7583 0.0504	3.5311 0.1134	0.1628 0.0325	2.2218 0.5133
		Non-Informative Prior	2.5174 0.0891	1.7201 0.0511	3.4893 0.1262	0.1601 0.0404	2.1915 0.6227
		ML	2.5210 0.0990	1.7131 0.0534	3.4871 0.1303	0.1751 0.0433	2.1655 0.6313

Table 3. Maximum Likelihood and Bayes Estimation Under *LINEX* Loss Function
($a = 7$)

n		Method	$\bar{\hat{\beta}}$ $V(\hat{\beta})$	$\bar{\hat{\gamma}}$ $V(\hat{\gamma})$	$\bar{\hat{\alpha}}$ $V(\hat{\alpha})$	$\bar{\hat{R}}(x^*)$ $V(\hat{R}(x^*))$	$\bar{\hat{h}}(x^*)$ $V(\hat{h}(x^*))$
30	B	Informative Prior	2.6295 0.1806	1.7714 0.0804	3.4420 0.2060	0.1873 0.0451	2.0513 0.5911
		Non-Informative Prior	2.6701 0.1942	1.7910 0.0815	3.4421 0.2331	0.1903 0.0603	1.9833 0.7005
		ML	2.7132 0.2230	1.8215 0.1084	3.3156 0.2447	0.2939 0.0733	1.8925 0.9761
40	B	Informative Prior	2.5234 0.0815	1.7340 0.0407	3.4726 0.1035	0.1791 0.0382	2.1766 0.4613
		Non-Informative Prior	2.5291 0.1153	1.7415 0.0570	3.4603 0.1203	0.1811 0.0476	2.1012 0.5312
		ML	2.6105 0.1423	1.7936 0.0790	3.4236 0.1678	0.2364 0.0633	2.0056 0.7009
50	B	Informative Prior	2.5043 0.0692	1.7021 0.0381	3.5016 0.0813	0.1651 0.0170	2.2165 0.3855
		Non-Informative Prior	2.5094 0.0735	1.7092 0.0470	3.5063 0.0948	0.1706 0.0232	2.1702 0.4622
		ML	2.5210 0.0990	1.7131 0.0534	3.4871 0.1303	0.1751 0.0433	2.1655 0.6313

Table 4. One-Sample prediction- 95 % *BPI* for $X_s^*, s = 1,2,3$.

1- Number of samples which cover the *BPI* from 10000 samples.
2- *BPI* for x_s^*, $s = 1,2,3$.
3- Length of the *BPI*.

r		x_1^*	x_2^*	x_3^*
	1	9690	9785	9907
10	2	(1.7859,3.4617)	(3.3671,5.1614)	(4.4959,6.8969)
	3	1.6758	1.7943	2.4010
	1	9606	9799	9806
20	2	(2.1725,3.9459)	(3.4280,5.5884)	(3.7467,5.8288)
	3	1.7734	2.1604	2.0821
	1	9577	9645	9704
45	2	(2.9762,3.9806)	(3.4981,5.1581)	(4.1514,6.0676)
	3	1.0044	1.6600	1.9162

Table 5. Two-Sample prediction- 95 % *BPI* for $X_s^*, s = 1, 2, 3$

1- Number of samples which cover the *BPI* from 10000 samples.
2- *BPI* for x_s^*, $s = 1, 2, 3$.
3- Length of the *BPI*.

r		z_1	z_2	z_3
	1	9683	9711	9768
10	2	(0.7941,1.1941)	(1.2930,1.8812)	(2.0906,2.8716)
	3	0.4000	0.5882	0.7810
	1	9625	9678	9755
20	2	(0.7922,1.1852)	(1.1237,1.5896)	(1.9954,2.6955)
	3	0.3930	0.4659	0.7001
	1	9543	9622	9753
45	2	(1.0883,1.3689)	(1.2271,1.5813)	(2.0735,2.4965)
	3	0.2806	0.3542	0.4230

Concluding Remarks

In our study, observe the following:

1. the variances of the $BE's$ (against the proposed subjective (informative) or objective (non-informative) prior) are smaller than the corresponding variances of the $MLE's$. This means that the $BE's$ (against the proposed priors) are better than the $MLE's$,

2. the variances of the $BE's$ in case of informative prior are smaller than the corresponding variances in case of non-informative prior,

3. under $LINEX$ loss function, $a = 1$, the variances of the $BE's$ are greater than the variances under SEL function. That is when $a = 1$, the use of SEL leads to better estimates than the $LINEX$ loss function.

4. under $LINEX$ loss function, $a = 7$, the variances of the $BE's$ are smaller than the variances under SEL function. That is when $a = 7$, the use of $LINEX$ loss function leads to better estimates than the SEL function.

5. in Bayesian estimation, if the hyperparameters are unknown, they can be estimated by using the empirical Bayes method [see Maritz and Lwin [16]] or the hierarchical method [see Bernardo and Smith [3],

6. the length of the $BPI's$ and the number of samples which cover these intervals increase by increasing s and decrease by increasing the informative sample size r, which means that the results become better as the informative sample size r gets larger.

7. In all cases, the simulated percentage coverages are at least 95%.

References

[1] Ateya, S. F. and Madhagi, E. A.(2012). On multivariate truncated generalized Cauchy distribution. *Statistical Papers* DOI: 10.1007/s00362-012-0467-9.

[2] Balmer, D. W., Boulton, M. and Sack, R. A. (1974). Optimal solutions in parameter estimation problems for the Cauchy distribution. *J. Amer. Statist. Assoc.*, 69, 238-242.

[3] Bernardo, J. M. and Smith, A. F. M. (1994). *Bayesian Theory.* Wiley, New York.

[4] Cane, G. J. (1974). Linear estimation of parameters of the Cauchy distribution based on sample quantiles. *J. Amer. Statist. Assoc.*, 69, 243-245.

[5] Chan, L. K. (1970). Linear estimation of location and scale parameters of the Cauchy distribution based on sample quantiles. *J. Amer. Statist. Assoc.*, 65, 851-859.

[6] Copas, J. B. (1975). On the unimodality of the likelihood for the Cauchy distribution. *Biometrika*, 62, 702-704.

[7] Dahiya, R.C., Staneski, P. G. and Chaganti, N. R.(2001). Maximum likelihood estimatation of the parameters of the truncated Cauchy distribution. *Commun-Statist.-Th. Methods.*, 30,1737-1750.

[8] Ferguson, T. S. (1978). Maximum likelihood estimates of the parameters of the Cauchy distribution for samples of size 3 and 4. *J. Amer. Statist. Assoc.*, 73, 211-213.

[9] Frank, W. K. (1981). The most powerful invariant test normal vs. Cauchy with applications to stable alternatives. *J. Amer. Statist. Assoc.*, 76, 1002-1005.

[10] Gabrielsen , G. (1982). On the unimodality of the Cauchy distribution: Some comments. *Biometrika*, 69, 677-678.

[11] Hinkley, D. V. (1978). Likelihood inference about location and scale parameters. *Biometrika*, 65, 253-261.

[12] Howlader, H. A. and Weiss, G. (1985). A survey of small-sample estimation of Cauchy location and scale. *Technical report 1.* Department of Statistics, University of Winnipeg, Winnipeg, Manitoba, Canada.

[13] Howlader, H. A. and Weiss, G. (1988). Bayesian reliability estimation of a two-parameter Cauchy distribution. *Biom. J.*, 30(3), 329-337.

[14] Howlader, H. A. and Weiss, G. (1988). On Bayesian estimation of the Cauchy parameters. *Indian J. Statist.*, B, 50(3), 350-361.

[15] Johnson, N. L., Kotz, S. and Balakrishnan, N. (1994). *Continuous Univariate Distributions*. Vol. 1, John Wiley and Sons, Inc., New York.

[16] Maritz, J. S. and Lwin, T.(1989). *Empirical Bayes Methods.* 2nd Ed. Chapman and Hall, London.

[17] Press, S. J. (2003). *Subjective and Objective Bayesian Statistics: Principles, Models and Applications.*Wiley.

[18] Rider, P. R.(1957). Generalized Cauchy distribution *Ann. Instit. Statist. Math.*9, 215-223.

[19] Spiegelhalter, D. J.(1985). Exact Baysian inference on the parameters of a Cauchy distribution with vague prior information. In Bayesian Statistics: *Proceeding of the Second Valencia International Meeting on Bayesian Statistics*, edited by J. M. Bernardo, M. H. Degroot, D. V. Lindley and A. F. M. Smith. Elsevier Publishers (North-Holland), Amsterdam.

[20] Thompson, R. D. and Basu, A. P. (1996). Asymmetric loss function for estimating reliability. In Berry, D. A., Chaloner, K. M. and Geweke, J. K. (Eds.): *Bayesian Analysis in Statistics and Econometrics.* Wiley, New York.

[21] Varian, H.(1975). A Bayesian approach to real estate assessment. In Fienberg, S. E. and Zellner, A. (Eds.): *Studies in Bayesian Econometrics and Statistics.* In honour of Leonard J. Savage, North Holland, Amestrdam, 195-208.

In: Applied Statistical Theory and Applications
Editor: Mohammad Ahsanullah

ISBN: 978-1-63321-858-1
© 2014 Nova Science Publishers, Inc.

Chapter 11

Unbiased Ridge Estimation with Multiple Sources of Prior Information

Robert H. Crouse and Chun Jin[*]

Department of Mathematical Sciences, Central Connecticut State University,
New Britain, Connecticut, US

Abstract

A procedure is illustrated to incorporate multiple sources of prior information in the ridge regression model. The resulting model is unbiased and robust estimates of the ridge parameters are developed.

Keywords and Phrases: Multicollinearity; Multiple sources of prior information; Mean square error; Ridge parameters

1. Introduction

Consider the standard linear regression model as

$$Y = X\beta + \varepsilon \tag{1}$$

where Y is an $n \times 1$ vector of responses, X is an $n \times p$ design matrix of the regressor variables, β is a $p \times 1$ vector of unknown parameters of interest, and ε is distributed normal $N(0, \sigma^2 I)$ with I being the identity matrix. It is well known that the least squares estimator (LSE) of β, $\hat{\beta} = (X'X)^{-1}X'Y$, is very unstable when multicollinearity is present in the design matrix and results in a large mean square error (MSE).

To deal with multicollinearity, a number of procedures have been developed for obtaining a biased estimator of β with a smaller MSE. One of these procedures is ridge regression, originally proposed by Hoerl and Kennard (1970a,b). Swindel (1976) illustrated a technique for combining prior information with ridge regression model, extending Hoerl and Kennard's model as follows:

$$\hat{\beta}(k,J) = (X'X + kI)^{-1}(X'Y + kJ) \tag{2}$$

[*]E-mail address: jinc@ccsu.edu

with J being a prior estimate of β. Swindel showed there exists a k value that results in a smaller MSE than the LSE for any prior information J when J is a fixed vector or when J is unbiased random vector and independent of $\hat{\beta}$. However, Swindel did not propose a way of estimating the ridge parameter k.

Crouse, Jin, and Hanumara (1995) proposed a stochastic estimate of the ridge parameter k, $\hat{k}$, so that $\hat{\beta}(\hat{k}, J)$ is an unbiased estimate of β. In addition they illustrated a substantial reduction in MSE for $\hat{\beta}(\hat{k}, J)$ when compared to the MSE for the LSE of β. Neither Swindel (1976) and nor Crouse, Jin, and Hanumara (1995) proposed a way to combine more than one source of prior information, or to estimate the ridge parameters for multiple sources of prior information.

A general procedure which incorporates several sources of prior information into the ridge regression model will be developed in this paper. Robust easily implemented calculations for the ridge parameters will be proposed, and two numerical examples will be presented to illustrate the performance of the resulting estimators. First, as a preliminary, a matrix convex combination of several random variables will be given in the following section.

2. Matrix Convex Combination of Several Random Variables

If interest is in minimizing the total MSE within the class of matrix convex combinations, then the best matrix convex combination of several unbiased and uncorrelated random variables does not depend on the underlying distribution, just the covariances of the random variables. The result can be summarized in the following known theorem:

Theorem 2.1 *Let $X_0, X_1, \ldots, X_{m-1}$ be m p-variate uncorrelated random variables with the common mean β and covariance matrices Σ_i, $i = 0, 1, \ldots, m - 1$, respectively. Assume that Σ_i, $i = 0, 1, \ldots, m - 1$ are full rank covariance matrices. Consider the matrix convex combination* *of* $X_0, X_1, \ldots, X_{m-1}$,

$$Y = C_0 X_0 + C_1 X_1 + \cdots + C_{m-1} X_{m-1},$$

where the C_i's are $p \times p$ fixed positive definite matrices with $\sum_{i=0}^{m-1} C_i = I$ and I being the $p \times p$ identity matrix. The total MSE of Y is defined as $E\left[(Y - \beta)'(Y - \beta)\right]$. Then the optimal C_i's in terms of minimum total MSE are

$$C_i = \left(\sum_{k=0}^{m-1} \Sigma_k^{-1} \right)^{-1} \Sigma_i^{-1}, \quad i = 0, 1, \ldots, m - 1.$$

A simple proof of Theorem 2.1 that relies only on matrix algebra is given as follows:

Proof: Define $\Sigma = \left(\sum_{k=0}^{m-1} \Sigma_k^{-1} \right)^{-1}$ and $A_i = \Sigma \Sigma_i^{-1}$,   and let $C_i = A_i + B_i$, $i = 0, 1, \ldots, m - 1$, where B_i's are $p \times p$ real matrices. Since $\sum_{i=0}^{m-1} C_i = I$, and $\sum_{i=0}^{m-1} A_i = I$, then we have $\sum_{i=0}^{m-1} B_i = 0$. The MSE can be written as

$$
\begin{aligned}
\text{MSE} &= \text{tr}E\left[(Y-\beta)(Y-\beta)'\right] \\
&= \text{tr}\sum_{i=0}^{m-1}(A_i+B_i)\Sigma_i(A_i+B_i)' \\
&= \text{tr}\left[\sum_{i=0}^{m-1}(A_i\Sigma_iA_i'+B_i\Sigma_iA_i'+A_i\Sigma_iB_i'+B_i\Sigma_iB_i')\right]
\end{aligned} \tag{3}
$$

Recall that $A_i\Sigma_i = \Sigma$, $i = 0,1,\ldots,m-1$, $\sum_{i=0}^{m-1}A_i = I$, and $\sum_{i=0}^{m-1}B_i = 0$. The MSE (3) can then be expressed as the following:

$$
\begin{aligned}
\text{MSE} &= \text{tr}\left[\sum_{i=0}^{m-1}(\Sigma A_i'+B_i\Sigma+\Sigma B_i'+B_i\Sigma_iB_i')\right] \\
&= \text{tr}\Sigma + \sum_{i=0}^{m-1}\text{tr}(B_i\Sigma_iB_i') \geq \text{tr}\Sigma
\end{aligned} \tag{4}
$$

and achieves the minimum MSE (4) when $B_i = 0$ for $i = 0,1,\ldots,m-1$. Thus the result follows.   □

Remark 2.1 It is easily seen from Theorem 2.1 that the more uncorrelated unbiased statistics that are available, the better matrix convex combination estimator we obtain in terms of decreasing the MSE.

3.   Composite Unbiased Ridge Estimator

Consider the standard linear regression model (1).   The LSE of β, $\hat{\beta} = (X'X)^{-1}X'Y$, is distributed normal $N(\beta,\sigma^2(X'X)^{-1})$. Given that there are a sequence of $(m-1)$ p-variate uncorrelated prior information, J_i, $i = 1,2,\ldots$, $m-1$, available, and each J_i is normally distributed as $N(\beta,(\sigma^2/k_i)I)$ where k_i is an unknown positive real number. The following theorem gives a generalized unbiased ridge estimate of β along with the multiple sources of prior information.

Theorem 3.1 Let $\hat{\beta}$ be a p-variate random variable with mean β and covariance $\sigma^2(X'X)^{-1}$. Consider a sequence of $(m-1)$ p-variate uncorrelated prior information, J_i, $i = 1,2,\ldots,m-1$, each J_i has the common mean β and the covariance $(\sigma^2/k_i)I$ for $k_i > 0$. Define the matrix convex combination of $\hat{\beta}, J_1,\ldots,J_{m-1}$ as

$$
C_0\hat{\beta} + C_1J_1 + \cdots + C_{m-1}J_{m-1}
$$

where the C_i's are $p \times p$ fixed positive definite matrices with $\sum_{i=0}^{m-1}C_i = I$ and I being the $p \times p$ identity matrix. Then, for the optimal C_i's in terms of minimum total MSE, the best matrix convex combination of $\hat{\beta}, J_1,\ldots,J_{m-1}$ is unbiased and can be expressed as

$$
\begin{aligned}
&\hat{\beta}(k_1,\ldots,k_{m-1},J_1,\ldots,J_{m-1}) \\
&= \left(X'X+(k_1+\cdots+k_{m-1})I\right)^{-1}(X'Y+k_1J_1+\cdots+k_{m-1}J_{m-1})
\end{aligned} \tag{5}
$$

Proof: Using Theorem 2.1, straightforward computations yield the results. □

The best matrix convex estimator (5) can be seen as a generalized Swindel-type ridge estimator compared with (2). However, the prior information J in (2) is a fixed vector while J_i's in (5) are random vectors with specified mean and covariances. As a matter of fact, the best matrix convex estimator $\hat{\beta}(k_1,\ldots,k_{m-1},J_1,\ldots,J_{m-1})$ in (5) is not an estimator in the usual sense because it depends upon $(m-1)$ unknown ridge parameters k_i's that need to be estimated. We will devote our attention to the problem of estimating the ridge parameters k_i's in the remainder of this section.

Crouse, Jin, and Hanumara (1995) proposed a stochastic estimate of the ridge parameter k when there is only one prior information J available. Using the similar idea, we can propose a general procedure to estimate several ridge parameters as follows.

Assume that there are $m-1$ independent sources of prior information, $J_1,J_2,\ldots,J_{m-1}$, as defined in Theorem 3.1. With the optimal values of C_i, the proposed ridge estimator (3.1) can be written as

$$\hat{\beta}(k_1,\ldots,k_{m-1},J_1,\ldots,J_{m-1}) = \hat{\beta}+C_1(J_1-\hat{\beta})+\cdots+C_{m-1}(J_{m-1}-\hat{\beta}), \qquad (6)$$

where

$$C_i = k_i\left(X'X+(k_1+\cdots+k_{m-1})I\right)^{-1} \quad \text{for } i=1,2,\ldots,m-1.$$

We now need to estimate those unknown positive ridge parameters k_i's.

It is assumed that each prior information J_i is uncorrelated with the LSE, $\hat{\beta}$. As discussed by Crouse, Jin, and Hanumara (1995), for each i, an unbiased estimate of $1/k_i$ is

$$\frac{1}{\hat{k}_i} = \frac{(J_i-\hat{\beta})'(J_i-\hat{\beta})-\sigma^2\text{tr}(X'X)^{-1}}{p\sigma^2} \qquad (7)$$

if σ^2 is known. When σ^2 is unknown, however, σ^2 can be estimated by an unbiased estimator $s^2 = (Y-X\hat{\beta})'(Y-X\hat{\beta})/(n-p)$, and an estimate of $1/k_i$ can then be shown as

$$\frac{1}{\hat{k}_i} = \frac{(J_i-\hat{\beta})'(J_i-\hat{\beta})-s^2\text{tr}(X'X)^{-1}}{ps^2}. \qquad (8)$$

One might note that we could use other estimates of σ^2 in above estimation.

Using (6), now the proposed ridge estimator (5) can be re-written as

$$\begin{aligned}
&\hat{\beta}(\hat{k}_1,\ldots,\hat{k}_{m-1},J_1,\ldots,J_{m-1}) \\
&= \left(X'X+(\hat{k}_1+\cdots+\hat{k}_{m-1})I\right)^{-1}\left(X'Y+\hat{k}_1J_1+\cdots+\hat{k}_{m-1}J_{m-1}\right) \\
&= \hat{\beta}+\left(X'X+(\hat{k}_1+\cdots+\hat{k}_{m-1})I\right)^{-1}\sum_{i=1}^{m-1}\hat{k}_i(J_i-\hat{\beta}), \qquad (9)
\end{aligned}$$

where $\hat{k}_i$'s can be obtained from (7) or (8).

The following theorem provides the unbiasedness of the proposed ridge estimator (9). Without loss of generality, we can simply assume that σ^2 is unknown.

Theorem 3.2 *Let $J_i - \hat{\beta}$ be independently distributed as $N\left(0, (\sigma^2/k_i)I + \sigma^2(X'X)^{-1}\right)$, for $i = 1, 2, \ldots, m - 1$. If σ^2 is unknown, then the proposed ridge estimator (9), $\hat{\beta}(\hat{k}_1, \ldots, \hat{k}_{m-1}, J_1, \ldots, J_{m-1})$, is unbiased where $\hat{k}_i$'s are given by (8).*

Proof: It can be shown that for each i,

$$\hat{k}_i = \frac{ps^2}{(J_i - \hat{\beta})'(J_i - \hat{\beta}) - s^2 \text{tr}(X'X)^{-1}},$$

where $s^2 = (Y - X\hat{\beta})'(Y - X\hat{\beta})/(n - p)$. Since the LSE, $\hat{\beta}$, is independent of s^2, conditioning on s^2, $\hat{k}_i$ is invariant to a sign change in $J_i - \hat{\beta}$, and then

$$E\left[\left(X'X + (\hat{k}_1 + \cdots + \hat{k}_{m-1})I\right)^{-1} \hat{k}_i(J_i - \hat{\beta})|s^2\right] = 0,$$

for $i = 1, 2, \ldots, m - 1$. Therefore, $E\left[\hat{\beta}(\hat{k}_1, \ldots, \hat{k}_{m-1}, J_1, \ldots, J_{m-1})\right] = E[\hat{\beta}] = \beta$. □

In equations (7) and (8), it is noted that the estimates of $1/\hat{k}_i$ could be negative which would make no sense because $k_i > 0$ for all $i = 1, 2, \ldots, m - 1$. In this case, similar to Crouse, Jin, and Hanumara (1995), for each i, $\hat{k}_i$ can be modified as follows:

$$\hat{k}_i^+ = \begin{cases} \dfrac{p\sigma^2}{(J_i - \hat{\beta})'(J_i - \hat{\beta}) - \sigma^2\text{tr}(X'X)^{-1}} & \text{if } (J_i - \hat{\beta})'(J_i - \hat{\beta}) > \sigma^2\text{tr}(X'X)^{-1} \\[3mm] \dfrac{p\sigma^2}{(J_i - \hat{\beta})'(J_i - \hat{\beta})} & \text{otherwise} \end{cases} \tag{10}$$

where σ^2 can be replaced by its estimator s^2 if σ^2 is unknown.

It is seen that $\hat{k}_i^+$ (10) is a generalization of Hoerl, Kennard and Baldwin's (1975) $p\sigma^2/(\hat{\beta}'\hat{\beta})$ to include several sources of prior information. In Section 4, simulation results will show that this generalization could greatly improve upon the performance of the estimators with one source of prior information proposed by Crouse, Jin, and Hanumara (1995).

4. Proposed Ridge Estimators with Multicollinearity

To illustrate the performance of the proposed ridge estimator with multiple sources of prior information in Section 3, two sources of prior information are considered along with a multicollinear design matrix originally considered by Hoerl and Kennard (1981, Table 1). The data was generated by taking a factor structure from a real data set, and choosing $\beta_1, \beta_2, \beta_3, \beta_4$, and β_5 with the constraint that $\beta'\beta = 300$ and a normal error ε with mean zero and $\sigma^2 = 1$ was added to form the observed response values Y_i. The data is given in Table 4.1. The resulting model is $Y = X\beta + \varepsilon$, where ε is normally distributed as $N(0, \sigma^2 I)$. It is noted that there is a high degree of multicollinearity among predictors, as evidenced by the eigenvalues of $X'X$ which are $.0138, .0583, .1549, .1941, 4.5789$. The ratio of the largest eigenvalue to the smallest eigenvalue is 331.804, indicating severe multicollinearity.

In addition, two sources of prior information, J_1 and J_2, were generated as $J_i \sim N(\beta, (\sigma^2/k_i)I)$ for selected values of the standard deviations for J_i's, $i = 1, 2$. The estimates of MSEs

Table 4.1.

X_1	X_2	X_3	X_4	X_5
−.4239	−.2943	−.1829	−.2857	−.3571
−.3912	−.2943	−.2815	−.2993	−.3135
−.1867	−.1723	−.3800	−.2452	−.1176
−.1704	−.1501	−.2158	−.2722	−.2482
−.1581	−.1057	−.3307	−.1235	−.1829
−.1009	−.1057	−.2486	−.1505	−.2047
−.0559	−.2943	.0306	−.1776	−.1611
−.0232	−.2277	.0471	−.1100	−.1611
−.0232	−.0170	.0142	.0117	.0131
.0177	−.0059	.0799	−.0288	.2961
.0586	.1826	.0964	.1875	.1872
.2549	.2714	.2442	.2957	.4267
.3080	.3157	.2771	.3498	.2961
.4266	.4044	.3592	.3633	.1219
.4675	.4932	.4906	.4850	.4050

Regression Coefficients				
β_1	β_2	β_3	β_4	β_5
9.0269	8.3384	3.0903	3.3411	11.3258

for the ridge estimators by incorporating one source of prior information, J_1, were calculated, and then for the proposed ridge estimators with two sources of prior information, J_1 and J_2 were also evaluated. All results are presented in Table 4.2. Although $\sigma^2 = 1$ is known, it was indeed estimated from the data by using s^2. Our simulation studies were done by taking 2500 replications. The percentages of improvement of the MSEs for the proposed ridge estimators with J_1 and J_2 over the ridge estimators with J_1 only are reported in parentheses in Table 4.2.

The MSE of the LSE of β can be easily computed and it results 101.20. As seen from Table 4.2, the proposed ridge estimators incorporating two sources of prior information always provide substantially smaller MSE than that of the LSE except when the standard deviations of both J_1 and J_2 are near a large number, say 30. In this case J_1 and J_2 could be considered as noninformative priors. Table 4.2 also shows that the proposed ridge estimators incorporating two sources of prior information, J_1 and J_2, have significant improvements across the board in MSE compared with only one J_1 when the standard deviations of J_2 are not too large. In other words, the proposed ridge estimator incorporating two sources of prior information has substantial improvement over the ridge estimator with only one source of prior information in terms of MSE as long as the second source of prior information is informative. The LSE always performs worse unless those two sources of prior information are noninformative.

Finally, let us consider a special case with an orthogonal design matrix $X = I$. Now the

MSE of the LSE of β is 5. Once again, two sources of prior information, J_1 and J_2, were generated as $J_i \sim N(\beta, (\sigma^2/k_i)I)$ for selected values of standard deviations for J_i's, $i = 1, 2$. Again $\sigma^2 = 1$, and since the rank of X and number of parameters estimated are 5, s^2 can not be estimated from the data, so it is just taken as known. Similar to the last example in Table 4.2, new simulations were done by taking 2500 replications and results are presented in Table 4.3.

Table 4.3 shows that a dramatic reduction in MSE by incorporating two sources of prior information when at least one of the two sources of prior information is informative. The estimates of MSEs of the orthogonal design matrix provide results similar to those of the multicollinear design matrix when the standard deviation of J_2 is relative small. It is noted that the percentages of improvement in MSE for orthogonal design matrix are less than those of the multicollinear design matrix, as would be expected.

Table 4.2. The Estimates of MSEs (Improvement% over J_1 only)

		$\sigma/\sqrt{k_1}$						
		0.50	1.00	2.00	3.00	5.00	10.0	30.0
	J_1 only	**20.05**	**22.09**	**26.40**	**35.13**	**51.69**	**80.78**	**103.49**
$\sigma/\sqrt{k_2}$								
0.50	J_1 and J_2	**10.82**	**11.79**	**13.18**	**16.51**	**20.67**	**21.85**	**20.09**
		(46%)	(47%)	(50%)	(53%)	(60%)	(73%)	(81%)
1.00	J_1 and J_2		**12.12**	**13.48**	**15.84**	**21.21**	**23.28**	**23.10**
			(45%)	(49%)	(55%)	(59%)	(71%)	(78%)
2.00	J_1 and J_2			**15.19**	**18.30**	**24.08**	**27.91**	**25.16**
				(42%)	(48%)	(53%)	(65%)	(76%)
3.00	J_1 and J_2				**21.71**	**30.68**	**34.03**	**33.68**
					(38%)	(41%)	(58%)	(67%)
5.00	J_1 and J_2					**38.20**	**46.99**	**49.67**
						(26%)	(42%)	(52%)
10.0	J_1 and J_2						**68.02**	**78.92**
							(16%)	(24%)
30.0	J_1 and J_2							**105.72**
								(-2%)

5. Summary

When multiple sources of prior information are available and the covariances of the prior information are not known, the proposed ridge estimator is a robust alternative to the

Table 4.3. The Estimates of MSEs for the Orthogonal Design Matrix

		$\sigma/\sqrt{k_1}$						
		0.50	1.00	1.50	2.00	3.00	4.00	5.00
	J_1 only	**1.497**	**2.900**	**3.915**	**4.496**	**4.726**	**4.941**	**4.998**
$\sigma/\sqrt{k_2}$								
0.50	J_1 and J_2	**0.895**	**1.497**	**1.876**	**1.925**	**1.832**	**1.737**	**1.719**
		(40%)	(48%)	(52%)	(57%)	(61%)	(65%)	(66%)
1.00	J_1 and J_2		**2.265**	**2.872**	**3.195**	**3.181**	**3.251**	**3.194**
			(22%)	(27%)	(29%)	(33%)	(34%)	(36%)
1.50	J_1 and J_2			**3.721**	**4.033**	**4.333**	**4.256**	**4.477**
				(5%)	(10%)	(8%)	(14%)	(10%)
2.00	J_1 and J_2				**4.437**	**4.518**	**4.362**	**4.516**
					(1%)	(4%)	(12%)	(10%)
3.00	J_1 and J_2					**5.457**	**5.168**	**5.066**
						(-15%)	(-5%)	(-1%)
4.00	J_1 and J_2						**5.319**	**5.495**
							(-8%)	(-10%)
5.00	J_1 and J_2							**5.308**
								(-6%)

MLE, or the ridge estimator with only one source of prior information. If additional sources of prior information are informative, then the proposed ridge estimator performs very well not only when multicollinearity is present in the design matrix, but also for the orthogonal design matrix. The simulation results illustrate that much is to be gained by incorporating two sources of informative prior information and little is lost by including noninformative prior information.

References

[1] Crouse, R.H., Jin, C. and Hanumara, R.C. (1995)."Unbiased Ridge Estimation with Prior Information and Ridge Trace," *Communications in Statistics, Theory and Methods*, 24, 2341-2354.

[2] Hoerl, A.E. and Kennard, R.W. (1970a). "Ridge regression: Biased estimation for nonorthogonal problems." *Technometrics*, 12, 55-67.

[3] Hoerl, A.E. and Kennard, R.W. (1970b). "Ridge regression: Applications to nonorthogonal problems." *Technometrics*, 12, 69-82.

[4] Hoerl, A.E., Kennard, R.W., and Baldwin, K.F. (1975). "Ridge regression: Some Simulations." *Communications in Statistics*, 4, 105-123.

[5] Hoerl, A.E. and Kennard, R.W. (1981). "Ridge Regression – 1980 Advances, Algorithms, and Applications." *American Journal of Mathematical and Management Sciences*, 1, 5-83.

[6] Swindel, B.F. (1976). "Good Ridge Estimators Based on Prior Information." *Communications in Statistics*, 11, 1065-1075.

In: Applied Statistical Theory and Applications
Editor: Mohammad Ahsanullah

ISBN: 978-1-63321-858-1
© 2014 Nova Science Publishers, Inc.

Chapter 12

ON AN ASYMPTOTIC COMPARISON OF MAXIMUM LIKELIHOOD AND BERKSON'S MODIFIED MINIMUM CHI-SQUARE ESTIMATES IN THE TWO PARAMETER DOSE RESPONSE MODELS

Wuttichai Srisodaphol[1], Montip Tiensuwan[1,*]and Bimal K. Sinha[2]
[1]Department of Mathematics, Faculty of Science,
Mahidol University, Bangkok, Thailand
[2]Department of Mathematics and Statistics,
University of Maryland Baltimore County (UMBC), Maryland, US

Abstract

This paper focuses on three standard dose response models, namely, the multistage Weibull, logistic and log-logistic models, each involving two unknown parameters. The maximum likelihood and Berkson's modified minimum chi-square methods are employed to estimate the two unknown parameters in each model, and the mean squared errors of these estimates are derived asymptotically to the order of approximation of n^{-2}, where n is the sample size.The AIC and deviance criteria are used for model selection. One real data set is used for illustration. The results show that, as expected, the mean squared errors of the estimates behave differently for different dose groups and dose levels.

Keywords and Phrases: asymptotic comparison; Berkson's modified minimum chi-square; logistic model; log-logistic model; maximum likelihood; mean squared errors; multistage Weibull model

AMS 2000 Subject Classifications:62F10, 62F12

---

* E-mail address: montip.tie@mahidol.ac.th (Corresponding Author)

1. Introduction

Dose response models are mathematical functions that relate the dose to the measure of observed effect, and the multistage Weibull, logistic and log-logistic models are three popular dose response models. Sinha [6] presented finite sample theory and also asymptotic results for comparing two relevant estimates in Berkson's bioassay problem based on the logistic model. Srisodaphol et al. [7, 8] considered the multistage Weibull, logistic and log-logistic models involving two parameters, and used the maximum likelihood and Berkson's modified minimum chi-square methods to estimate one unknown parameter, assuming the other parameter is known.

In this study, we consider the above three dose response models where both parameters are unknown. We derive the maximum likelihood and Berkson's modified minimum chi-square estimates of them and study their large sample properties via mean squared error (MSE) to the order of n^{-2}. Further, a real data set is used for illustration.

The paper is organized as follows. In Section 2 we present the three dose response models and the general conditions of asymptotically efficient estimates. The asymptotic properties of the maximum likelihood and Berkson's modified minimum chi-square estimates based on the multistage Weibull, logistic and log-logistic models are given in Sections 3, 4 and 5, respectively. Finally, Section 6 contains conclusions and discussions of our methods from one data set.

2. Models and Notations

We assume that there are $m+1$ dose groups with doses $d_0 = 0$ (control), $d_1,...,d_m > 0$ and n_i subjects in the ith dose group. The number of respondents X_i are independent and distributed as binomial, $X_i \sim B[n_i, \pi_i(d_i, \underline{\theta})]$, where $\pi_i(d_i, \underline{\theta})$ stands for the response probability at dose d_i. The three popular dose response models that we consider are given below along with the natural restriction on the two parameters.

$$\text{Multistage Weibull model: } \pi(d, \underline{\theta}) = 1 - e^{-(\theta_0 + \theta_1 d)}, \ \theta_0, \theta_1 > 0.$$

$$\text{Logistic model: } \pi(d, \underline{\theta}) = \frac{1}{1 + e^{-(\theta_0 + \theta_1 d)}}, \ -\infty < \theta_0, \theta_1 < \infty.$$

$$\text{Log-logistic model: } \pi(d, \underline{\theta}) = \frac{1}{1 + e^{-(\theta_0 + \theta_1 \ln(d))}}, \ -\infty < \theta_0, \theta_1 < \infty.$$

We consider mean squared errors(MSEs) of the estimates of θ_0 and θ_1 as a basis of their performance evaluation and derive their asymptotic expressions to the order of approximation n^{-2} as follows.

Suppose $\hat{\underline{\theta}} = \begin{pmatrix} \hat{\theta}_0 & \hat{\theta}_1 \end{pmatrix}'$ is an estimate of $\underline{\theta} = \begin{pmatrix} \theta_0 & \theta_1 \end{pmatrix}'$ with $E(\hat{\theta}_0) = \theta_0 + b_0(\underline{\theta})$,

$E(\hat{\theta}_1) = \theta_1 + b_1(\underline{\theta})$, $E\left[\left(\hat{\theta}_i - E(\hat{\theta}_i) \right) \left(\hat{\theta}_j - E(\hat{\theta}_j) \right) \right] = v_{ij}$, $i, j = 0, 1$. Often the bias

terms $b_0(\underline{\theta})$ and $b_1(\underline{\theta})$ could be asymptotically expressed as

$$b_0(\underline{\theta}) = \frac{b_0(\underline{\theta})}{n} + o(n^{-1}), \ b_1(\underline{\theta}) = \frac{b_1(\underline{\theta})}{n} + o(n^{-1}). \tag{1}$$

The MSEs of $\hat{\theta}_0$ and $\hat{\theta}_1$ can be written as

$$E(\hat{\theta}_0 - \theta_0)^2 = v_{00} + b_0^2(\underline{\theta}), E(\hat{\theta}_1 - \theta_1)^2 = v_{11} + b_1^2(\underline{\theta}),$$

$E\left[\left(\hat{\theta}_0 - E(\hat{\theta}_0) \right) \left(\hat{\theta}_1 - E(\hat{\theta}_1) \right) \right] = v_{01} + b_0(\underline{\theta})b_1(\underline{\theta})$, implying the MSE matrix of

estimates of θ_0 and θ_1 is given by

$$V + \begin{pmatrix} b_0^2(\underline{\theta}) & b_0(\underline{\theta})b_1(\underline{\theta}) \\ b_1(\underline{\theta})b_0(\underline{\theta}) & b_1^2(\underline{\theta}) \end{pmatrix}.$$

From Rao-Cramer information inequality [5], $V \geq \Delta I^{-1}(\underline{\theta})\Delta'$ where $I(\underline{\theta})$ is Fisher

information matrix and

$$\Delta = \begin{pmatrix} \dfrac{\partial g_0(\underline{\theta})}{\partial \theta_0} & \dfrac{\partial g_0(\underline{\theta})}{\partial \theta_1} \\ \dfrac{\partial g_1(\underline{\theta})}{\partial \theta_0} & \dfrac{\partial g_1(\underline{\theta})}{\partial \theta_1} \end{pmatrix},$$

with $g_i(\underline{\theta}) = E(\hat{\theta}_i) = \theta_i + b_i(\underline{\theta})$, so that

$$\Delta = \begin{pmatrix} 1 + \dfrac{\partial b_0(\underline{\theta})}{\partial \theta_0} & \dfrac{\partial b_0(\underline{\theta})}{\partial \theta_1} \\ \dfrac{\partial b_1(\underline{\theta})}{\partial \theta_0} & 1 + \dfrac{\partial b_1(\underline{\theta})}{\partial \theta_1} \end{pmatrix}.$$

From (1) we can then write

$$\Delta \approx I + \frac{1}{n}\Lambda, \text{ where } \Lambda = \begin{pmatrix} \dfrac{\partial b_0(\underline{\theta})}{\partial \theta_0} & \dfrac{\partial b_0(\underline{\theta})}{\partial \theta_1} \\ \dfrac{\partial b_1(\underline{\theta})}{\partial \theta_0} & \dfrac{\partial b_1(\underline{\theta})}{\partial \theta_1} \end{pmatrix}.$$

Using $I^{-1}(\underline{\theta}) = \frac{1}{n}\Sigma = \frac{1}{n}\begin{pmatrix} \sigma_{00} & \sigma_{01} \\ \sigma_{10} & \sigma_{11} \end{pmatrix}$ so that

$$\Delta I^{-1}(\underline{\theta})\Delta' = \left[I + \frac{1}{n}\Lambda\right]\frac{\Sigma}{n}\left[I + \frac{1}{n}\Lambda'\right] = \frac{\Sigma}{n} + \frac{1}{n^2}[\Lambda\Sigma + \Sigma\Lambda'],$$

the MSE matrix of $\hat{\theta}_0$ and $\hat{\theta}_1$ is written as

$$\frac{\Sigma}{n} + \frac{1}{n^2}[\Lambda\Sigma + \Sigma\Lambda'] + \frac{1}{n^2}\begin{pmatrix} b_0^2(\underline{\theta}) & b_0(\underline{\theta})b_1(\underline{\theta}) \\ b_1(\underline{\theta})b_0(\underline{\theta}) & b_1^2(\underline{\theta}) \end{pmatrix} + o(n^{-2}). \quad (2)$$

From (2), the asymptotic mean squared errors of $\hat{\theta}_0$ and $\hat{\theta}_1$ are obtained as

$$E(\hat{\theta}_0 - \theta_0)^2 = \frac{\sigma_{00}}{n} + \frac{1}{n^2}\left[2\left(\frac{\partial b_0(\underline{\theta})}{\partial \theta_0}\sigma_{00} + \frac{\partial b_0(\underline{\theta})}{\partial \theta_1}\sigma_{01}\right)\right] + \frac{b_0^2(\underline{\theta})}{n^2} = \frac{\sigma_{00}}{n} + \varphi_0^*(\theta_0), \quad (3)$$

$$E(\hat{\theta}_1 - \theta_1)^2 = \frac{\sigma_{11}}{n} + \frac{1}{n^2}\left[2\left(\frac{\partial b_1(\underline{\theta})}{\partial \theta_0}\sigma_{10} + \frac{\partial b_1(\underline{\theta})}{\partial \theta_1}\sigma_{11}\right)\right] + \frac{b_1^2(\underline{\theta})}{n^2} = \frac{\sigma_{11}}{n} + \varphi_1^*(\theta_1). \quad (4)$$

Given the above general scenario, in the next section we carry out the various computations for the MLEs and Berkson's estimates for the three specified dose response models.

3. Multistage Weibull Model

3.1. Maximum Likelihood Estimates

The likelihood function of multistage Weibull model is given by

$$L(\theta_0, \theta_1 \mid \text{data}) = \prod_{i=0}^{m}\binom{n_i}{x_i}\left[1 - e^{-(\theta_0 + \theta_1 d_i)}\right]^{x_i}\left[e^{-(\theta_0 + \theta_1 d_i)}\right]^{n_i - x_i}$$

$$\propto \prod_{i=0}^{m}\left[e^{(\theta_0 + \theta_1 d_i)} - 1\right]^{x_i}\left[e^{-(\theta_0 + \theta_1 d_i)}\right]^{n_i}.$$

Differentiating $\log L\left(\theta_0, \theta_1 \mid \text{data}\right)$ with respect to θ_0 and θ_1, and setting the derivatives equal to zero, the normal equations are

$$\sum_{i=0}^{m} n_i = \sum_{i=0}^{m} \frac{x_i}{1 - e^{-\left(\hat{\theta}_{0MLE} + \hat{\theta}_{1MLE}d_i\right)}} \tag{5}$$

$$\sum_{i=0}^{m} n_i d_i = \sum_{i=0}^{m} \frac{x_i d_i}{1 - e^{-\left(\hat{\theta}_{0MLE} + \hat{\theta}_{1MLE}d_i\right)}} \tag{6}$$

Where $\hat{\theta}_{0MLE}$ and $\hat{\theta}_{1MLE}$ denote the maximum likelihood estimates of θ_0 and θ_1. We assume for simplicity that $n_i = n$ for all i and write $p_i = x_i / n$, then (5) and (6) reduce to

$$m + 1 = \sum_{i=0}^{m} \frac{p_i}{1 - e^{-\left(\psi_0\left(p_0, \ldots, p_m\right) + \psi_1\left(p_0, \ldots, p_m\right)d_i\right)}} \tag{7}$$

$$\sum_{i=0}^{m} d_i = \sum_{i=0}^{m} \frac{d_i p_i}{1 - e^{-\left(\psi_0\left(p_0, \ldots, p_m\right) + \psi_1\left(p_0, \ldots, p_m\right)d_i\right)}} \tag{8}$$

where $\hat{\theta}_{0MLE} = \psi_0\left(p_0, \ldots, p_m\right)$ and $\hat{\theta}_{1MLE} = \psi_1\left(p_0, \ldots, p_m\right)$. To study the asymptotic properties of $\hat{\theta}_{0MLE}$ and $\hat{\theta}_{1MLE}$, we use Taylor series to expand $\psi_0\left(p_0, \ldots, p_m\right)$ and $\psi_1\left(p_0, \ldots, p_m\right)$, and find the means of $\hat{\theta}_{0MLE}$ and $\hat{\theta}_{1MLE}$ by ignoring the terms of smaller order than n^{-2} as

$$E\left(\hat{\theta}_{0MLE}\right) = \theta_0 + \frac{1}{2} \sum_{i=0}^{m} \frac{P_i\left(1 - P_i\right)}{n} \left. \frac{\partial^2 \psi_0}{\partial p_i^2} \right|_{P_i},$$

$$E\left(\hat{\theta}_{1MLE}\right) = \theta_1 + \frac{1}{2} \sum_{i=0}^{m} \frac{P_i\left(1 - P_i\right)}{n} \left. \frac{\partial^2 \psi_1}{\partial p_i^2} \right|_{P_i}.$$

To determine the first order bias terms

$$b_{0MLE}\left(\underline{\theta}\right) = \frac{1}{2n} \sum_{i=0}^{m} P_i\left(1 - P_i\right) \left. \frac{\partial^2 \psi_0}{\partial p_i^2} \right|_{P_i} \tag{9}$$

$$b_{1MLE}\left(\underline{\theta}\right) = \frac{1}{2n} \sum_{i=0}^{m} P_i\left(1 - P_i\right) \left. \frac{\partial^2 \psi_1}{\partial p_i^2} \right|_{P_i}, \tag{10}$$

we compute the second derivative of $\psi_0 (p_0,\ldots,p_m)$ and $\psi_1 (p_0,\ldots,p_m)$ with respect to p_i which is then replaced by P_i for $i = 0,1,\ldots,m$. Upon simplification we get

$$b_{0MLE}(\underline{\theta}) = \left[-A_3^2 B_1 + 3A_2 A_3 B_2 - A_1 A_3 B_3 - 2A_2^2 B_3 + A_1 A_2 B_4 \right]\bigg/ n\left[A_1 A_3 - A_2^2\right]^2$$

$$+ \left\{-\frac{3}{2}A_1 A_2 A_3^2 C_2 + \frac{3}{2}A_2^3 A_3 C_2 + \frac{1}{2}A_1^2 A_3^2 C_3 + \frac{1}{2}A_1 A_2^2 A_3 C_3 - A_2^4 C_3 + \frac{1}{2}A_1 A_3^3 C_1 \right.$$

$$\left. -\frac{1}{2}A_2^2 A_3^2 C_1 - \frac{1}{2}A_1^2 A_2 A_3 C_4 + \frac{1}{2}A_1 A_2^3 C_4 \right\}\bigg/ n\left[A_1 A_3 - A_2^2\right]^3, \tag{11}$$

$$b_{1MLE}(\underline{\theta}) = \left[-A_1 A_3 B_2 + 3A_1 A_2 B_3 - A_1^2 B_4 + A_2 A_3 B_1 - 2A_2^2 B_2 \right]\bigg/ n\left[A_1 A_3 - A_2^2\right]^2$$

$$+ \left\{\frac{1}{2}A_1^2 A_3^2 C_2 + \frac{1}{2}A_1 A_2^2 A_3 C_2 - A_2^4 C_2 - \frac{3}{2}A_1^2 A_2 A_3 C_3 + \frac{3}{2}A_1 A_2^3 C_3 - \frac{1}{2}A_1^2 A_2^2 C_4 \right.$$

$$\left. +\frac{1}{2}A_1^3 A_3 C_4 - \frac{1}{2}A_1 A_2 A_3^2 C_1 + \frac{1}{2}A_2^3 A_3 C_1 \right\}\bigg/ n\left[A_1 A_3 - A_2^2\right]^3, \tag{12}$$

where

$$A_1 = \sum_{i=0}^{m} \frac{(1-\pi_i)}{\pi_i}, \; A_2 = \sum_{i=0}^{m} \frac{d_i(1-\pi_i)}{\pi_i}, \; A_3 = \sum_{i=0}^{m} \frac{d_i^2(1-\pi_i)}{\pi_i},$$

$$B_1 = \sum_{i=0}^{m} \frac{(1-\pi_i)^2}{\pi_i^2}, \; B_2 = \sum_{i=0}^{m} \frac{d_i(1-\pi_i)^2}{\pi_i^2}, \; B_3 = \sum_{i=0}^{m} \frac{d_i^2(1-\pi_i)^2}{\pi_i^2}, \; B_4 = \sum_{i=0}^{m} \frac{d_i^3(1-\pi_i)^2}{\pi_i^2}$$

$$C_1 = \sum_{i=0}^{m} \frac{(1-\pi_i)(2-\pi_i)}{\pi_i^2}, \; C_2 = \sum_{i=0}^{m} \frac{d_i(1-\pi_i)(2-\pi_i)}{\pi_i^2}, \; C_3 = \sum_{i=0}^{m} \frac{d_i^2(1-\pi_i)(2-\pi_i)}{\pi_i^2},$$

$$C_4 = \sum_{i=0}^{m} \frac{d_i^3(1-\pi_i)(2-\pi_i)}{\pi_i^2}.$$

Finally, to compute $\varphi_0^*(\theta_0)$ and $\varphi_1^*(\theta_1)$ in (3) and (4) based on MLEs for multistage Weibull model, the expressions of $\dfrac{\partial b_{0MLE}(\underline{\theta})}{\partial \theta_0}$, $\dfrac{\partial b_{0MLE}(\underline{\theta})}{\partial \theta_1}$, $\dfrac{\partial b_{1MLE}(\underline{\theta})}{\partial \theta_0}$ and $\dfrac{\partial b_{1MLE}(\underline{\theta})}{\partial \theta_1}$

which are required in the sequel are obtained by Maple, and the values of $\varphi_{0MLE}^{*}(\theta_0)$ and $\varphi_{1MLE}^{*}(\theta_1)$ are computed by MATLAB and shown in Section 6.1 for one data set.

3.2. Berkson's Modified Minimum Chi-Square Estimates

Since $1 - \pi(\theta_0, \theta_1) = e^{-(\theta_0 + \theta_1 d_i)}$ implies $-\ln(1 - \pi(\theta_0, \theta_1)) = \theta_0 + \theta_1 d_i$, asymptotically we have $E[-\ln(1 - p_i)] \approx \theta_0 + \theta_1 d_i$ and $Var[-\ln(1 - p_i)] \approx \pi_i / [n_i(1 - \pi_i)]$. A modified chi-square function, $Q(\theta_0, \theta_1)$, is defined by

$$Q(\theta_0, \theta_1) = \sum_{i=0}^{m} \frac{n_i(1 - p_i)}{p_i} \left[\ln(1 - p_i) + \theta_0 + \theta_1 d_i\right]^2.$$

Berkson's modified minimum chi-square estimates of θ_0 and θ_1, $\hat{\theta}_{0B}$ and $\hat{\theta}_{1B}$, are obtained by minimizing $Q(\theta_0, \theta_1)$ with respect to θ_0 and θ_1. A direct minimization produces

$$\sum_{i=0}^{m} \frac{n_i(1 - p_i)}{p_i} \left[\ln(1 - p_i) + \theta_0 + \theta_1 d_i\right] = 0 \tag{13}$$

$$\sum_{i=0}^{m} \frac{n_i d_i(1 - p_i)}{p_i} \left[\ln(1 - p_i) + \theta_0 + \theta_1 d_i\right] = 0, \tag{14}$$

which can be readily solved to yield

$$\hat{\theta}_{0B} = \frac{\sum_{i=0}^{m} \frac{d_i(1 - p_i)}{p_i} \sum_{i=0}^{m} \frac{d_i(1 - p_i)}{p_i} \ln(1 - p_i) - \sum_{i=0}^{m} \frac{d_i^2(1 - p_i)}{p_i} \sum_{i=0}^{m} \frac{(1 - p_i)}{p_i} \ln(1 - p_i)}{\sum_{i=0}^{m} \frac{(1 - p_i)}{p_i} \sum_{i=0}^{m} \frac{d_i^2(1 - p_i)}{p_i} - \left[\sum_{i=0}^{m} \frac{d_i(1 - p_i)}{p_i}\right]^2} \tag{15}$$

$$\hat{\theta}_{1B} = \frac{\sum_{i=0}^{m} \frac{d_i(1 - p_i)}{p_i} \sum_{i=0}^{m} \frac{(1 - p_i)}{p_i} \ln(1 - p_i) - \sum_{i=0}^{m} \frac{(1 - p_i)}{p_i} \sum_{i=0}^{m} \frac{d_i(1 - p_i)}{p_i} \ln(1 - p_i)}{\sum_{i=0}^{m} \frac{(1 - p_i)}{p_i} \sum_{i=0}^{m} \frac{d_i^2(1 - p_i)}{p_i} - \left[\sum_{i=0}^{m} \frac{d_i(1 - p_i)}{p_i}\right]^2}. \tag{16}$$

We write $\hat{\theta}_{0B} = \tilde{\psi}_0(p_0, \ldots, p_m)$ and $\hat{\theta}_{1B} = \tilde{\psi}_1(p_0, \ldots, p_m)$. By Taylor expansion, ignoring the terms of smaller order than n^{-2}, we obtain the means of $\hat{\theta}_{0B}$ and $\hat{\theta}_{1B}$,

$$E\left(\hat{\theta}_{0B}\right) = \theta_0 + \frac{1}{2}\sum_{i=0}^{m}\frac{P_i(1-P_i)}{n}\frac{\partial^2\tilde{\psi}_0}{\partial p_i^2}\bigg|_{P_i} , \ E\left(\hat{\theta}_{1B}\right) = \theta_1 + \frac{1}{2}\sum_{i=0}^{m}\frac{P_i(1-P_i)}{n}\frac{\partial^2\tilde{\psi}_1}{\partial p_i^2}\bigg|_{P_i}$$

so that

$$b_{0B}(\underline{\theta}) = \frac{1}{2n}\sum_{i=0}^{m}P_i(1-P_i)\frac{\partial^2\tilde{\psi}_0}{\partial p_i^2}\bigg|_{P_i} \tag{17}$$

$$b_{1B}(\underline{\theta}) = \frac{1}{2n}\sum_{i=0}^{m}P_i(1-P_i)\frac{\partial^2\tilde{\psi}_1}{\partial p_i^2}\bigg|_{P_i}. \tag{18}$$

Computing the second derivatives of $\tilde{\psi}_0(p_0, \ldots, p_m)$ and $\tilde{\psi}_1(p_0, \ldots, p_m)$ from (15) and (16) yields upon complicated simplication

$$b_{0B}(\underline{\theta}) = \left\{(A_2/2)[A_2 + I_2 + 2D_2 + 4\theta_0 E_2] + E_2 F_2 - (A_3/2)[A_1 + I_1 + 2D_1 + 2\theta_0 E_1]\right.$$

$$-E_3 F_1 - A_1 E_3 \theta_0\big\}/\big[nA_1 A_3 - A_2^2\big] + \big\{-A_1 A_2[E_4 + H_4 + 2G_4\theta_0] - A_1 F_2 G_4$$

$$+A_1 A_3[E_3 + H_3 + G_3\theta_0] + A_1 F_1 G_5 + A_1^2 G_5\theta_0 - A_2 A_3[E_2 + H_2 + 2G_2\theta_0] - A_3 F_2 G_2$$

$$+A_3^2[E_1 + H_1 + G_1\theta_0] + A_3 F_1 G_3 + A_1 A_3 G_3\theta_0 + 2A_2^2[E_3 + H_3 + 2G_3\theta_0] + 2A_2 F_2 G_3$$

$$-2A_2 A_3[E_2 + H_2 + G_2\theta_0] - 2A_2 F_1 G_4 - 2A_1 A_2 G_4\theta_0\big\}/n\big[A_1 A_3 - A_2^2\big]^2, \tag{19}$$

$$b_{1B}(\underline{\theta}) = \left\{(A_2/2)[A_1 + I_1 + 2D_2 + 4E_2\theta_1] + E_2 F_1 - A_1[A_2 + I_2 + 2D_2 + 2E_3\theta_1] - E_1 F_2\right.$$

$$-A_3 E_1\theta_1\big\}/\big[nA_1 A_3 - A_2^2\big]$$

$$+\big\{-A_1 A_2[E_3 + H_3 + 2G_4\theta_1] - A_1 F_1 G_4 + A_1^2[E_4 + H_4 + G_5\theta_1] + A_1 F_2 G_3$$

$$+A_1 A_3 G_3\theta_1 - A_2 A_3[A_1 + D_1 + 2E_2\theta_1] - A_3 E_2 F_1 + A_1 A_3[A_2 + D_2 + E_3\theta_1] + A_3 E_1 F_2$$

$$+A_3^2 E_1\theta_1 - 2A_2^2[E_2 + H_2 + 2G_3\theta_1] + 2A_2 F_1 G_3 - 2A_1 A_2[E_3 + H_3 + G_4\theta_1]$$

$$-2A_2F_2G_2 - 2A_2A_3G_2\theta_1\}/n\left[A_2A_3 - A_2^2\right]^2, \quad (20)$$

where

$$D_1 = \sum_{i=0}^{m} \frac{(1-\pi_i)}{\pi_i^2}\ln(1-\pi_i), \, D_2 = \sum_{i=0}^{m} \frac{d_i(1-\pi_i)}{\pi_i^2}\ln(1-\pi_i)$$

$$E_1 = \sum_{i=0}^{m} \frac{(1-\pi_i)}{\pi_i^2}, \, E_2 = \sum_{i=0}^{m} \frac{d_i(1-\pi_i)}{\pi_i^2}, \, E_3 = \sum_{i=0}^{m} \frac{d_i^2(1-\pi_i)}{\pi_i^2}, \, E_4 = \sum_{i=0}^{m} \frac{d_i^3(1-\pi_i)}{\pi_i^2}$$

$$F_1 = \sum_{i=0}^{m} \frac{(1-\pi_i)}{\pi_i}\ln(1-\pi_i), \, F_2 = \sum_{i=0}^{m} \frac{d_i(1-\pi_i)}{\pi_i}\ln(1-\pi_i)$$

$$G_1 = \sum_{i=0}^{m} \frac{(1-\pi_i)}{\pi_i^3}, \, G_2 = \sum_{i=0}^{m} \frac{d_i(1-\pi_i)}{\pi_i^3}, \, G_3 = \sum_{i=0}^{m} \frac{d_i^2(1-\pi_i)}{\pi_i^3}, \, G_4 = \sum_{i=0}^{m} \frac{d_i^3(1-\pi_i)}{\pi_i^3},$$

$$G_5 = \sum_{i=0}^{m} \frac{d_i^4(1-\pi_i)}{\pi_i^3}$$

$$H_1 = \sum_{i=0}^{m} \frac{(1-\pi_i)}{\pi_i^3}\ln(1-\pi_i), \, H_2 = \sum_{i=0}^{m} \frac{d_i(1-\pi_i)}{\pi_i^3}\ln(1-\pi_i),.$$

$$H_3 = \sum_{i=0}^{m} \frac{d_i^2(1-\pi_i)}{\pi_i^3}\ln(1-\pi_i),$$

$$H_4 = \sum_{i=0}^{m} \frac{d_i^3(1-\pi_i)}{\pi_i^3}\ln(1-\pi_i), \, I_1 = \sum_{i=0}^{m} \frac{1}{\pi_i}, \, . I_2 = \sum_{i=0}^{m} \frac{d_i}{\pi_i}.$$

To find $\varphi_0^*(\theta_0)$ and $\varphi_1^*(\theta_1)$ in (3) and (4) based on Berkson's modified minimum chi-square estimates for multistage Weibull model, the expressions of $\dfrac{\partial b_{0B}(\underline{\theta})}{\partial\theta_0}$, $\dfrac{\partial b_{0B}(\underline{\theta})}{\partial\theta_1}$, $\dfrac{\partial b_{1B}(\underline{\theta})}{\partial\theta_0}$ and $\dfrac{\partial b_{1B}(\underline{\theta})}{\partial\theta_1}$ which are required in the sequel are obtained by using Maple. The values of $\varphi_{0B}^*(\theta_0)$ and $\varphi_{1B}^*(\theta_1)$ are computed by MATLAB and shown in Section 6.1 for one data set.

4. Logistic Model

4.1. Maximum Likelihood Estimates

The likelihood function of logistic model is given by

$$L\left(\theta_0,\theta_1 \mid \text{data}\right) = \prod_{i=0}^{m} \binom{n_i}{x_i} \left[\frac{1}{1+e^{-(\theta_0+\theta_1 d_i)}}\right]^{x_i} \left[\frac{e^{-(\theta_0+\theta_1 d_i)}}{1+e^{-(\theta_0+\theta_1 d_i)}}\right]^{n_i-x_i}$$

$$\propto e^{-\sum_{i=0}^{m}(\theta_0+\theta_1 d_i)(n_i-x_i)} \prod_{i=0}^{m}\left[\frac{1}{1+e^{-(\theta_0+\theta_1 d_i)}}\right]^{n_i}.$$

Differentiating $\ln L\left(\theta_0,\theta_1 \mid \text{data}\right)$ with respect to θ_0 and θ_1, and setting these derivatives equal to zero yields the normal equations

$$\sum_{i=0}^{m} x_i = \sum_{i=0}^{m} \frac{n_i}{1+e^{-\left(\hat{\theta}_{0MLE}+\hat{\theta}_{1MLE}d_i\right)}} \tag{21}$$

$$\sum_{i=0}^{m} d_i x_i = \sum_{i=0}^{m} \frac{n_i d_i}{1+e^{-\left(\hat{\theta}_{0MLE}+\hat{\theta}_{1MLE}d_i\right)}}, \tag{22}$$

where $\hat{\theta}_{0MLE}$ and $\hat{\theta}_{1MLE}$ are the maximum likelihood estimates of θ_0 and θ_1. Taking $n_i = n$, $\forall_i$, we get

$$\sum_{i=0}^{m} p_i = \sum_{i=0}^{m} \frac{1}{1+e^{-\left(\psi_0\left(p_0,\ldots,p_m\right)+\psi_1\left(p_0,\ldots,p_m\right)d_i\right)}} \tag{23}$$

$$\sum_{i=0}^{m} d_i p_i = \sum_{i=0}^{m} \frac{d_i}{1+e^{-\left(\psi_0\left(p_0,\ldots,p_m\right)+\psi_1\left(p_0,\ldots,p_m\right)d_i\right)}} \tag{24}$$

where we write $\hat{\theta}_{0MLE} = \psi_0\left(p_0,\ldots,p_m\right)$ and $\hat{\theta}_{1MLE} = \psi_1\left(p_0,\ldots,p_m\right)$. We use Taylor series to expand $\psi_0\left(p_0,\ldots,p_m\right)$ and $\psi_1\left(p_0,\ldots,p_m\right)$, and find the means of $\hat{\theta}_{0MLE}$ and $\hat{\theta}_{1MLE}$ by ignoring the terms of smaller order than n^{-1} as

$$E\left(\hat{\theta}_{0MLE}\right) = \theta_0 + \frac{1}{2}\sum_{i=0}^{m} \frac{P_i(1-P_i)}{n}\frac{\partial^2 \psi_0}{\partial p_i^2}\bigg|_{P_i}, \; E\left(\hat{\theta}_{1MLE}\right) = \theta_1 + \frac{1}{2}\sum_{i=0}^{m} \frac{P_i(1-P_i)}{n}\frac{\partial^2 \psi_1}{\partial p_i^2}\bigg|_{P_i}.$$

With the bias terms of $\hat{\theta}_{0MLE}$ and $\hat{\theta}_{1MLE}$, $b_{0MLE}\left(\underline{\theta}\right)$ and $b_{1MLE}\left(\underline{\theta}\right)$, are given by

$$b_{0MLE}(\underline{\theta}) = \frac{1}{2n}\sum_{i=0}^{m} P_i(1-P_i)\frac{\partial^2\psi_0}{\partial p_i^2}\bigg|_{P_i} \tag{25}$$

$$b_{1MLE}(\underline{\theta}) = \frac{1}{2n}\sum_{i=0}^{m} P_i(1-P_i)\frac{\partial^2\psi_1}{\partial p_i^2}\bigg|_{P_i}. \tag{26}$$

The second derivatives of $\psi_0(p_0,\ldots,p_m)$ and $\psi_1(p_0,\ldots,p_m)$ with respect to p_i are computed from (23) and (24) and simplified to produce

$$b_{0MLE}(\underline{\theta}) = \left\{ \frac{1}{2}J_1J_3^3K_1 - \frac{1}{2}J_2^2J_3^2K_1 - \frac{3}{2}J_1J_2J_3^2K_2 + \frac{3}{2}J_2^3J_3K_2 + \frac{1}{2}J_1^2J_3^2K_3 + \frac{1}{2}J_1J_2^2J_3K_3 - J_2^4K_3 \right.$$
$$\left. - \frac{1}{2}J_1^2J_2J_3K_4 + \frac{1}{2}J_1J_2^3K_4 \right\} \bigg/ n\left[J_1J_3 - J_2^2\right]^3, \tag{27}$$

$$b_{1MLE}(\underline{\theta}) = \left\{ \frac{1}{2}J_1^2J_3^2K_2 + \frac{1}{2}J_1J_2^2J_3K_2 - J_2^4K_2 - \frac{3}{2}J_1^2J_2J_3K_3 + \frac{3}{2}J_1J_2^3K_3 + \frac{1}{2}J_1^3J_3K_4 \right.$$
$$\left. - \frac{1}{2}J_1^2J_2^2K_4 - \frac{1}{2}J_1J_2J_3^2K_1 + \frac{1}{2}J_2^3J_3K_1 \right\} \bigg/ n\left[J_1J_3 - J_2^2\right]^3, \tag{28}$$

where

$$J_1 = \sum_{i=0}^{m}\pi_i(1-\pi_i),. \quad J_2 = \sum_{i=0}^{m}d_i\pi_i(1-\pi_i), \quad J_3 = \sum_{i=0}^{m}d_i^2\pi_i(1-\pi_i)$$

$$K_1 = \sum_{i=0}^{m}\pi_i(1-\pi_i)(2\pi_i-1), \quad K_2 = \sum_{i=0}^{m}d_i\pi_i(1-\pi_i)(2\pi_i-1),$$

$$K_3 = \sum_{i=0}^{m}d_i^2\pi_i(1-\pi_i)(2\pi_i-1), \quad K_4 = \sum_{i=0}^{m}d_i^3\pi_i(1-\pi_i)(2\pi_i-1).$$

To find $\varphi_0^*(\theta_0)$ and $\varphi_1^*(\theta_1)$ in (3) and (4) based on MLEs for logistic model, the expressions of $\dfrac{\partial b_{0MLE}(\underline{\theta})}{\partial\theta_0}$, $\dfrac{\partial b_{0MLE}(\underline{\theta})}{\partial\theta_1}$, $\dfrac{\partial b_{1MLE}(\underline{\theta})}{\partial\theta_0}$ and $\dfrac{\partial b_{1MLE}(\underline{\theta})}{\partial\theta_1}$ which are needed in the sequel are obtained by Maple. The values of $\varphi_{0MLE}^*(\theta_0)$ and $\varphi_{1MLE}^*(\theta_1)$ are computed by MATLAB and shown in Section 6.2 for one data set.

4.2. Berkson's Modified Minimum Chi-Square Estimates

Since $1 - \pi(\theta_0, \theta_1) = \dfrac{e^{-(\theta_0 + \theta_1 d_i)}}{1 + e^{-(\theta_0 + \theta_1 d_i)}}$ implies $\ln\left(\dfrac{\pi(\theta_0, \theta_1)}{1 - \pi(\theta_0, \theta_1)}\right) = \theta_0 + \theta_1 d_i$,

asymptotically we get

$$E\left[\ln\left(p_i/(1-p_i)\right)\right] \approx \theta_0 + \theta_1 d_i \text{ and } Var\left[\ln\left(p_i/(1-p_i)\right)\right] \approx \left[n_i \pi_i (1 - \pi_i)\right]^{-1}.$$

A modified chi-square function, $Q(\theta_0, \theta_1)$, is defined by

$$Q(\theta_0, \theta_1) = \sum_{i=0}^{m} n_i p_i (1 - p_i)\left[\ln\left(\frac{p_i}{1 - p_i}\right) - \theta_0 - \theta_1 d_i\right]^2.$$

Berkson's modified minimum chi-square estimates of θ_0 and θ_1, $\hat{\theta}_{0B}$ and $\hat{\theta}_{1B}$, are obtained by minimizing $Q(\theta_0, \theta_1)$ with respect to θ_0 and θ_1. A direct differentiation and simplification produces

$$\hat{\theta}_{0B} = \frac{\sum_{i=0}^{m} d_i^2 p_i (1 - p_i) \sum_{i=0}^{m} p_i (1 - p_i)\ln\left(\frac{p_i}{1 - p_i}\right) - \sum_{i=0}^{m} d_i p_i (1 - p_i) \sum_{i=0}^{m} d_i p_i (1 - p_i)\ln\left(\frac{p_i}{1 - p_i}\right)}{\sum_{i=0}^{m} p_i (1 - p_i) \sum_{i=0}^{m} d_i^2 p_i (1 - p_i) - \left[\sum_{i=0}^{m} d_i p_i (1 - p_i)\right]^2}, \quad (29)$$

$$\hat{\theta}_{1B} = \frac{\sum_{i=0}^{m} p_i (1 - p_i) \sum_{i=0}^{m} d_i p_i (1 - p_i)\ln\left(\frac{p_i}{1 - p_i}\right) - \sum_{i=0}^{m} d_i p_i (1 - p_i) \sum_{i=0}^{m} p_i (1 - p_i)\ln\left(\frac{p_i}{1 - p_i}\right)}{\sum_{i=0}^{m} p_i (1 - p_i) \sum_{i=0}^{m} d_i^2 p_i (1 - p_i) - \left[\sum_{i=0}^{m} d_i p_i (1 - p_i)\right]^2}. \quad (30)$$

We write $\hat{\theta}_{0B} = \tilde{\psi}_0(p_0, \ldots, p_m)$ and $\hat{\theta}_{1B} = \tilde{\psi}_1(p_0, \ldots, p_m)$. By Taylor expansion, ignoring the terms of smaller order than n^{-1}, we obtain the means of $\hat{\theta}_{0B}$ and $\hat{\theta}_{1B}$,

$$E\left(\hat{\theta}_{0B}\right) = \theta_0 + \frac{1}{2}\sum_{i=0}^{m}\frac{P_i(1 - P_i)}{n}\frac{\partial^2 \tilde{\psi}_0}{\partial p_i^2}\bigg|_{P_i}, \quad E\left(\hat{\theta}_{1B}\right) = \theta_1 + \frac{1}{2}\sum_{i=0}^{m}\frac{P_i(1 - P_i)}{n}\frac{\partial^2 \tilde{\psi}_1}{\partial p_i^2}\bigg|_{P_i},$$

providing the bias terms of $\hat{\theta}_{0B}$ and $\hat{\theta}_{1B}$, $b_{0B}(\underline{\theta})$ and $b_{1B}(\underline{\theta})$, as

$$b_{0B}(\underline{\theta}) = \frac{1}{2n}\sum_{i=0}^{m} P_i(1 - P_i)\frac{\partial^2 \tilde{\psi}_0}{\partial p_i^2}\bigg|_{P_i}, \quad b_{1B}(\underline{\theta}) = \frac{1}{2n}\sum_{i=0}^{m} P_i(1 - P_i)\frac{\partial^2 \tilde{\psi}_1}{\partial p_i^2}\bigg|_{P_i}.$$

The second derivatives of $\tilde{\psi}_0\left(p_0,\ldots,p_m\right)$ and $\tilde{\psi}_1\left(p_0,\ldots,p_m\right)$ with respect to p_i can be readily obtained from (29) and (30) and used to give

$$b_{0B}\left(\underline{\theta}\right)=\left\{(J_3/2)\left[-L_1-2M_1+2J_1\theta_0\right]-J_3M_1-\frac{1}{2}J_2\left[-L_2-2M_2+4J_2\theta_0\right]+J_2M_2\right.$$

$$\left.+J_1J_3\theta_0\right\}/\left[nJ_1J_3-J_2^2\right]$$

$$+\left\{-J_1J_2K_3+J_1J_3O_3-J_1J_3N_3\theta_0-J_1M_1N_5-J_1J_2K_4+J_1J_2O_4-2J_1J_2N_4\theta_0\right.$$

$$+J_1M_2N_4+J_1^2N_5\theta_0+J_3^2K_1-J_3^2O_1+J_3^2N_1\theta_0-J_3M_1N_3-J_2J_3K_2+J_2J_3O_2$$

$$-2J_2J_3N_2\theta_0+J_3M_2N_2+J_1J_3N_3\theta_0-2J_2J_3K_2+2J_2J_3O_2-2J_2J_3N_2\theta_0$$

$$\left.+2J_2M_1N_4+2J_2^2K_3-2J_2^2O_3+4J_2^2N_3\theta_0-2J_2M_2N_3-2J_1J_2N_4\theta_0\right\}/n\left[J_1J_3-J_2^2\right]^2, \quad (31)$$

$$b_{1B}\left(\underline{\theta}\right)=\left\{\left[-L_2-2M_2+2J_3\theta_1\right](J_1/2)-J_1M_2+\frac{1}{2}\left[L_1+2M_1-4J_2\theta_1\right]J_2+J_2M_1+J_1J_3\theta_1\right\}/\left[nJ_1J_3-J_2^2\right]$$

$$+\left\{J_1^2K_4-J_2^2O_4+J_1^2N_5\theta_1-J_1M_2N_3-J_1J_2K_3+J_1J_2O_3-2J_1J_2N_4\theta_1+J_1M_1N_4\right.$$

$$+J_1J_3N_3\theta_1+J_1J_3K_2-J_1J_3O_2+J_1J_3N_3\theta_1-J_3M_2N_1-J_2J_3K_1+J_2J_3O_1-2J_2J_3N_2\theta_1$$

$$+J_3M_1N_2+J_3^2N_1\theta_1-2J_1J_2K_3+2J_1J_2O_3-2J_1J_2N_4\theta_1-2J_2M_2N_2+2J_2^2K_2$$

$$\left.-2J_2^2O_2+4J_2^2N_3\theta_1-2J_2M_1N_3-2J_2J_3N_2\theta_1\right\}/n\left[J_1J_3-J_2^2\right]^2, \quad (32)$$

where

$$L_1=\sum_{i=0}^{m}\left(2\pi_i-1\right),\ L_2=\sum_{i=0}^{m}d_i\left(2\pi_i-1\right),\ M_1=\sum_{i=0}^{m}\pi_i\left(1-\pi_i\right)\ln\left(\frac{\pi_i}{1-\pi_i}\right),$$

$$M_2=\sum_{i=0}^{m}d_i\pi_i\left(1-\pi_i\right)\ln\left(\frac{\pi_i}{1-\pi_i}\right),$$

$$N_1=\sum_{i=0}^{m}\pi_i\left(1-\pi_i\right)\left(2\pi_i-1\right)^2,$$

$$N_2 = \sum_{i=0}^{m} d_i \pi_i (1 - \pi_i)(2\pi_i - 1)^2,$$

$$N_3 = \sum_{i=0}^{m} d_i^2 \pi_i (1 - \pi_i)(2\pi_i - 1)^2,$$

$$N_4 = \sum_{i=0}^{m} d_i^3 \pi_i (1 - \pi_i)(2\pi_i - 1)^2,$$

$$N_5 = \sum_{i=0}^{m} d_i^4 \pi_i (1 - \pi_i)(2\pi_i - 1)^2,$$

$$O_1 = \sum_{i=0}^{m} \pi_i (1 - \pi_i)(2\pi_i - 1)^2 \ln\left(\frac{\pi_i}{1 - \pi_i}\right),$$

$$O_2 = \sum_{i=0}^{m} d_i \pi_i (1 - \pi_i)(2\pi_i - 1)^2 \ln\left(\frac{\pi_i}{1 - \pi_i}\right),$$

$$O_3 = \sum_{i=0}^{m} d_i^2 \pi_i (1 - \pi_i)(2\pi_i - 1)^2 \ln\left(\frac{\pi_i}{1 - \pi_i}\right),$$

$$O_4 = \sum_{i=0}^{m} d_i^3 \pi_i (1 - \pi_i)(2\pi_i - 1)^2 \ln\left(\frac{\pi_i}{1 - \pi_i}\right).$$

To find $\varphi_0^*(\theta_0)$ and $\varphi_1^*(\theta_1)$ in (3) and (4) based on Berkson's modified minimum chi-square estimates for logistic model, the expressions of $\partial b_{0B}(\underline{\theta})/\partial\theta_0$, $\partial b_{0B}(\underline{\theta})/\partial\theta_1$, $\partial b_{1B}(\underline{\theta})/\partial\theta_0$ and $\partial b_{1B}(\underline{\theta})/\partial\theta_1$ which are required in the sequel are obtained by using Maple. The values of $\varphi_{0B}^*(\theta_0)$ and $\varphi_{1B}^*(\theta_1)$ are obtained by using MATLAB and shown in Section 6.2 for one data set.

5. Log-Logistic Model

The log-logistic model could be processed in the same manner as the logistic model with "d" replaced by "$\ln(d)$". The comparison of MSEs of MLEs and Berkson's modified minimum chi-square estimates are shown in Section 6.3 for one data set.

6. Discussion of the Data Set

In this section we provide a comparison of MLEs and Berkson's modified minimum chi-square estimates under the three dose response models. Obviously a direct comparison of the asymptotic MSEs of MLEs and Berkson's modified minimum chi-square estimates would involve computing these expressions for various values of θ_0 and θ_1. The data set in Table 1 are used to estimate parameters based on the two methods. Data contain the number of female B6C3F1 rats exhibiting heart hemangiosarcomas after they were exposed to 1, 3-Butadiene [4]. We can compare the two estimates (MLE and Berkson) by choosing the values of θ_0 and θ_1 around the estimates $\hat{\theta}_0$ and $\hat{\theta}_1$, and then computing and comparing the expressions of $\varphi^*_{0MLE}(\theta_0)$ and $\varphi^*_{0B}(\theta_0)$ for $\hat{\theta}_0$, and the expressions of $\varphi^*_{1MLE}(\theta_1)$ and $\varphi^*_{1B}(\theta_1)$ for $\hat{\theta}_1$. The appropriate estimates are preferred when $\varphi^*_0(\theta_0)$ or $\varphi^*_1(\theta_1)$ are smaller. A similar idea holds in the other two models.

Table 1. Data set with dose, number responding, and number in experiment

Dose	Number of respondents	Number of animals tested
0	0	50
6.25	0	50
20	0	50
62.5	1	49
200	21	50

6.1. Multistage Weibull Model

We estimate the parameters θ_0 and θ_1 by using MATLAB based on the two methods for the multistage Weibull model (MWM). The estimates are shown in Table 2.

Table 2. Values of $\hat{\theta}_{0MLE}$, $\hat{\theta}_{0B}$, $\hat{\theta}_{1MLE}$ and $\hat{\theta}_{1B}$ for MWM

$\hat{\theta}_{0MLE}$	$\hat{\theta}_{0B}$	$\hat{\theta}_{1MLE}$	$\hat{\theta}_{1B}$
1.485e-10	1.000e-10	1.816e-03	8.397e-04

Table 3. Values of $\varphi^*_{0MLE}(\theta_0)$ and $\varphi^*_{0B}(\theta_0)$ of MWM when values of θ_0 and θ_1 around the estimates from MLE and Berkson

θ_1 \ θ_0		1.000e-12	1.000e-11	1.000e-10	1.000e-09	1.000e-08
0.0001	$\varphi^*_{0MLE}(\theta_0)$	-2.125e-20	-2.124e-19	-2.123e-18	-2.123e-17	-2.123e-16
	$\varphi^*_{0B}(\theta_0)$	-1.078e-15	-1.078e-14	-1.078e-13	-1.131e-12	-1.077e-11
0.0010	$\varphi^*_{0MLE}(\theta_0)$	-2.900e-20	-2.883e-19	-2.884e-18	-2.884e-17	-2.884e-16
	$\varphi^*_{0B}(\theta_0)$	-1.064e-16	-1.064e-15	-1.064e-14	-1.597e-13	-1.059e-12
0.0015	$\varphi^*_{0MLE}(\theta_0)$	-3.309e-20	-3.316e-19	-3.315e-18	-3.315e-17	-3.315e-16
	$\varphi^*_{0B}(\theta_0)$	-7.042e-17	-7.042e-16	-7.042e-15	-1.237e-13	-6.989e-13
0.0020	$\varphi^*_{0MLE}(\theta_0)$	-3.754e-20	-3.750e-19	-3.751e-18	-3.751e-17	-3.751e-16
	$\varphi^*_{0B}(\theta_0)$	-5.239e-17	-5.240e-16	-5.240e-15	-1.057e-13	-5.186e-13
0.0025	$\varphi^*_{0MLE}(\theta_0)$	-4.195e-20	-4.189e-19	-4.189e-18	-4.189e-17	-4.189e-16
	$\varphi^*_{0B}(\theta_0)$	-4.157e-17	-4.157e-16	-4.157e-15	-9.486e-14	-4.103e-13

Table 4. Values of $\varphi^*_{1MLE}(\theta_1)$ and $\varphi^*_{1B}(\theta_1)$ of MWM when values of θ_0 and θ_1 around the estimates from MLE and Berkson

θ_1 \ θ_0		1.000e-12	1.000e-11	1.000e-10	1.000e-09	1.000e-08
0.0001	$\varphi^*_{1MLE}(\theta_1)$	3.017e-14	3.017e-14	3.017e-14	3.017e-14	3.017e-14
	$\varphi^*_{1B}(\theta_1)$	1.922e-12	1.926e-12	1.926e-12	1.926e-12	1.929e-12
0.0010	$\varphi^*_{1MLE}(\theta_1)$	3.713e-13	3.713e-13	3.713e-13	3.713e-13	3.713e-13
	$\varphi^*_{1B}(\theta_1)$	1.983e-12	1.983e-12	1.983e-12	1.983e-12	1.983e-12
0.0015	$\varphi^*_{1MLE}(\theta_1)$	6.227e-13	6.227e-13	6.227e-13	6.227e-13	6.227e-13
	$\varphi^*_{1B}(\theta_1)$	2.003e-12	2.006e-12	2.006e-12	2.006e-12	2.006e-12
0.0020	$\varphi^*_{1MLE}(\theta_1)$	9.260e-13	9.260e-13	9.260e-13	9.260e-13	9.260e-13
	$\varphi^*_{1B}(\theta_1)$	2.016e-12	2.018e-12	2.018e-12	2.018e-12	2.018e-12
0.0025	$\varphi^*_{1MLE}(\theta_1)$	1.288e-12	1.288e-12	1.288e-12	1.288e-12	1.288e-12
	$\varphi^*_{1B}(\theta_1)$	2.005e-12	2.013e-12	2.013e-12	2.013e-12	2.013e-12

We consider values of θ_0 and θ_1 around the estimates $\hat{\theta}_0$ and $\hat{\theta}_1$, and then compute the expressions of $\varphi^*_{0MLE}(\theta_0)$ and $\varphi^*_{0B}(\theta_0)$ for $\hat{\theta}_0$ and, the expressions of $\varphi^*_{1MLE}(\theta_1)$ and $\varphi^*_{1B}(\theta_1)$ for $\hat{\theta}_1$. These values are shown in Tables 3-4.

We find that there are intervals I_0 of θ_0 and I_1 of θ_1 within which $\varphi^*_{0MLE}(\theta_0)$ is greater than $\varphi^*_{0B}(\theta_0)$ (see Table 3) and $\varphi^*_{1B}(\theta_1)$ is greater than $\varphi^*_{1MLE}(\theta_1)$ (see Table 4). Therefore, we conclude that $\hat{\theta}_{0B}$ is preferred to $\hat{\theta}_{0MLE}$ and $\hat{\theta}_{1MLE}$ is preferred to $\hat{\theta}_{1B}$ when the true values lie within such an interval while outside this interval it is the other way around.

6.2. Logistic Model

For data in Table 1, we estimate the parameters θ_0 and θ_1 by using MATLAB based on the two methods for logistic model (LM). The estimates are shown in Table 5.

Table 5. Values of $\hat{\theta}_{0MLE}$, $\hat{\theta}_{0B}$, $\hat{\theta}_{1MLE}$ and $\hat{\theta}_{1B}$ for LM

$\hat{\theta}_{0MLE}$	$\hat{\theta}_{0B}$	$\hat{\theta}_{1MLE}$	$\hat{\theta}_{1B}$
-6.401	-4.959	3.044e-02	2.314e-02

Table 6. Values of $\varphi^*_{0MLE}(\theta_0)$ and $\varphi^*_{0B}(\theta_0)$ of LM when values of θ_0 and θ_1 around the estimates from MLE and Berkson

θ_1 \ θ_0		-7	-6	-5	-4	-3
0.01	$\varphi^*_{0MLE}(\theta_0)$	1.230e-02	1.671e-03	2.286e-04	3.186e-05	4.687e-06
	$\varphi^*_{0B}(\theta_0)$	-1.038e-02	-1.418e-03	-1.967e-04	-2.843e-05	-4.560e-06
0.02	$\varphi^*_{0MLE}(\theta_0)$	7.243e-03	9.864e-04	1.359e-04	1.945e-05	3.245e-06
	$\varphi^*_{0B}(\theta_0)$	-6.166e-03	-8.470e-04	-1.195e-04	-1.817e-05	-3.304e-06
0.03	$\varphi^*_{0MLE}(\theta_0)$	3.631e-03	4.982e-04	7.093e-05	1.246e-05	5.247e-06
	$\varphi^*_{0B}(\theta_0)$	-3.073e-03	-4.269e-04	-6.319e-05	-1.124e-05	-2.068e-06
0.04	$\varphi^*_{0MLE}(\theta_0)$	1.581e-03	2.270e-04	4.684e-05	3.069e-05	8.534e-06
	$\varphi^*_{0B}(\theta_0)$	-1.291e-03	-1.888e-04	-3.375e-05	-9.269e-06	-1.483e-05
0.05	$\varphi^*_{0MLE}(\theta_0)$	6.552e-04	1.904e-04	1.834e-04	3.859e-05	4.992e-06
	$\varphi^*_{0B}(\theta_0)$	-4.941e-04	-8.922e-05	-7.731e-05	-8.057e-05	-7.910e-06

We consider the values of θ_0 and θ_1 around the estimates $\hat{\theta}_0$ and $\hat{\theta}_1$, and then compute the expressions of $\varphi_{0MLE}^*(\theta_0)$ and $\varphi_{0B}^*(\theta_0)$ for $\hat{\theta}_0$ and, the expressions of $\varphi_{1MLE}^*(\theta_1)$ and $\varphi_{1B}^*(\theta_1)$ for $\hat{\theta}_1$. These values are shown in Tables 6-7.

For logistic model in Tables 6-7, we see that there are intervals I_0 of θ_0 and I_1 of θ_1 within which $\varphi_{0MLE}^*(\theta_0)$ is greater than $\varphi_{0B}^*(\theta_0)$ and also $\varphi_{1MLE}^*(\theta_1)$ is greater than $\varphi_{1B}^*(\theta_1)$. Therefore, the Berkson's modified minimum chi-square estimates are better than the MLEs within these intervals while outside these intervals it is the other way around.

Table 7. Values of $\varphi_{1MLE}^*(\theta_1)$ and $\varphi_{1B}^*(\theta_1)$ of LM when values of θ_0 and θ_1 around the estimates from MLE and Berkson

θ_1 \ θ_0		-7	-6	-5	-4	-3
0.01	$\varphi_{1MLE}^*(\theta_1)$	3.585e-07	4.900e-08	6.812e-09	9.967e-10	1.732e-10
	$\varphi_{1B}^*(\theta_1)$	-2.842e-08	-4.027e-09	-6.132e-00	-1.088e-10	-2.225e-11
0.02	$\varphi_{1MLE}^*(\theta_1)$	1.763e-07	2.409e-08	3.369e-09	5.316e-10	1.862e-10
	$\varphi_{1B}^*(\theta_1)$	-1.355e-07	-1.866e-08	-2.669e-09	-4.311e-10	-6.007e-11
0.03	$\varphi_{1MLE}^*(\theta_1)$	9.026e-08	1.251e-08	1.971e-09	8.729e-10	1.672e-09
	$\varphi_{1B}^*(\theta_1)$	-7.480e-08	-1.052e-08	-1.682e-09	-2.534e-10	9.671e-11
0.04	$\varphi_{1MLE}^*(\theta_1)$	4.008e-08	6.725e-09	4.693e-09	8.941e-09	1.754e-09
	$\varphi_{1B}^*(\theta_1)$	-3.251e-08	-5.243e-09	-7.899e-10	-2.921e-09	-1.081e-08
0.05	$\varphi_{1MLE}^*(\theta_1)$	2.237e-08	2.819e-08	4.947e-08	6.749e-09	6.441e-10
	$\varphi_{1B}^*(\theta_1)$	-1.410e-08	-2.935e-09	-3.395e-08	-3.628e-08	-1.193e-09

6.3. Log-Logistic Model

For data in Table 1, we estimate the parameters θ_0 and θ_1 by using MATLAB based on the two methods for log-logistic model (LLM). The estimates are shown in Table 8.

Table 8. Values of $\hat{\theta}_{0MLE}$, $\hat{\theta}_{0B}$, $\hat{\theta}_{1MLE}$ and $\hat{\theta}_{1B}$ for LLM

$\hat{\theta}_{0MLE}$	$\hat{\theta}_{0B}$	$\hat{\theta}_{1MLE}$	$\hat{\theta}_{1B}$
-16.774	-2.586	3.105	3.529e-01

Table 9. Values of $\varphi_{0MLE}^{*}(\theta_0)$ and $\varphi_{0B}^{*}(\theta_0)$ of LLM when values of θ_0 and θ_1 around $\hat{\theta}_{0MLE}$ and $\hat{\theta}_{1MLE}$

θ_1 \ θ_0		-19	-17	-15	-13	-11
2.5	$\varphi_{0MLE}^{*}(\theta_0)$	1.137e+02	2.086e+00	3.859e-02	7.854e-04	2.088e-04
	$\varphi_{0B}^{*}(\theta_0)$	3.745e+03	6.910e+01	1.338e+00	3.786e-02	6.543e-03
2.8	$\varphi_{0MLE}^{*}(\theta_0)$	1.007e+01	1.854e-01	3.542e-03	2.186e-04	3.361e-04
	$\varphi_{0B}^{*}(\theta_0)$	3.633e+02	6.843e+00	1.566e-01	1.483e-02	7.841e-03
3.1	$\varphi_{0MLE}^{*}(\theta_0)$	8.794e-01	1.642e-02	4.318e-04	8.897e-04	1.704e-04
	$\varphi_{0B}^{*}(\theta_0)$	3.407e+01	6.955e-01	3.345e-02	2.245e-02	8.057e-03
3.4	$\varphi_{0MLE}^{*}(\theta_0)$	7.631e-02	1.569e-03	9.319e-04	6.714e-04	5.145e-04
	$\varphi_{0B}^{*}(\theta_0)$	3.201e+00	9.526e-02	3.907e-02	2.227e-02	1.568e-02
3.7	$\varphi_{0MLE}^{*}(\theta_0)$	6.777e-03	7.085e-04	3.037e-03	3.272e-04	1.784e-03
	$\varphi_{0B}^{*}(\theta_0)$	3.419e-01	5.142e-02	7.981e-02	1.929e-02	3.892e-02

Table 10. Values of $\varphi_{1MLE}^{*}(\theta_1)$ and $\varphi_{1B}^{*}(\theta_1)$ of LLM when values of θ_0 and θ_1 around $\hat{\theta}_{0B}$ and $\hat{\theta}_{1B}$

θ_1 \ θ_0		-5	-4	-3	-2	-1
0.1	$\varphi_{1MLE}^{*}(\theta_1)$	8.655e-05	1.202e-05	1.737e-06	2.751e-07	5.190e-08
	$\varphi_{1B}^{*}(\theta_1)$	5.103e-05	7.275e-06	1.118e-06	1.983e-07	4.227e-08
0.2	$\varphi_{1MLE}^{*}(\theta_1)$	1.545e-04	2.276e-05	3.787e-06	7.891e-07	2.078e-07
	$\varphi_{1B}^{*}(\theta_1)$	-1.126e-04	-1.396e-05	-1.352e-06	6.337e-08	1.127e-07
0.3	$\varphi_{1MLE}^{*}(\theta_1)$	-1.048e-05	-3.948e-07	5.477e-07	5.604e-07	5.006e-07
	$\varphi_{1B}^{*}(\theta_1)$	-4.614e-04	-6.864e-05	-1.149e-05	-2.140e-06	-1.531e-07
0.4	$\varphi_{1MLE}^{*}(\theta_1)$	-4.137e-05	-7.104e-06	-1.612e-06	-4.469e-07	3.738e-07
	$\varphi_{1B}^{*}(\theta_1)$	-1.663e-04	-3.037e-05	-8.054e-06	-3.682e-06	-1.946e-06
0.5	$\varphi_{1MLE}^{*}(\theta_1)$	-6.717e-06	-1.586e-06	-6.429e-07	-5.375e-07	-3.984e-07
	$\varphi_{1B}^{*}(\theta_1)$	3.421e-05	4.051e-06	-3.492e-07	-1.841e-06	-4.382e-06

We consider the values of θ_0 and θ_1 around the estimates $\hat{\theta}_0$ and $\hat{\theta}_1$, and then compute the expressions of $\varphi^*_{0MLE}(\theta_0)$ and $\varphi^*_{0B}(\theta_0)$ for $\hat{\theta}_0$ and, the expressions of $\varphi^*_{1MLE}(\theta_1)$ and $\varphi^*_{1B}(\theta_1)$ for $\hat{\theta}_1$. These values are shown in Tables 9- 10.

We find from the above tables that $\varphi^*_{0MLE}(\theta_0)$ is less than $\varphi^*_{0B}(\theta_0)$ when we consider the values of θ_0 and θ_1 around MLEs (see Table 9). We also see that $\varphi^*_{0B}(\theta_0)$ is less than $\varphi^*_{0MLE}(\theta_0)$ when we consider the values of θ_0 and θ_1 around Berkson estimates (see Table 10). Therefore, there are intervals I_0 of θ_0 and I_1 of θ_1 within which $\hat{\theta}_{0MLE}$ is preferred to $\hat{\theta}_{0B}$ and $\hat{\theta}_{1B}$ is preferred to $\hat{\theta}_{1MLE}$ while outside these intervals it is the other way around.

6.4. Model Selection

We have used the following two well-known criteria for model selection for our data.

1. Akaike's information criterion (AIC) [1, 2] is computed as $\text{AIC} = 2k - 2\ln(L)$, where k is the number of parameters in the model, and L is the maximized value of the likelihood function for the estimated model.

2. Log-likelihood ratio statistic (Deviance) [3] is defined as

$$D = 2\sum_{i=0}^{m}\left[y_i \log\left(\frac{y_i}{\hat{y}_i}\right) + (n_i - y_i)\log\left(\frac{n_i - y_i}{n_i - \hat{y}_i}\right)\right],$$ where y_i is the observed value, $\hat{y}_i$

denotes the fitted value and n_i is the number of subjects or cases tested in the ith group.

Table 11. AIC and deviance values for one data set of MWM, LM and LLM

AIC			Deviance		
MWM	LM	LLM	MWM	LM	LLM
95.127	87.765	136.916	0.239	0.053	0.983

From Table 11 we conclude that, according to AIC and deviance criteria the preferred model for our data set is the logistic model.

Overall Conclusion

A direct comparison of the MSEs of MLE and Berkson's modified minimum chi-square estimate in general is rather difficult because both depend on unknown parameters. For a given data set though we can provide such a comparison by considering the values of the parameters around their estimated values. For the three dose response models we have considered in this paper, it is extremely difficult to establish the exact small sample properties of MLE & Berkson's modified minimum chi-square estimates. By assuming a large sample size and using Taylor expansion, we are able to derive the asymptotic expressions of the MSEs of MLE and Berkson's estimate in the two parameters case. We hope that such methods will be useful in other dose response models too.

Acknowledgments

We would like to thank the Institute for the Promotion of Teaching Science and Technology (IPST), the Thailand Research Fund (TRF) and the Mahidol University for financial support.

References

[1]　Akaike, H. (1973). Information theory and an extension of the maximum likelihood principle, *Proc.2nd International Symposium on Information Theory* (Eds.B.N.Petrov and F.Csaki), Akademiai Kiado, Budapest, 267-281.

[2]　Akaike, H. (1974). A new look at the statistical model identification, *IEEE Transactions on Automatic Control*, AC-19, 716-723.

[3]　Dobson, A.J. (1990). *An introduction to generalized linear models*, Chapman & Hall, London, UK.

[4]　National Toxicology Program (1993). Toxicology and carcinogenesis studies of 1,3-Butadiene (CAS NO. 106-99-0) in B6C3F1 mice (Inhalation Studies), *NTP TR* 434.

[5]　Rao, C.R. (1973). Linear statistical inference and its applications, John Wiley and Sons, Inc., New York, USA.

[6]　Sinha, B.K. (2007). On some aspects of Berkson's bioassay problem: issues and controversies. *International Conference on Advances in Interdisciplinary Statistics and Combinatorics.* October 12-14, 2007, University of North Carolina at Greensboro, North Carolina, USA.

[7]　Srisodaphol, W., Tiensuwan, M. and Sinha, B.K. (2009). On an asymptotic comparison of maximum likelihood and Berkson's minimum chi-square estimates in the multistage Weibull logistic and log-logistic models, *Proceeding of the 5th Asian Mathematical Conference (AMC 2009)*, Putra World Trade Centre, Kuala Lumpur, Malaysia, 22-26 June 2009, 603-612.

[8]　Srisodaphol, W., Tiensuwan, M. and Sinha, B.K. (2010). On an asymptotic comparison of the maximum likelihood and Berkson's minimum chi-square estimators in some standard dose response models with one unknown parameter, *Model Assisted Statistics and Applications*, Vol. 6(1), 21-38.

In: Applied Statistical Theory and Applications
Editor: Mohammad Ahsanullah

ISBN: 978-1-63321-858-1
© 2014 Nova Science Publishers, Inc.

Chapter 13

STATISTICAL INFERENCE ON THE GENERALIZED GAMMA DISTRIBUTION BASED ON GENERALIZED ORDER STATISTICS

M. Ahsanullah[1]*, M. Maswadah[2],† and M. Seham[2],‡

[1]Department of Management Science, Rider University,
Lawrenceville, New Jersey, US
[2]Department of Mathematics, Faculty of Science,
Aswan University, Aswan, Egypt

Abstract

In this paper, a practical approach based on the adaptive kernel density estimation (AKDE) has been applied for deriving the confidence intervals (CIs) of the generalized gamma distribution parameters based on the generalized order statistics (GOS). The efficiency of this technique has been studied comparing to the conditional inference based on the mean lengths, the covering percentages and the standard errors, via Monte Carlo simulations and some real data. From our results, it appears that the kernel approach mostly competes with the conditional approach. Finally, a numerical example is given to illustrate the inferential methods developed in this paper.

Keywords: Generalized gamma distribution; Generalized order statistics; Maximum likelihood estimation; Adaptive Kernel density estimation; Conditional inference

1. Introduction

The generalized gamma distribution (GGD) has been proposed by Stcay (1962) as a flexible model with many applications in lifetime data analysis and several other fields, and it has probability density distribution (PDF) in the form:

* E-mail address: ahsan@rider.edu
† E-mail address: maswadah@hotmail.com
‡ E-mail address: seham_1elwany @yahoo.com

$$f(x;\alpha,\beta,\lambda) = \frac{\alpha}{\Gamma(\lambda)}\beta^{-\alpha\lambda}x^{\alpha\lambda-1}\exp\left[-(x/\beta)^{\alpha}\right], \quad x>0 \; \alpha,\beta,\lambda>0, \quad (1.1)$$

where $\Gamma(\lambda)$ is gamma function, α, β and λ are the shape, scale and index parameters respectively. The corresponding cumulative distribution (CDF) is given by:

$$F(x;\alpha,\beta,\lambda) = \frac{IG(\lambda,(x/\beta)^{\alpha})}{\Gamma(\lambda)}, \quad x>0,$$

where $IG(\lambda,(x/\beta)^{\alpha}) = \int_{0}^{(x/\beta)^{\alpha}} t^{\lambda-1}e^{-t}dt$, is the lower incomplete gamma function.

The GGD reduces to the two-parameter Weibull distribution for $\lambda=1$, the two-parameter gamma distribution for $\alpha=1$, and the one parameter exponential distribution for $\alpha=\lambda=1$. Thus, this distribution incorporates many life-testing models, which is the reason that,it has many applications in lifetime data analysis. In early work with the GGD, there wasa difficulty in developing inference procedures except the maximum likelihood estimation method with large samples. In the last decades, the statistical inference on the GGD has been studied extensively in the literature, see Stacy and Mihram (1965),Parr and Webter (1965), Harter (1967), Hager and Bain (1970), Prentice (1974), Lawless (1980, 1982), Di Ciccio (1987), Wingo (1987), Cohen and Norgaard (1977) and Maswadah (1989,1991).Hwang and Huag (2006) derived the moment estimators for the GGD parameters. Dadpay et al. (2007) introduced some concepts on the GGD in information theory. Gomes et al. (2008) described many difficulties in estimating the parameters and used their perception in developing inference procedures with the GGD, especially the maximum likelihood parameter estimation, by justifying the model in terms of a simpler alternative form. Geng and Yuhlong (2009) proposed a new re-parameterization of the GGD to sustain the numerical stability for the maximum likelihood estimation based on the progressively type-II censored sample. Mukherjee et al. (2011) carried out a Bayesian study for the comparison of the generalized gamma model with its components. In this paper, the adaptive kernel density estimation has been applied for deriving the confidence intervals for the unknown parameters of the GGD comparing to those using the conditional inference based on the GOS, that introduced by Kamps (1995) as a unified model that includes several models, such as ordinary order statistics, type-II censored order statistics, type-II progressive censored order statistics, record values and sequential order statistics. For more details about the GOS, see Ahsanullah (1995, 2000).

Let $X(1,n,\tilde{m},k),\ldots,X(n,n,\tilde{m},k)$, ($k \geq 1, \tilde{m} > -1$ is a real number)be n generalized order statistics from a continuous population with CDF $F(x)$ and PDF $f(x)$, thus their joint PDF has the form

$$f_{X(1,n,\tilde{m},k),\ldots,X(n,n,\tilde{m},k)}(x_1,x_2,\ldots,x_n) = k\prod_{i=1}^{n-1}\gamma_i f(x_i)[1-F(x_i)]^{m_i}$$

$$\times [1 - F(x_n)]^{k-1} f(x_n),$$ (1.2)

on the cone

$$F^{-1}(0) < x_1 < ... < x_n < F^{-1}(1)$$

of R^n where

$$\tilde{m} = (m_1, m_2, ..., m_{n-1}) \in R^{n-1}, \quad \gamma_r = k + (n - r) + M_r > 0$$

such that

$$M_r = \sum_{j=r}^{n-1} m_j, \quad \gamma_n = k > 0.$$

Particular cases from (1.2):

1- Ordinary order statistics: for $k = 1$ and $\tilde{m} = 0$.

2- Type-II right censored order statistics: for $k = 1$ and $m_i = 0, i = 1, 2, .., n-1$, $m_n = n - r$.

3- Type-II progressive e censored order statistics: for $m_i \neq 0, i = 1, 2, ..., n-1$, $m_n = k - 1$.

4- Record values for $k = 1$ and $\tilde{m} = -1$.

2. Main Results

2.1. Kernel Estimation

In this section, we apply the kernel approach for deriving the confidence intervals to the unknown parameters based on the adaptive kernel density estimation, which is asymptotically converged to any density function depending only on a random sample, though the underlying distribution is not known. This approach has been applied for some lifetime distributions, see Maswadah (2006, 2007, 2010). In the univariate case, the adaptive kernel density estimation based on a random sample of size n from the random variable X with unknown probability density function $f(x)$ and support on $(0, \infty)$ is given by:

$$\hat{f}(x) = \frac{1}{n} \sum_{i=1}^{n} \frac{1}{h_i} K\left(\frac{x - x_i}{h_i}\right),$$ (2.1)

where $h_i = h\lambda_i$ and λ_i is a local bandwidth factor which narrows the bandwidth near the modes and widens it in the tails, which can be defined as:

$$\lambda_i = \left(\frac{G}{\hat{f}(x_i)} \right)^{0.5},$$

(2.2)

where G is the geometric mean of the $\hat{f}(x_i)$, $i = 1, 2, \ldots, n$ and h is a fixed (pilot) bandwidth. We can see that our estimate $\hat{f}(x)$ is bin-independent regardless of our choice of K, where the role of K is to spread out the contribution of each data point in our estimate of the parent distribution, that controls the shape. The most important part in the kernel estimation method is to select the bandwidth (scaling) or the smoothing parameter. Thus, its selection has been studied by many authors, see Abramson (1982) and Jones (1991), based on minimizing the mean square errors, however, the optimal choice in most cases is $h = 1.059 \cdot S \cdot n^{-0.2}$, where S is the sample standard deviation and we will consider it as the pilot bandwidth. Although, it must be mentioned that the optimal choice of h cannot possibly be optimal in every application, and its choice is really depended on the application under consideration to different bandwidths. Though there is a variety of kernel functions with different properties have been used in literature, however, the obvious and natural choice of the kernel functions is the standard Gaussian kernel, for its continuity, differentiability, and locality properties. For more details about the kernel density estimation function, see Guillamon et al. (1999) and Scott (1992).

The kernel approach depending on finding the kernel density estimation for pivotal random variables, that depending on the unknown parameters and whose distributions are free of the unknown parameters. For the GGD (1.1), $(x_i / \beta)^\alpha, \ldots, (x_n / \beta)^\alpha$ be a sample of size n from the gamma distribution $G(\lambda, 1)$, Thus if $\hat{\alpha}$ and $\hat{\beta}$ are the MLEs of α and β respectively, thus:

$$(x_i / \beta)^\alpha = ((x_i / \beta)^{\hat{\alpha}})^{\alpha/\hat{\alpha}} = [(\hat{\beta}/\beta)^{\hat{\alpha}} \cdot (x_i / \hat{\beta})^{\hat{\alpha}}]^{\alpha/\hat{\alpha}} = [a_i z_2]^{z_1},$$

for $i = 1, 2, \ldots, n$ are independent of the unknown parameters α and β when λ is known. Therefore, $Z_1 = \alpha / \hat{\alpha}$ and $Z_2 = (\hat{\beta}/\beta)^{\hat{\alpha}}$ are pivotal quantities and $a_i = (x_i / \hat{\beta})^{\hat{\alpha}}$, $i = 1, 2, \ldots, n$ form a set of ancillary statistics. Note that the ancillary statistics satisfy the maximum likelihood equations, therefore, any $n - 2$ of a_i's, say $a_1, \ldots, a_{n-2}$ form a set of $n - 2$ functionally independent ancillary statistics. For utilizing the kernel function for estimating the probability density function (PDF) of a pivotal, we can summarize the method in the following algorithm:

1- Let $(x_1, x_2, \ldots, x_n)$ be a random sample of size n from the random variable X, with PDF $f(x;\theta)$, where θ represents the unknown parameter with support on $(0, \infty)$.

2- Bootstrapping with replacement n samples X_i^* of size n from the parent sample in step 1, where $X_i^* = (x_1^*, x_1^*, \ldots, x_n^*)$, $i = 1, 2, \ldots, n$.

3- For each sample in step 2, calculate a consistent estimator as the MLE for the parameter and calculate the pivotal quantity Z based on the unknown parameter and its MLE. Thus, we have an objective and informative random sample from the pivotal quantities $Z = (z_1, z_1, \ldots, z_n)$ of size n, which constitute the sampling distribution for the pivotal Z.

4- Finally, based on the informative sample in step 3 we can use the AKDE for estimating $g(z)$ at any given value for Z and thus, the confidence interval of the unknown parameter can be derived fiducially.

Utilizing the above algorithm, the AKDE of the quantile Z_p of order p, for Z can be derived as:

$$G(z_p) = \int_{-\infty}^{z_p} \widehat{g}(z)dz = \frac{1}{n}\sum_{i=1}^{n} \int_{-\infty}^{z_p} \frac{1}{h_i} K\left(\frac{z - z_i}{h_i}\right) dz = p, \qquad (2.3)$$

thus

$$\sum_{i=1}^{n} I\left(\frac{z_p - z_i}{h_i}\right) = np, \qquad (2.4)$$

where

$$I(x) = \int_{-\infty}^{x} k(y)dy.$$

For deriving the value of the quantile estimator Z_p, equation (2.4) can be solved recurrently as the limit to the sequence $\{\tilde{Z}_1, \tilde{Z}_2, \tilde{Z}_3, \ldots\}$, that defined by the formulas:

$$\tilde{Z}_1 = \frac{1}{n}\sum_{i=1}^{n} Z_i,$$

$$\tilde{Z}_{r+1} = \tilde{Z}_r + C\left[np - \sum_{i=1}^{n} I\left(\frac{\tilde{Z}_r - Z_i}{h_i}\right)\right], r = 1, 2, 3, \ldots \tag{2.5}$$

The convergence of (2.5) is guaranteed by the condition $0 < C < \dfrac{2h_i}{nL_1}$, where $L_1 = k(0)$, see Kulczycki (1999).

For censored samples, we have to introduce another form to the kernel density estimation function which is the weighted kernel density estimation function, that has the form:

$$\hat{f}(x) = \sum_{i=1}^{n} \frac{1}{h_i \alpha_i^r} K\left(\frac{x - x_i}{h_i}\right), r < n \tag{2.6}$$

where

$$\alpha_i^r = \sum_{i=1}^{r} \frac{1}{r - m_i + 1}.$$

In this case, the kernel function can be taken as the truncated normal distribution which is defined as:

$$K(x) = \begin{bmatrix} \left[\dfrac{1}{h_i\sqrt{2\Pi}\Phi(x_{i+1})}\exp\left(-\dfrac{1}{2}\left(\dfrac{x-x_i}{h_i}\right)^2\right)\right] & if\ m_i = 0, \quad i = 1,\ldots r \\[4mm] \left[\dfrac{1}{h_i\sqrt{2\Pi}\Phi(m_i x_i)}\exp\left(-\dfrac{1}{2}\left(\dfrac{x-x_i}{h_i}\right)^2\right)\right] & if\ m_i \neq 0, \quad i = 1,\ldots r \end{bmatrix}, \tag{2.7}$$

where $\Phi(z) = \dfrac{1}{\sqrt{2\Pi}}\displaystyle\int_{-\infty}^{z} e^{-\frac{x^2}{2}}\, dx$, see Bordes (2004).

2.2. Conditional Inference

In this section, the confidence intervals for the generalized gamma parameters have been constructed based on the conditional inference. For more details about this method see Lawless (1980, 1982) and Maswadah (2003, 2005) who applied this approach on some lifetime distributions.

Let $\hat{\alpha}$ and $\hat{\beta}$ be the maximum likelihood estimators (MLEs) of α and β, basedonthe generalized order statistics $X(1, n, \tilde{m}, k), \ldots, X(n, n, \tilde{m}, k)$, and Z_1 and Z_2 are pivotal quantities for the parameter α and β, depending on their MLEs $\hat{\alpha}$ and $\hat{\beta}$ respectively, as as defined in section (2.1).Thus, the joint conditional PDF of Z_1 and Z_2 given $A = (a_1, a_2, \ldots, a_{n-2})$ is of the form:

$$g(z_1, z_2 \mid A) = C \cdot z_1^{n-1} z_2^{n\lambda z_1 - 1} \prod_{i=1}^{n} (a_i)^{\lambda z_1}$$

$$\times \exp\left[\sum_{i=1}^{n} m_i \ln[1 - IG(\lambda, (a_i z_2)^{z_1})] - z_2^{z_1} \sum_{i=1}^{n} a_i^{z_1} \right], \quad m_n = k - 1, \tag{2.8}$$

where C is the normalizing constant and is a function of n and A only, see Maswadah (2003).To evaluate C, one may use the fact that (2.8) must integrate to one, we get:

$$C^{-1} = \int_0^\infty \int_0^\infty z_1^{n-1} z_2^{n\lambda z_1 - 1} \prod_{i=1}^{n} (a_i)^{\lambda z_1}$$

$$\times \exp\left[\sum_{i=1}^{n} m_i \ln[1 - IG(\lambda, (a_i z_2)^{z_1})] - z_2^{z_1} \sum_{i=1}^{n} a_i^{z_1} \right] dz_1 dz_2 . \tag{2.9}$$

The marginal density of Z_1 given A, can be obtained by integrating (2.8) with respect to Z_2 as:

$$g_1(z_1 \mid A) = C \int_0^\infty z_1^{n-1} z_2^{n\lambda z_1 - 1} \prod_{i=1}^{n} (a_i)^{\lambda z_1}$$

$$\times \exp\left[\sum_{i=1}^{n} m_i \ln[1 - IG(\lambda, (a_i z_2)^{z_1})] - z_2^{z_1} \sum_{i=1}^{n} a_i^{z_1} \right] dz_2 . \tag{2.10}$$

Similarly, the marginal density of Z_2 given A, can be obtained as:

$$g_2(z_2 \mid A) = C \int_0^\infty z_1^{n-1} z_2^{n\lambda z_1 - 1} \prod_{i=1}^{n} (a_i)^{\lambda z_1}$$

$$\times \exp\left[\sum_{i=1}^{n} m_i \ln[1 - IG(\lambda, (a_i z_2)^{z_1})] - z_2^{z_1} \sum_{i=1}^{n} a_i^{z_1} \right] dz_1 . \tag{2.11}$$

Special Cases:

1-If $k = 1$ and $\tilde{m} = 0$, then (2.8) will be the joint conditional PDF of Z_1 and Z_2 given the ancillary statistics A based on the n ordinary order statistics.

2-If $k = 1$ and $m_i = 0$ for $i = 1, 2, ..., n-1$, $m_n = n - r$, then (2.8) will be the joint conditional PDF of Z_1 and Z_2 given A based on the type-II right censored samples.

3-If $m_i \geq 0, i = 1, 2, ..., r-1$, n, r, $k \in N$, and $m_r = k - 1$,

$n = r + \sum_{i=1}^{r} m_i$, then (2.8) will be the joint conditional PDF of Z_1 and Z_2 given the A based on the type-II progressive censored samples.

3. Simulation Study and Comparisons

The statistical performance of the conditional inference has been compared, via Monte Carlo simulation, to the performance of the Kernel inference in terms of the following criteria:

i) Covering percentage (CP), which is defined as the fraction of times the confidence interval covers the true value of the parameter in repeated sampling.

ii) The mean length of intervals (MLI).

iii) The standard error of the covering percentage (SDE), which is defined for the nominal level $(1 - \alpha)100\%$ by $SDE(\hat{\alpha}) = \sqrt{\dfrac{\hat{\alpha}(1 - \hat{\alpha})}{M}}$, where $(1 - \hat{\alpha})100\%$ denote the corresponding Monte Carlo estimate and M is the number of Monte Carlo trials. Thus, for the nominal level 95% and 1000 simulation trails, say, the standard error of the covering percentage is 0.0049, which is approximately $\pm 1\%$. Therefore, we say the procedure is adequate if the SDE is within $\pm 2\%$ error for the nominal level 95%.

The results, based on 1000 Monte Carlo simulations are given for samples of sizes

n = 20 and 80, which have been generated for values to the scale parameter $\beta = 2, 3$, shape parameter $\alpha = 1, 2, 3$ and $\lambda = 1, 2$ based on the complete, the type-II censored and the type-II progressive censored samples at binomial random removals $P = 0.5$ with uncensored levels r equal to [n/2] and [3n/4]. From the simulation results, we summarized some of the interesting features in the following points:

1.The results in Tables2-4 indicated that, as the sample size increases, the two approaches have values of *MLIs* decrease and the values of *CPs* increase, while the values of *SDEs* decrease for all values of α, for the complete and censored samples.

2. The values of *MLIs* for the parameter α increase as the shape parameter increases as would be expected. On the contrary, for the parameter β the values of *MLIs* decrease as the shape parameter α increases for the complete, type-II censored and type-II progressive censored samples.

3. As the true value of β increases, the values of *MLIs* increase and the *CPs* mostly increase, while the values of *SDEs* decrease based on the complete, type-II censored and type-II progressive censored samples.

4. As the true value of λ increases the *MLIs* decrease, and the *CPs* mostly increase, while the values of *SDEs* decrease based on the complete, type-II censored and type-II progressive censored samples.

5. The two procedures are adequate because the values of *SDEs* are less than ± 2 for the nominal level 95% for the complete, type-II censored and type-II progressive censored samples.

6. The kernel approach is conservative for estimating the parameters α and β because the covering percentages are much greater than the nominal level than those based on the conditional inference for all sample sizes. On the contrary, the conditional approach is anti-conservative for α and almost conservative for β, when the sample sizes greater than 20.

7. Finally, it is worthwhile to note that, the values of *MLIs* and *SDEs* based on the type-II progressive censored samples are less than those based on the type-II censored samples. Moreover, the *CPs* for type-II progressive censored samples are greater than those based on type-II censored samples.

4. An Illustrative Example

Consider the results of tests, the endurance of deep groove ball bearings. The data are quoted from Lawless (1982) consist of a complete sample of size n=23, that represent the results of the test, in millions of revolutions before failures are:

17.88, 28.92, 33.00, 41.52, 41.12, 45.60, 48.48, 51.84, 51.96, 54.12, 55.56, 67.80, 68.64, 68.64, 68.88, 84.12, 93.12, 98.64, 105.12, 105.84, 127.92, 128.04, 173.40.

Thus, for the purpose of comparison, the 95% *CIs* for the parameters α and β are derived using the two approaches based on the data for complete, type-II censored and type-II progressive censored samples with binomial removal at $P = 0.5$, and uncensored levels r equal to [n/2] and [3n/4] at $\lambda = 1,2$.

The results in Table 1, have been indicated that the length of intervals for α and β based on the kernel approach are slightly greater, for one decimal point, than those based on the conditional inference. Also, as the true value of λ increases, the length of intervals decrease. Moreover, as the uncensored level increases, the length of intervals for the parameters α and β decrease based on complete, type-II censored and type-II progressive censored samples. Finally, it is worthwhile to note that, the length of intervals based on the type-II progressively censored samples are smaller than those based on the type-II censored samples, which ensure the simulation results.

Table 1. The Lower (LL) and the Upper limits (UL), Maximum likelihood estimates (MLE), and the lengths of the 95% confidence intervals (CI) for the parameters α and β using the kernel and conditional approaches based on GOS for ball bearings data

| | | Approaches | | | | Kernel | | Conditional | |
| | | CI | | | | 95% | | 95% | |
S	n	r	λ	Par.	LL	UL	LL	UL
		11	1		1.3999	5.4360	1.7114	5.6181
						(4.0361)		(3.9067)
			2		0.8424	3.1518	1.0390	3.2485
						(2.3094)		(2.2095)
Type-II	23	17	1	α	0.8195	2.6492	1.3504	3.1719
censored						(1.8297)		(1.8215)
sample			2		0.5672	1.7131	0.8900	2.0240
						(1.1459)		(1.1340)
		23	1		1.3975	2.5569	1.4385	2.7261
						(1.1593)		(1.2876)
			2		1.0002	1.7598	0.9906	1.8518
						(0.7596)		(0.8612)
		11	1		1.1876	5.2150	2.5238	6.2393
						(4.0274)		(3.7155)
Type-II			2		2.2245	4.3105	1.8706	3.8178
progressive	23			α		(2.0860)		(1.9472)
censored		17	1		1.1725	3.7747	2.0299	4.2126
sample						(2.6022)		(2.1827)
			2		1.5660	2.9320	1.4702	2.7926
						(1.3660)		(1.3224)

Table 1. (Continued)

S	n	r	λ	Par.	Kernel 95% LL	Kernel 95% UL	Conditional 95% LL	Conditional 95% UL
		11	1		60.1484	98.9387	55.2798	90.1386
						(38.7903)		(34.8588)
			2		36.2246	60.2878	35.9278	55.8029
						(24.0632)		(19.8751)
Type-II censored sample	23	17	1	β	71.5374	129.0789	65.3485	105.5123
						(57.5415)		(40.1638)
			2		32.3249	55.3321	33.6026	60.0579
						(23.0072)		(26.4553)
		23	1		59.9192	112.4036	65.4721	102.2297
						(52.4844)		(36.7576)
			2		29.6682	61.7362	32.6251	59.8381
						(32.0680)		(27.2130)
		11	1		45.2633	59.0386	44.9310	57.4086
						(13.7753)		(12.4776)
			2		31.8807	45.4237	31.4181	42.5814
						(13.5430)		(11.1633)
Type-II progressive censored sample		17	1	β	58.1276	86.8869	55.5121	75.2494
						(28.7593)		(19.7373)
			2		33.7310	51.1446	34.5821	50.7146
						(17.4136)		(16.1325)

Table 2. The (MLIs), (CPs) and (SDEs) for the kernel and the conditional approaches when the nominal level is 95% for the parameter α with ($\beta = 2, 3$) with censored levels (50% and 75%)

| App. | | | Kernel | | | | | Conditional | | | | |
| | | | MLI, α | | | | | MLI, α | | | | |
n	r	λ	1.0	2.0	3.0	CP	SDE	1.0	2.0	3.0	CP	SDE
complete and Type-II censored samples												
20	1	10	1.7687	3.5373	5.3060	0.945	0.0072	1.3107	2.6215	3.9323	0.946	0.0071
		15	1.1243	2.2486	3.3728	0.944	0.0073	0.9620	1.9241	2.8861	0.955	0.0066
		20	0.8344	1.6688	2.5032	0.943	0.0073	0.7331	1.4662	2.1993	0.956	0.0065
	2	10	1.7914	3.5816	5.3743	0.946	0.0071	1.2284	2.4569	3.6853	0.954	0.0066
		15	1.1173	2.2345	3.3518	0.945	0.0072	0.9136	1.8272	2.7408	0.947	0.0071
		20	0.7889	1.5779	2.3668	0.932	0.008	0.7055	1.4110	2.1165	0.938	0.0076
80	1	40	0.7057	1.4114	2.1171	0.952	0.0068	0.5937	1.1873	1.7810	0.949	0.0070
		60	0.5128	1.0255	1.5383	0.955	0.0066	0.4532	0.9063	1.3595	0.952	0.0068
		80	0.3831	0.7662	1.1493	0.957	0.0064	0.3491	0.6983	1.0474	0.955	0.0066
	2	40	0.6828	1.3657	2.0485	0.958	0.0063	0.5642	1.1285	1.6927	0.961	0.0061
		60	0.4982	0.9964	1.4946	0.955	0.0066	0.4284	0.8568	1.2852	0.953	0.0067
		80	0.3667	0.7333	1.1000	0.951	0.0068	0.3386	0.6771	1.0157	0.947	0.0071
Type-II progressively censored samples												
20	1	10	1.4774	2.9549	4.4323	0.972	0.0052	1.4375	2.8692	4.3125	0.978	0.0046
		15	1.0995	2.1991	3.2986	0.960	0.0062	0.9198	1.8378	2.7595	0.965	0.0058
	2	10	1.2121	2.4242	3.6364	0.958	0.0063	1.2254	2.4509	3.6763	0.979	0.0045
		15	1.0708	2.1416	3.2124	0.958	0.0063	0.8952	1.7905	2.6857	0.969	0.0055
80	1	40	0.7147	1.4295	2.1442	0.959	0.0063	0.5400	1.0799	1.6199	0.954	0.0066
		60	0.6544	1.3088	1.9632	0.975	0.0049	0.4580	0.9161	1.3741	0.981	0.0043
	2	40	0.6970	1.3940	2.0911	0.976	0.0048	0.5182	1.0364	1.5546	0.950	0.0069
		60	0.6479	1.2958	1.9437	0.971	0.0053	0.4468	0.8936	1.3404	0.953	0.0067

Table 3. The (MLIs), (CPs) and (SDEs) for the kernel and the conditional approaches when the nominal level is 95% for the parameter β with (β=2,3) based on the complete and type-II censored samples with censored levels (50% and 75%)

$\beta = 2$

App.				Kernel					Conditional				
				MLI, β					MLI, β				
n	r	λ		1.0	2.0	3.0	CP	SDE	1.0	2.0	3.0	CP	SDE
20	10	1		6.7292	3.5565	1.9383	0.841	0.0116	4.5278	1.6850	1.0425	0.943	0.0073
	15			3.2168	1.4051	0.9092	0.947	0.0071	2.6845	1.2015	0.7800	0.947	0.0071
	20			2.5416	1.1738	0.7705	0.957	0.0064	2.0382	0.9844	0.6537	0.953	0.0067
	10	2		2.0419	1.0072	0.6750	0.933	0.0079	1.9012	0.9250	0.6157	0.933	0.0079
	15			1.9159	0.9302	0.6192	0.933	0.0079	1.6875	0.8422	0.5648	0.927	0.0082
	20			1.8545	0.9292	0.6256	0.914	0.0089	1.7413	0.8797	0.5925	0.948	0.0070
80	40	1		2.3158	1.0163	0.6530	0.964	0.0059	1.6326	0.7655	0.5018	0.964	0.0059
	60			1.3850	0.6562	0.4309	0.958	0.0063	1.0683	0.5247	0.3485	0.958	0.0063
	80			1.0921	0.5466	0.3654	0.974	0.0050	0.9387	0.4668	0.3112	0.961	0.0061
	40	2		1.1189	0.5417	0.3580	0.962	0.0060	0.9061	0.4537	0.3031	0.956	0.0065
	60			0.9220	0.4602	0.3071	0.963	0.0060	0.8812	0.4426	0.2960	0.956	0.0065
	80			0.9446	0.4721	0.3152	0.962	0.0060	0.8682	0.4353	0.2909	0.962	0.0060

Table 3. (Continued)

$\beta = 3$

App.			Kernel					Conditional				
			MLI, β					MLI, β				
n	λ	r	1.0	2.0	3.0	CP	SDE	1.0	2.0	3.0	CP	SDE
20	1	10	11.0938	5.3348	2.9074	0.841	0.0116	10.2199	3.3898	2.0378	0.943	0.0073
		15	4.8251	2.1076	1.3638	0.947	0.0071	4.0268	1.8022	1.1700	0.947	0.0071
		20	3.8124	1.7607	1.1558	0.957	0.0064	3.0573	1.4766	0.9805	0.953	0.0067
	2	10	3.0628	1.5108	1.0124	0.933	0.0079	2.8518	1.3876	0.9235	0.933	0.0079
		15	2.8738	1.3953	0.9288	0.933	0.0079	2.5312	1.2633	0.8472	0.927	0.0082
		20	2.7817	1.3939	0.9384	0.914	0.0089	2.6119	1.3196	0.8888	0.948	0.0070
80	1	40	3.4737	1.5245	0.9795	0.964	0.0059	2.4489	1.1483	0.7527	0.964	0.0059
		60	2.0776	0.9843	0.6464	0.958	0.0063	1.6025	0.7870	0.5227	0.958	0.0063
		80	1.6114	0.7965	0.5301	0.974	0.0050	1.4080	0.7002	0.4668	0.961	0.0061
	2	40	1.6784	0.8125	0.5370	0.962	0.0060	1.3592	0.6805	0.4547	0.956	0.0065
		60	1.3830	0.6903	0.4607	0.963	0.0060	1.3217	0.6638	0.4439	0.956	0.0065
		80	1.4169	0.7081	0.4728	0.962	0.0060	1.3023	0.6529	0.4363	0.962	0.0060

Table 4. The (MLIs), (CPs) and (SDEs) for the kernel and the conditional approaches when the nominal level is 95%for the parameter β (β=2,3) based on type-II progressively censored samples with censored levels (50% and75%)

$\beta = 2$

App.			Kernel					Conditional				
			MLI, β			CP	SDE	MLI, β			CP	SDE
n	r	λ	1.0	2.0	3.0			1.0	2.0	3.0		
20	10	1	3.7357	1.6194	1.0478	0.945	0.0072	3.1987	1.4434	0.9444	0.937	0.0077
	15		2.5122	1.2250	0.8195	0.958	0.0063	2.5599	1.2019	0.7930	0.945	0.0072
	10	2	2.9915	1.3663	0.8957	0.917	0.0087	1.9976	1.0267	0.6989	0.890	0.0099
	15		1.9672	1.0085	0.6843	0.945	0.0072	1.6280	0.8128	0.5453	0.894	0.0097
40	20	1	2.2367	1.1289	0.7625	0.975	0.0049	2.0620	1.0077	0.6720	0.960	0.0062
	30		1.5854	0.7887	0.5276	0.954	0.0066	1.6688	0.8304	0.5557	0.960	0.0062
	20	2	1.9092	0.9932	0.6767	0.964	0.0059	1.5268	0.7825	0.5292	0.916	0.0088
	30		1.5262	0.7581	0.5066	0.955	0.0066	1.4509	0.7457	0.5042	0.949	0.0070
80	40	1	1.4886	0.7516	0.5049	0.967	0.0056	1.3762	0.6916	0.4636	0.959	0.0063
	60		1.2961	0.6742	0.4570	0.960	0.0062	1.2265	0.6234	0.4192	0.965	0.0058
	40	2	1.4576	0.7373	0.4954	0.977	0.0047	1.3902	0.7274	0.4944	0.961	0.0061
	60		1.2683	0.6600	0.4473	0.972	0.0052	1.0651	0.5511	0.3726	0.946	0.0071

Table 4. (Continued)

$$\beta = 3$$

App.				Kernel					Conditional				
				MLI, β					MLI, β				
n	r	λ		1.0	2.0	3.0	CP	SDE	1.0	2.0	3.0	CP	SDE
20	10	1		5.6035	2.4291	1.5717	0.945	0.0072	4.7980	2.1651	1.4166	0.937	0.0077
	15			3.7683	1.8375	1.2292	0.958	0.0063	3.8398	1.8029	1.1895	0.945	0.0072
	10	2		4.4872	2.0495	1.3436	0.917	0.0087	2.9965	1.5400	1.0484	0.890	0.0099
	15			2.9508	1.5127	1.0264	0.945	0.0072	2.4421	1.2192	0.8180	0.894	0.0097
40	20	1		3.3550	1.6934	1.1437	0.975	0.0049	3.0929	1.5072	1.0080	0.960	0.0062
	30			2.3780	1.1831	0.7914	0.954	0.0066	2.5033	1.2456	0.8336	0.960	0.0062
	20	2		2.8637	1.4898	1.0151	0.964	0.0059	2.2903	1.1738	0.7938	0.916	0.0088
	30			2.2893	1.1371	0.7599	0.955	0.0066	2.1764	1.1186	0.7562	0.949	0.0070
80	40	1		2.2329	1.1274	0.7573	0.967	0.0056	2.0643	1.0374	0.6955	0.959	0.0063
	60			1.9442	1.0113	0.6855	0.960	0.0062	1.8397	0.9351	0.6287	0.965	0.0058
	40	2		2.1863	1.1059	0.7432	0.977	0.0047	2.0853	1.0911	0.7417	0.961	0.0061
	60			1.9024	0.9900	0.6710	0.972	0.0052	1.5976	0.8266	0.5589	0.946	0.0071

5. Conclusion

The kernel estimation technique constitutes a strong basis for statistical inference, and it has a number of benefits relative to the conditional inference. First, it is easy to be implemented, and it doesn't need tedious work as the conditional inference. Second, it can perform quite well even when the number of bootstraps is extremely small up to 20 replications. Finally, it is uniquely determined based on the information content in the pivotal quantities, and thus we can consider the kernel inference as an alternative and reliable technique for estimation than the conditional inference.

References

Abramson, I. (1982). On Bandwidth Variation in Kernel Estimates: A Square Root Law. *Ann. Statist.*10, 1217-1223.

Ahsanullah, M. (1995). The generalized order statistics and a characteristic property of the exponential distribution. *Pak. J. Statist.*, 11(3),215-218.

Ahsanullah, M. (2000). Generalized order statistics from exponential distribution. *Journal of Statistical Planning and Inference*, 85, 85-91.

Bordes, L. (2004). Non-parametric estimation under progressive censoring. *J. Statist. Plann. Inference*, 119, 171–189.

Cohen, A. C. and Norgaard, N. J. (1977). Progressively type-II Censored sampling on the three parameter Gamma Distribution, *Technometrics*, 19, 333-340.

Geng, C. and Yuhiong, L. (2009). A Note on the Maximum Likelihood Estimationfor the Generalized Gamma Distribution Parameters under Progressive Type-II Censoring. *International Journal of Intelligent Technology and Applied Statistics*, 2(2), 57-64.

Dadpay, A., Soofi, E. and Soyer, R. (2007).Information measures for generalized gamma family. *Journal of Econometrics*, 56, 568-585.

Di Ciccio, T. (1987). Approoximate inference for the generalized gamma distribution. *Technometrics*, 33-40.

Guillamon, A. Navarro, J. and Ruiz, J. M. (1999). A note on kernel estimators for positive values random variables. *Sankhya*, A, 6, 276-281.

Gomes, O., Combes, C. and Dussauchoy, A. (2008). Parameter estimation of the generalized gamma distribution. *Mathematics and Computers in Simulation*,79, 955-963.

Hager, H. and Bain, L.(1970). Inferential procedures for the generalized gamma distribution. *Journal of the American Statistical Association*,65, 1601-1609.

Harter, H. L. (1967).Maximum Likelihood Estimation of the Parameters of a four-Parameter Generalized Gamma Population from Complete and Censored Samples, *Technometrics*, 9, 159-5.

Hwang T. and Huang P. (2006).On new moment estimation of parameters of the Generalized Gamma distribution and its characterization, *Taiwanese journal of Mathematics*, 10(4), 1083-1093.

Kamps, U. (1995). *A concept of generalized order statistics*. Germany: B. G. Teubner Stuttgart.

Kulczycki, P. (1999). Parameter Identification Using Bayes and Kernel Approaches. *Proceedings of the National Science Council* ROC(A), 23(2), 205-213.

Lawless, J. (1980).Inference on the generalized gamma and log gamma distributions. *Technometrics*, 22, 409-419.

Lawless, J. (1982).*Statistical Models and Methods for Lifetime Data*. John Wiley and Sons, New York.

Maswadah, M. S. (1989). Two approaches based on the structural model to inference on the generalized Gamma parameters. *Egyptian Statist. J.*, 33(1), 110-129.

Maswadah, M. S. (1991). Structural inference on the generalized Gamma distribution based on type -II progressively censored sample. *J. Austral. Math. Soc.* A,50 (1), 15-22.

Maswadah, M. (2003).Conditional Confidence Interval Estimation for the Inverse Weibull Distribution Based on Censored Generalized Order Statistics. *J. statist. Comput. Simul.*, 73(12), P.887-898.

Maswadah, M. (2005). Conditional Confidence Interval Estimation for the Type-II Extreme Value Distribution Based on Censored Generalized Order Statistics. *Journal of Applied Statistical Science.* 14(1/2), 71-84.

Maswadah, M. (2006). Kernel Inference on the Inverse Weibull Distribution". *TheKorean Communications in Statistics.* 13(3), 503- 512.

Maswadah, M. (2007). Kernel Inference on the Weibull Distribution. *Proc. Third National Statistical Conference*, Lahore, Pakistan. May 28-29, Vol.14, 77-86.

Maswadah, M. (2010). *Statistical Inferences on the Type-II Extreme Value Distribution Based on the Kernel Approach.* (ICCS-X), vol. II, 870-880.

Mukherjee, B., Ashutosh Gupta and Upadhyay, S. K. (2011). A Bayesian study for the comparison of generalized gamma model with its components. *Sankhya*, B, 72, 154–174.

Parr, V. B. and Webster, J. T. (1965). A Method for Discriminating between Failure Density Functions used in Reliability Predictions, *Technometrics*, 7, 1-10.

Prentice, R. (1974). A log gamma model and its maximum likelihood estimation. *Biometrika*, 61, 539-544.

Scott, D. W. (1992). *Multivariate Density Estimation*. New York; Wiley inter-science.

Stacy, E. (1962). A generalization of the gamma distribution. *Annals of Mathematical Statistics*, 1187-1192.

Stacy, E. and Mihram, G. (1965). Parameter estimation for a generalized gamma distribution. *Technometrics*, 7, 349-358.

Wingo, D. R. (1987). Computing maximum-likelihood parameter estimates of the generalized gamma distribution by numerical root isolation. *IEEE Transactions on Reliability*, 36, 586-590.

In: Applied Statistical Theory and Applications
Editor: Mohammad Ahsanullah

ISBN: 978-1-63321-858-1
© 2014 Nova Science Publishers, Inc.

Chapter 14

ON STATISTICAL CHARACTERISTICS
OF THE PRODUCT OF TWO CORRELATED
CHI-SQUARE VARIABLES

Anwar H. Joarder[1] and M. Hafidz Omar[2]
Department of Mathematics and Statistics
King Fahd University of Petroleum and Minerals, Dhahran, Saudi Arabia

Abstract

The distribution of the product of two variables is important in portfolio diversification model and in economic forecasting. We derive the distribution of the product of two chi-square variables when they are correlated through a bivariate chi-square distribution. Closed form expressions for raw moments, centered moments, coefficient of skewness and kurtosis are obtained. The density function is also graphed. The results match with the distribution of the product of two independent chi-square variables in case the coefficient correlation in our model vanishes. They are often extended to sample variances of bivariate normal distribution.

Keywords and Phrases: Correlated chi-square variables; distribution of product of the chi-square variables; centered moments

AMS Mathematics Subject Classification (2000): 62E15, 60E05, 60E10

1. Introduction

Let $X'_j = (X_{1j}, X_{2j})$, $j = 1, 2, \cdots, N$, be two-dimensional independent normal random vectors with mean vector $\bar{X} = (\bar{X}_1, \bar{X}_2)'$ so that the sums of squares and cross product

---

[1] E-mail address: anwarj@kfupm.edu.sa
[2] E-mail address: omarmh@kfupm.edu.sa

matrix is given by $\sum_{j=1}^{N}(X_j - \bar{X})(X_j - \bar{X})' = A$ which can be denoted by

$A = (a_{ik})$, $i = 1, 2$; $k = 1, 2$ where $a_{ii} = ms_i^2$, $m = N - 1$, $(i = 1, 2)$ and $a_{12} = mrs_1s_2$.

Also let $\Sigma = (\sigma_{ik})$, $i = 1, 2$; $k = 1, 2$ where $\sigma_{11} = \sigma_1^2$, $\sigma_{22} = \sigma_2^2$, $\sigma_{12} = \rho\sigma_1\sigma_2$ with

$\sigma_1 > 0$, $\sigma_2 > 0$. The quantity ρ $(-1 < \rho < 1)$ is the product moment correlation

coefficient between the parent variables X_{1j} and X_{2j} $(j = 1, 2, \cdots, N)$.

The joint density function of $U = mS_1^2 / \sigma_1^2$ and $V = mS_2^2 / \sigma_2^2$, called the bivariate chi-square distribution, was derived by Joarder (2009) from the joint density function of the sample variances and correlation coefficient. The product moment correlation coefficient between U and V can be derived to be ρ^2. For the estimation of correlation coefficient by modern techniques, we refer to Ahmed (1992). In case the correlation coefficient ρ of the parent variables vanishes, the density function of U and V becomes that of the product of two independent chi-square variables each with m degrees of freedom.

The distribution of the product of two variables arises in many contexts. Certain cases in traditional portfolio selection models involve the distribution of the product of two variables. The best examples of this are in the case of investment in a number of different overseas markets. In portfolio diversification models (see, e.g., Grubel, 1968), not only are the prices of shares in local markets uncertain but also the exchange rates, and so the value of the portfolio in domestic currency is related to a product of random variables. Similarly, in models of diversified production by multinationals (see e.g. Rugman 1979), there are local production uncertainty and exchange rate uncertainty, and so profits in home currency are again related to a product of random variables.

While forecasting from an estimated equation in econometrics, Feldstein (1971), pointed out that both the parameter and the value of the exogenous variable in the forecast period could be considered as random variables. Hence the forecast was proportional to a product of random variables.

Wells, Anderson and Cell (1962) derived the distribution of the product of two independent chi-square variables with degrees of freedom m_1 and m_2. Note that Springer (1979, 365) also derived the same but with some misprints.

We derive the distribution of $W = UV$ in Theorem 4.1 when $U = mS_1^2 / \sigma_1^2$ and $V = mS_2^2 / \sigma_2^2$ have a bivariate chi-square distribution with common degrees of freedom m. Our contribution is more general than Wells, Anderson and Cell (1962) or Springer (1979) in the sense of accommodating correlated chi-square variables U and V. In case the chi-square variables are uncorrelated, Theorem 4.1 matches exactly with Wells, Anderson and Cell for $m_1 = m_2$.

Higher order raw moments of W are derived in Theorem 5.1 although they can follow from Joarder, Laradji and Omar (2012). Centered moments of W are derived in Theorem 5.2 and Theorem 5.3. The coefficient of skewness and kurtosis are presented in Corollary 5.5. The results are often simply extended to sample variances of bivariate normal distribution. In case the correlation coefficient ρ of the parent variables vanishes, the findings of the paper match with the case of the distribution of the product of the independent chi-square variables.

2. Mathematical Preliminaries

The product of k consecutive numbers is denoted by the following:

$$a_{\{k\}} = a(a+1)\cdots(a+k-1), \quad a^{\{k\}} = a(a-1)\cdots(a-k+1),$$

with $a_{\{0\}} = 1$ and $a^{\{0\}} = 1$. (2.1)

The duplication formula of gamma function is given by

$$\Gamma(2z)\sqrt{\pi} = 2^{2z-1}\Gamma(z)\Gamma[z+(1/2)].$$ (2.2)

The hypergeometric function $_pF_q(a_1,a_2,\cdots,a_p;b_1,b_2,\cdots,b_q;z)$ is defined by

$$_pF_q(a_1,a_2,\cdots,a_p;b_1,b_2,\cdots,b_q;z) = \sum_{k=0}^{\infty} \frac{(a_1)_{\{k\}}(a_2)_{\{k\}}\cdots(a_p)_{\{k\}}}{(b_1)_{\{k\}}(b_2)_{\{k\}}\cdots(b_q)_{\{k\}}} \frac{z^k}{k!},$$ (2.3)

(Gradshteyn and Ryzhik, 1994, 1071, #9.14). The function $_2F_1(a,b;c;z)$ can be transformed to

$$_2F_1(a,b;c;z) = (1-z)^{c-a-b} {}_2F_1(c-a,c-b;c;z)$$ (2.4)

(Gradshteyn and Ryzhik, 1994, 1069).

If a, b and c are integers, then the function $_2F_1(a,b;c;z)$ has the following finite representation:

$$_2F_1(a,b;c;\rho^2) = \sum_{k=0}^{a} \frac{a_{\{k\}}b_{\{k\}}}{c_{\{k\}}} \frac{\rho^k}{k!},$$ (2.5)

(See 15.4.1 of Abramowitz and Stegun, 1972, p561).

The function $_2F_1(a,b;c;z)$ is also related to Jacobi's polynomial $P_n^{(\alpha,\beta)}(z)$ by the following relation:

$$_2F_1(-n,\alpha+1+\beta+n;\alpha+1;z) = \frac{n!}{(n+1)_{\{n\}}} P_n^{(\alpha,\beta)}(1-2z).$$ (2.6)

The Modified Bessel Function of the second kind admits the following integral representations:

$$K_\alpha(z) = \frac{(\frac{z}{2})^\alpha \sqrt{\pi}}{\Gamma(\alpha + \frac{1}{2})} \int_1^\infty (t^2 - 1)^{(2\alpha-1)/2} e^{-zt} dt \,, \ \alpha > -1/2, \ z > 0 \qquad (2.7)$$

(Gradshteyn and Ryzhik, 1994, 969, #8.432), and

$$K_\alpha(z) = \frac{1}{2}\left(\frac{z}{2}\right)^\alpha \int_0^\infty t^{-(\alpha+1)} \exp\left(-t - \frac{z^2}{4t}\right) dt \,, \ z > 0 \qquad (2.8)$$

(Gradshteyn and Ryzhik, 1994, 969, #8.432).

3. The Bivariate Chi-Square Distribution

Theorem 3.1 Let S_1^2 and S_2^2 be sample variances of a bivariate normal distribution as discussed in Section 1. Then the joint density function of $U = mS_1^2 / \sigma_1^2$ and $V = mS_2^2 / \sigma_2^2$ is given by the following function:

$$f(u,v) = \frac{(uv)^{(m-2)/2}}{2^m \, \Gamma^2(m/2)(1-\rho^2)^{m/2}} \exp\left(-\frac{u+v}{2-2\rho^2}\right) \, {}_0F_1\left(\frac{m}{2}; \frac{\rho^2 uv}{(2-2\rho^2)^2}\right), \qquad (3.1)$$

where $-1 < \rho < 1$, $m > 2$ and ${}_0F_1(;b;z)$ is defined in (2.3).

The variables U and V are said to have a correlated bivariate chi-square distribution each with m degrees of freedom. In case $\rho = 0$, the density function in (3.1) would be that of the product of two independent chi-square random variables. By a simple transformation in (3.1), we have the following corollary.

Corollary 3.1 The joint density of S_1^2 and S_2^2 is given by

$$f(s_1^2, s_2^2) = \left(\frac{m}{2\sigma_1\sigma_2}\right)^m \frac{(s_1^2 s_2^2)^{(m-2)/2}}{(1-\rho^2)^{m/2}\Gamma^2(m/2)} \exp\left[\frac{-m}{2-2\rho^2}\left(\frac{s_1^2}{\sigma_1^2} + \frac{s_2^2}{\sigma_2^2}\right)\right]$$
$$\times \, {}_0F_1\left(\frac{m}{2}; \frac{(m\rho)^2 s_1^2 s_2^2}{(2-2\rho^2)^2 \sigma_1^2 \sigma_2^2}\right), \qquad (3.2)$$

where $m = N - 1 > 2$, $-1 < \rho < 1$ and the hypergeometric function ${}_0F_1(a; z)$ is defined by (2.3).

By integrating out s_2^2 in (3.2), it can be easily checked that $U = mS_1^2 / \sigma_1^2 \sim \chi_m^2$. Similarly, it can be proved that $V = mS_2^2 / \sigma_2^2 \sim \chi_m^2$. Thus we have the following corollary.

Corollary 3.2 Let S_1^2 and S_2^2 be two correlated chi-square variables with density function given by (3.2). Then $S_i^2 (i = 1, 2)$ has the following density function

$$g_i(s_i^2) = \left(\frac{m}{2\sigma_i^2}\right)^{m/2} \frac{(s_i^2)^{(m-2)/2}}{\Gamma(m/2)} \exp\left(\frac{-ms_i^2}{2\sigma_i^2}\right), \quad (i = 1, 2), \tag{3.3}$$

where $m = N - 1 > 2$.

In case S_1^2 and S_2^2 are independent, then the density function of S_1^2 and S_2^2 would be

$$f(s_1^2, s_2^2) = \left(\frac{m}{2\sigma_1\sigma_2}\right)^m \frac{(s_1^2 s_2^2)^{(m-2)/2}}{\Gamma^2(m/2)} \exp\left[\frac{-m}{2}\left(\frac{s_1^2}{\sigma_1^2} + \frac{s_2^2}{\sigma_2^2}\right)\right], \tag{3.4}$$

where $m = N - 1 > 2$.

4. Main Results

Theorem 4.1 Let U and V be two correlated chi-square variables with density function given by (3.1). Then the density function of $W = UV$ is given by

$$f_W(w) = \frac{(1-\rho^2)^{-m/2} w^{(m-2)/2}}{2^{m-1}\Gamma^2(m/2)} K_0\left(\frac{\sqrt{w}}{1-\rho^2}\right) {}_0F_1\left(\frac{m}{2}; \frac{\rho^2 w}{(2-2\rho^2)^2}\right), \quad w > 0, \tag{4.1}$$

where $m > 2$, $-1 < \rho < 1$, ${}_0F_1(x)$ is given by (2.3) and $K_\alpha(x)$ is given by (2.7) or (2.8).

Proof. Let $y = h_1(u, v) = u + v$, $w = h_2(u, v) = uv$, $u = h_1^{-1}(y, w)$, $v = h_2^{-1}(y, w)$ in (3.1) so that the joint density function of Y and W is given by

$$f(y, w) = f(h_1^{-1}(y, w), h_2^{-1}(y, w))|J_1| + f(h_1^{-1}(y, w), h_2^{-1}(y, w))|J_2|, \tag{4.2}$$

where $|J_i|, (i = 1, 2)$ is the Jacobian of transformation in the domain $D_1 = \{(u, v), u > v\}$ and $D_2 = \{(u, v) : u < v\}$ respectively. In $D_1 = \{(u, v) : u > v\}$, we have $2u = y + \sqrt{y^2 - 4w}$, $2v = y - \sqrt{y^2 - 4w}$ so that $\dfrac{\partial u}{\partial y}\dfrac{\partial v}{\partial w} - \dfrac{\partial u}{\partial w}\dfrac{\partial v}{\partial y} = (y^2 - 4w)^{-1/2}$

yielding $J(u, v \to y, w) = (y^2 - 4w)^{-1/2}$, $y > 2\sqrt{w}$. In $D_2 = \{(u, v) : u < v\}$, we have $2u = y - \sqrt{y^2 - 4w}$, $2v = y + \sqrt{y^2 - 4w}$ and as above, it can be proved that

$$\frac{\partial u}{\partial y}\frac{\partial v}{\partial w} - \frac{\partial u}{\partial w}\frac{\partial v}{\partial y} = -(y^2 - 4w)^{-1/2},$$

so that the Jacobian of the transformation is

$$|J(u, v \to y, w)| = (y^2 - 4w)^{-1/2}, \quad y > 2\sqrt{w}.$$

Then the joint probability density function of Y and W is given by

$$f_{Y,W}(y, w) \propto w^{(m-2)/2}(y^2 - 4w)^{-1/2}\exp\left(\frac{-y}{2-2\rho^2}\right)\,_0F_1\left(\frac{m}{2}; \frac{\rho^2 w}{(2-2\rho^2)^2}\right),$$

where $w > 0$, $y > 2\sqrt{w}$, $m > 2$ and $-1 < \rho < 1$.

By integrating out y, it follows from the above that

$$f_W(w) \propto w^{(m-2)/2}\,_0F_1\left(\frac{m}{2}; \frac{\rho^2 w}{(2-2\rho^2)^2}\right)I(w, \rho), \tag{4.3}$$

where

$$I(w, \rho) = \int_{2\sqrt{w}}^{\infty}(y^2 - 4w)^{-1/2}\exp\left(\frac{-y}{2-2\rho^2}\right)dy.$$

By a bit of simplification and using (2.7), we have

$$I(w, \rho) = K_0\left(\frac{\sqrt{w}}{1-\rho^2}\right),$$

so that (4.3) simplifies to (4.1).

Figure 1 in the Appendix 1 shows the graph of the density function (4.1) of the product of two chi-square variables for various values of ρ for $m = 5$. If W is the product of two independent chi-square variables with degrees of freedom m_1 and m_2, then

$$f_W(w) = \frac{w^{[(m_1+m_2)/4]-1}}{2^{[(m_1+m_2)/2]-1}\Gamma(m_1/2)\Gamma(m_2/2)}K_{(m_1-m_2)/2}(\sqrt{w}), \quad w > 0, \tag{4.4}$$

(Wells, Anderson and Cell, 1962) where $K_\alpha(x)$ is the modified Bessel function of the second kind defined in (2.7) or (2.8). Note that Springer (1979, 365) derived the above but there is a misprint in the density function. If $\rho = 0$ and $m_1 = m_2 = m$ in (4.4), it reduces to the joint density of the product of two independent chi-square variables each having m degrees of freedom.

Corollary 4.1 Let S_1^2 and S_2^2 be two correlated variables with density function given by (3.2). Then the density function of $W = S_1^2 S_2^2$ is given by

$$f_W(w) = \frac{m^m w^{(m/2)-1}}{2^{m-1}(1-\rho^2)^{m/2} \Gamma^2(m/2)(\sigma_1\sigma_2)^m} \, _0F_1\left(\frac{m}{2}; \frac{(m\rho)^2 w}{(2-2\rho^2)^2 \sigma_1^2 \sigma_2^2}\right) K_0\left(\frac{m\sqrt{w}}{(1-\rho^2)\sigma_1\sigma_2}\right), (4.5)$$

where $w > 0$, $-1 < \rho < 1$, $m > 2$, $_0F_1(b;z)$ is given by (2.3) and $K_\alpha(x)$ is given by (2.7) or (2.8).

Corollary 4.2 Let S_1^2 and S_2^2 be independent chi-square random variable with density functions given by (3.3). Then the density function of $W = S_1^2 S_2^2$ is given by

$$f_W(w) = \frac{m^m}{2^{m-1}\,\Gamma^2(m/2)(\sigma_1\sigma_2)^m}\, w^{(m-2)/2} K_0\left(\frac{m}{\sigma_1\sigma_2}\sqrt{w}\right), \tag{4.6}$$

where $w > 0$, and $m > 2$.

5. Higher Order Moments

Theorem 5.1 Let W have the density function given by (4.1). Then for $m > 2$ and $-1 < \rho < 1$, the a-th moment of W denoted by $\mu_a' = E(W^a)$, is given by

$$E(W^a) = 4^a(1-\rho^2)^{2a+(m/2)}\left((m/2)_{\{a\}}\right)^2 \, _2F_1\left(a+(m/2),\ a+(m/2);\ m/2;\ \rho^2\right), (5.1)$$

where $_2F_1(a_1, a_2; b_1; z)$ is the generalized hypergeometric function defined by (2.3).

Proof. It follows from (4.1) that the a-th moment $E(W^a)$ is given by

$$E(W^a) = \frac{4^a(1-\rho^2)^{2a+(m/2)}}{\sqrt{\pi}\,\Gamma(m/2)} \sum_{k=0}^{\infty} \frac{(2\rho)^{2k}}{(2k)!\Gamma(k+(m/2))}\Gamma^2\left(k+a+(m/2)\right)\Gamma\left(k+(1/2)\right),$$

which, by virtue of duplication formula of gamma function (2.2), can be written as

$$E(W^a) = \frac{4^a(1-\rho^2)^{2a+(m/2)}}{\Gamma(m/2)} \sum_{k=0}^{\infty} \frac{\rho^{2k}}{k!\Gamma(k+(1/2))} \frac{\Gamma^2\left(k+a+(m/2)\right)\Gamma\left(k+(1/2)\right)}{\Gamma\left(k+(m/2)\right)},$$

which simplifies to

$$E(W^a) = \frac{4^a(1-\rho^2)^{2a+(m/2)}}{\Gamma(m/2)} \sum_{k=0}^{\infty} \frac{\rho^{2k}}{k!} \frac{\Gamma^2\left(k+a+(m/2)\right)}{\Gamma\left(k+(m/2)\right)}. \tag{5.2}$$

Then by hypergeometric function (2.3), we have

$$E(W^a) = 4^a (1-\rho^2)^{2a+(m/2)} \frac{\Gamma^2(a+(m/2))}{\Gamma^2(m/2)} \, {}_2F_1(a+(m/2), a+(m/2); m/2; \rho^2),$$

which is equivalent to (5.1). By virtue of (2.4), the above can also be transformed to

$$E(W^a) = 4^a \left((m/2)_{\{a\}}\right)^2 \, {}_2F_1(-a, -a; m/2; \rho^2).$$

We remark that the above theorem can also follow from Joarder, Laradji and Omar (2012).

Corollary 5.1 Let W have the density function given by (4.1). Then for any nonnegative integer a, $E(W^a)$ is given by

$$E(W^a) = 4^a (m/2)_{\{a\}} \sum_{k=0}^{a} \binom{a}{k} (1+a-k)_{\{k\}} \left((m/2)+k\right)_{\{a-k\}} \rho^{2k}, \qquad (5.3)$$

where $m > 2$ and $-1 < \rho < 1$ and $k_{\{a\}}$ is defined by (2.1).

Proof. Since a is an integer, by (2.5), we have

$$ {}_2F_1(-a, -a; m/2; \rho^2) = \sum_{k=0}^{a} \frac{(-a)_{\{k\}}(-a)_{\{k\}}}{(m/2)_{\{k\}}} \frac{\rho^k}{k!},$$

and hence, from (5.1), we have

$$E(W^a) = 4^a \frac{\Gamma^2(a+(m/2))}{\Gamma^2(m/2)} \sum_{k=0}^{a} \frac{[(-a)_{\{k\}}]^2}{(m/2)_{\{k\}}} \frac{\rho^k}{k!}.$$

Further by virtue of $(-a)_{\{k\}} = (-1)^k (a-k+1)_{\{k\}}$, we have

$$E(W^a) = 4^a (m/2)_{\{a\}} \sum_{k=0}^{a} \binom{a}{k} \frac{\Gamma(a+(m/2))(a-k+1)_{\{k\}}}{\Gamma((m/2)+k)} \rho^{2k},$$

which is equivalent to (5.3).

The above moments are represented by Jacobi's Polynomials in the following corollary:

Corollary 5.2 Let W have the density function given by (4.1). Then for any nonnegative integer a, we have the following:

$$E(W^a) = 4^a(m/2)_{\{a\}}(1-\rho^2)^{-2a}a!P_a^{((m/2)-1,-2a-(m/2))}(1-2\rho^2), \ m > 2, \quad (5.4)$$

where $m > 2$, $-1 < \rho < 1$, $P_n^{(\alpha,\beta)}(z)$ is defined by (2.6) and $k_{\{a\}}$ is defined by (2.1),

Proof. Putting $a = n$, $\alpha + 1 + \beta + a = -b$, $a = b$, $\alpha + 1 = m/2$, $z = \rho^2$ in (2.6), we have

$$_2F_1(-a,-b;m/2;\rho^2) = \frac{a!}{(m/2)_{\{a\}}}P_a^{((m/2)-1,-a-b-(m/2))}(1-2\rho^2).$$

Then (5.4) follows from (5.1).

The corollary below follows from Corollary 5.1 (cf. Joarder , 2009).

Corollary 5.3 For $m > 2, -1 < \rho < 1$, the first raw four moments $E(W^a)$, $a = 1,2,3,4$ of $W = UV$ are respectively given by

$$E(W) = m(m + 2\rho^2),$$

$$E(W^2) = m(m+2)[8\rho^4 + 8(m+2)\rho^2 + m(m+2)],$$

$$E(W^3) = m(m+2)(m+4)[48\rho^6 + 72(m+4)\rho^4 + 18(m+2)(m+4)\rho^2) + m(m+2)(m+4)],$$

$$E(W^4) = m(m+2)(m+4)(m+6)\Big[m(m+2)(m+4)(m+6) + 32(m+2)(m+4)(m+6)\rho^2$$
$$+ 288(m+4)(m+6)\rho^4 + 768(m+6)\rho^6 + 384\rho^8\Big].$$

Since $m^2 S_1^2 S_2^2 = \sigma_1^2 \sigma_2^2 W$, moments, coefficient of skewness and kurtosis of $S_1^2 S_2^2$ can be simply derived from the results in this section. In particular,in the following corollary we report the mean and variance.

Corollary 5.4 The mean and variance of $S_1^2 S_2^2$ are respectively given by

$$E(S_1^2 S_2^2) = \frac{1}{m}(m + 2\rho^2)\sigma_1^2\sigma_2^2,$$

and

$$Var(S_1^2 S_2^2) = \frac{1}{m^3}[4(1+\rho^2)m^2 + 4(1+8\rho^2 - \rho^4)m + 16\rho^4]\sigma_1^4\sigma_2^4,$$

where $m > 2$ and $-1 < \rho < 1$.

The centered moments of W are given by $\mu_a = E(W - E(W))^a$. In the following theorem, we provide compact expressions for the second, the third and the fourth order mean centered moments.

Theorem 5.2 Let W have the density function given by (4.1). Then the second, third and fourth centered moments of W are given respectively by

$$\mu_2 = 4m[(m+4)\rho^4 + (m^2 + 8m + 8)\rho^2 + m(m+1)], \qquad (5.5)$$

$$\mu_3 = 8m[m(5m^2 + 12m + 8) + 6(2m^3 + 17m^2 + 36m + 24)\rho^2 + 3(m+4)(m^2 + 16m + 24)\rho^4 \\ + 2(m^2 + 12m + 24)\rho^6], \qquad (5.6)$$

$$\mu_4 = 48m[m(m(m^4 + 16m^3 + 59m^2 + 88m + 48) + 2(m^5 + 37m^4 + 304m^3 + 976m^2 \\ + 1408m + 768)\rho^2 + (m^5 + 56m^4 + 798m^3 + 4176m^2 + 9024m + 6912)\rho^4 \qquad (5.7) \\ + 2(3m^4 + 84m^3 + 728m^2 + 2304m + 2304)\rho^6 + (3m^3 + 56m^2 + 288m + 384\rho^8],$$

where $m > 2$ and $-1 < \rho < 1$.

Proof. By using the raw moments $E(W^a)$, $a = 1, 2, 3, 4$, from Corollary 5.3, in the following relations,

$$\mu_2 = E(W^2) - \mu^2,$$

$$\mu_3 = E(W^3) - 3E(W^2)\mu + 2\mu^3,$$

$$\mu_4 = E(W^4) - 4E(W^3)\mu + 6E(W^2)\mu^2 - 3\mu^4,$$

and performing a lengthy calculation, we get the central moments given by (5.5), (5.6) and (5.7).

By substituting $\rho = 0$, it follows from Theorem 5.2 that the second, third and fourth order centered moments of the product of two independent chi-square variables with the same degrees of freedom m are given respectively by

$$\mu_2 = 4m^2(m+1),$$

$$\mu_3 = 8m^2(5m^2 + 12m + 8),$$

$$\mu_4 = 48m^2(m^4 + 16m^3 + 59m^2 + 88m + 48),$$

which can be checked alternatively.

Corollary 5.5 Let W have the density function given by (4.1). The coefficient of skewness and coefficient of kurtosis of W are respectively given by the moment ratios

$$\alpha_3(W) = \frac{\mu_3}{\mu_2^{3/2}}, \quad \text{and} \quad \alpha_4(W) = \frac{\mu_4}{\mu_2^2},$$

where μ_2, μ_3 and μ_4 are given by Theorem 5.2.

The asymptotic behaviour of coefficient of skewness and kurtosis can be studied. If $\rho = 0$, then W will be the product of two independent chi-square random variables each with m degrees of freedom and evidently the resulting moments are in agreement with that situation of independence. In that case the coefficient of skewness and kurtosis of W are respectively given by

$$\frac{5m^2 + 12 + 8}{m(m+1)^{3/2}}, \text{ and } \frac{3(m^4 + 16m^3 + 59m^2 + 88m + 48)}{[m(m+1)]^2}.$$

If m increases indefinitely, the above coefficients asymptotically converge to 0 and 3 of the univariate normal distribution.

Theorem 5.3 Let W have the density function given by (4.1). Then for any real number a, $\mu_a = E(W - E(W))^a$ is given by the following:

$$\mu_a = \left(m(m+2\rho^2)\right)^a (1-\rho^2)^{m/2} \sum_{i=0}^{\infty} (-1)^{a-i} \frac{a^{\{i\}}}{i!} \frac{4^i(1-\rho^2)^{2i}}{\left(m(m+2\rho^2)\right)^i} \qquad (5.8)$$

$$\times \left((m/2)_{\{i\}}\right)^2 {}_2F_1(i+(m/2), i+(m/2); m/2; \rho^2),$$

where $m > 2$, $-1 < \rho < 1$ with $a^{\{i\}}$ and $a_{\{i\}}$ being given by (2.1).

Proof. Expanding $\mu_a = E(W - E(W))^a$ by binomial theorem, we have

$$\mu_a = \left(E(W)\right)^a \sum_{i=0}^{\infty} (-1)^{a-i} \frac{a^{\{i\}}}{i!} E(W^i)\left(E(W)\right)^{-i},$$

which, by (5.1), can be simplified to the following:

$$\mu_a = \left(E(W)\right)^a \sum_{i=0}^{\infty} (-1)^{a-i} \frac{a^{\{i\}}}{i!} 4^i(1-\rho^2)^{2i+(m/2)}$$

$$\times \frac{\Gamma^2\left(i+(m/2)\right)}{\Gamma^2(m/2)} {}_2F_1(i+(m/2), i+(m/2); m/2; \rho^2)\left(E(W)\right)^{-i}.$$

Then by using (2.3) in the above equation and noting that $E(W) = m(m+2\rho^2)$, the theorem is proved.

Corollary 5.8 Let W have the density function given by (4.1). Then for any nonnegative integer a, the centered moments of W denoted by $\mu_a = E(W - E(W))^a$ is given by

$$\mu_a = \left(m(m+2\rho^2)\right)^a \sum_{i=0}^a (-1)^{a-i} \binom{a}{i} \frac{4^i (m/2)_{\{i\}}}{\left(m(m+2\rho^2)\right)^i} \sum_{k=0}^i \binom{i}{k} (1+i-k)_{\{k\}} \left((m/2)+k\right)_{\{i-k\}} \rho^{2k}, \quad (5.9)$$

where $m > 2$, $-1 < \rho < 1$ and $a_{\{i\}}$ is given by (2.1).

Proof. Expanding $\mu_a = E(W - E(W))^a$ by binomial theorem, we have

$$\mu_a = \left(E(W)\right)^a \sum_{i=0}^a (-1)^{a-i} \frac{a^{\{i\}}}{i!} E(W^i)\left(E(W)\right)^{-i}.$$

Then by using (5.3), we have (5.9).

Appendix 1

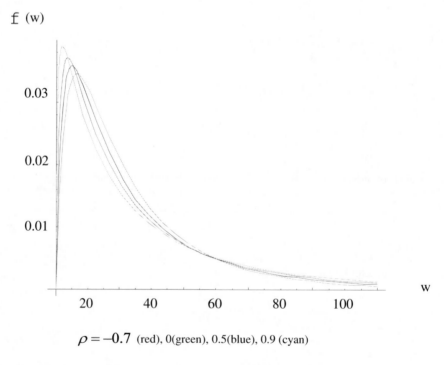

$\rho = -0.7$ (red), 0(green), 0.5(blue), 0.9 (cyan)

Figure 1. Density function of W for $m = 5$ and various ρ values.

Acknowledgments

The authors gratefully acknowledge the excellent research facility provided by King Fahd University of Petroleum and Minerals. In particular, the authors gratefully acknowledge the research support provided through the project FT100007.

References

Abramowitz, M. and Stegun, I. A. (1972). Handbook of Mathematical Functions with Formulas, *Graphs and Mathematical Tables*. Dover

Ahmed, S.E.(1992). Large sample pooling procedure for correlation. *The Statistician*, 41, 415-428.

Feldstein, M.S. (1971). The error of forecast in econometric models when the forecast period exogenus variables are stochastic. *Econometrica*, 39(1), 55-60.

Gradshteyn, I.S. and Ryzhik, I.M. (1994). *Table of Integrals, Series and Products*, Academic Press.

Grubel, H.G. (1968). Internationally diversified portfolios: welfare gains capital flows. *American Economic Reviews*, 58(5), 1299-1314.

Joarder, A.H. (2009). Moments of the product and ratio of two correlated chi-square random variables, *Statistical Papers*, 50(3), 581-592.

Joarder, A.H.; Laradji, A. and Omar, M.H. (2012). On some characteristics of bivariate chi-square distribution. *Statistics*, 46(5), 577-586.

Rugman, A.M. (1979). *International Diversification and Multinational Enterprise*, Lexington Books, Lexington, MA.

Springer, M.D. (1979). *The Algebra of Random Variables*. John Wiley and Sons.

Wells, W.T.; Anderson, R.L. and Cell, J.W. (1962). The distribution of the product of two central or noncentral chi-square variates. *Annals of Statistics*, 33(3), 1016-1020.

In: Applied Statistical Theory and Applications
Editor: Mohammad Ahsanullah

ISBN: 978-1-63321-858-1
© 2014 Nova Science Publishers, Inc.

Chapter 15

SEQUENTIAL ESTIMATION OF THE MEAN SURVIVAL TIME OF THE TWO-PARAMETER EXPONENTIAL DISTRIBUTION

Sandeep Bhougal[1,] and Sunil Kumar[2,†]*

[1]School of Mathematics, Shri Mata Vaishno Devi University,
Kakryal, Jammu (J & K).
[2]Visiting Scientist, SOSU, ISI Kolkata

Abstract

The problem of fixed-width Confidence Interval for the mean survival time is considered. Sequential procedures are adopted based on the maximum likelihood estimators (MLE) and uniform minimum variance unbiased estimators (UMVUE) of the scale parameter. A comparative study of the two sequential procedures is done and second-order approximations are obtained and they are proved to be 'asymptotically efficient and consistent.'

Keywords: Exponential Distribution, Sequential Estimation

1. Introduction

Exponential distribution plays an important part in life-testing and reliability problems and it is the simplest and the most widely exploited model in this area. Early work by Sukhatme (1973) and later work by Epstein and Sobel (1953, 1954, 1955) and Epstein (1954, 1960) gave numerous results and popularized the exponential as a lifetime distribution, especially in the area of industrial life testing. Sequential techniques have been utilized by several researchers to deal with various inferential problems related to one-parameter and two-parameter exponential distributions. For some citations one may refer to Basu (1971), Starr and Woodroofe (1972), Mukhopadhay (1974), Mukhopadhay and Hilton (1986),

---

[*] E-mail address: sandeep.bhougal@smvdu.ac.in
[†] E-mail address: sunilbhougal06@gmail.com

Chaturvedi and Shukla (1990), Chaturvedi (1996), Manisha, P., M.M. Ali and J. woo (2005) and Gupta and Bhougal (2006).

In this paper, we consider the problem of constructing fixed-width confidence interval for the mean survival time, for addressing which in section 3, we consider the problem of sequential interval estimation. Sequential procedures are adopted based on the maximum likelihood estimator (MLE) and uniformly minimum variance unbiased estimator (UMVUE) of the scale parameter. A comparative study of the two sequential procedures is done and they are proved to be 'asymptotically efficient and consistent.' In section 4, the problem of sequential point estimation of the mean survival time is tackled. Consideration is given to squared-error loss function and linear cost of sampling. Two sequential procedures (one based on the MLE and the other based on the UMVUE of the scale parameter) are proposed. Second-order approximations are obtained and a comparative study is done.

2. The Set-up of the Estimation Problems

Let $\{X_i\}_{i=1,2,.....}$ be a sequence of independent and identically distributed (i.i.d.) random variables from two-parameter exponential distribution having the probability density function p.d.f. given by

$$f(x;\mu,\sigma) = \frac{1}{\sigma}\exp\left(-\frac{(x-\mu)}{\sigma}\right); \ x > \mu, \ \sigma > 0 \tag{2.1}$$

Both $\mu \in (-\infty,\infty)$ and $\sigma \in (0,\infty)$ are unknown. Have been recorded a random sample $X_1,.....,X_n$ of size $n(\geq 2)$, the MLE's of μ and σ are $X_{n(1)} = \min(X_1,.....,X_n)$ and

$\hat{\sigma}_n = n^{-1}\sum_{i=1}^{n}(X_i - X_{n(1)})$, respectively and the UMVUE of σ is $\hat{\sigma}_n^* = (n-1)^{-1}\sum_{i=1}^{n}(X_i - X_{n(1)})$

Our first estimation problem is to construct fixed-width confidence interval for the mean survival time. For the model (2.1), the mean survival time is $E(X) = \mu + \sigma = \theta$. For pre-assigned $d > 0$ and $\alpha \in (0,1)$, suppose one wishes to construct a Confidence Interval for θ having width $2d$ and coverage probability atleast $1 - \alpha$. The MLE, as well as, the UMVUE of

θ is $\overline{X}_n = n^{-1}\sum_{i=1}^{n}X_i$. We define $I_n = \left[\overline{X}_n - d\,\overline{X}_n + d,\right]$ Using the facts that

$E(\overline{X}_n) = \theta, \ Var(\overline{X}_n) = \frac{\sigma^2}{n}$ and applying the central limit theorem (CLT), we conclude that

$$\frac{(\overline{X}_n - \theta)}{\left(\sigma/\sqrt{n}\right)} \xrightarrow{L} N(0,1) \tag{2.2}$$

Using (2.2) and denoting by $\Phi(y)$, the cumulative distribution function (c.d.f.) of the standard normal variate (SNV), we get

$$P[\theta \in I_n] = P\left[\frac{\left|\overline{X}_n - \theta\right|}{\left(\sigma/\sqrt{n}\right)} \le \frac{d\sqrt{n}}{\sigma}\right] = 2\Phi\left(\frac{d\sqrt{n}}{\sigma}\right) - 1. \tag{2.3}$$

Let 'a' be the constant defined by

$$2\Phi(a) - 1 = 1 - \alpha. \tag{2.4}$$

Using the monotonicity property of the c.d.f., it follows from (2.3) and (2.4) that, in order to achieve $P[\theta \in I_n] \ge 1 - \alpha$, the sample size required is the smallest positive integer $n \ge n_0$. where

$$n_0 = \left(\frac{a}{d}\right)^2 \sigma^2. \tag{2.5}$$

However, in the absence of any knowledge about σ, no fixed sample size procedure achieves the goals of 'preassigned width and coverage probability' simultaneously for all values of σ. In such a situation, motivated by (2.5), in Section 3, we develop sequential procedures based on the MLE and UMVUE of σ.

Our second estimation problem is the minimum risk point estimation of θ. Let the loss incurred in estimating θ by $\overline{X}_n$ be squared-error plus linear cost of sampling, that is,

$$L\left(\theta, \overline{X}_n\right) = A\left(\overline{X}_n - \theta\right)^2 + n, \tag{2.6}$$

where $A(> 0)$ is the known weight. The risk corresponding to the loss function (2.6) is

$$R_n(A) = \frac{A\sigma^2}{n} + \theta. \tag{2.7}$$

Treating n as a continuous variable, the value n^* of n minimizing the risk (2.7) is

$$n^* = A^{1/2}\sigma, \tag{2.8}$$

and substituting $n = n^*$ in (2.7), the corresponding minimum risk is

$$R_{n^*}(A) = 2n^*. \tag{2.9}$$

But, in the absence of any knowledge about σ, no fixed sample size procedure minimizes the risk for all values of σ. As a solution to the problem, in conformity with (2.8), in Section 4, we propose sequential procedure based on the MLE and UMVUE of σ.

3. Sequential Procedures for Fixed-Width Confidence Interval Estimation of the Mean Survival Time

We first consider the sequential procedure based on the MLE of σ.

Let us start with a sample of size $m(\geq 2)$. Then, the stopping time $N_1 \equiv N_1(d)$ is the smallest positive integer $n_1 \geq m$ such that

$$n_1 \geq \left(\frac{a}{d}\right)^2 \hat{\sigma}_{n_1}^2 \qquad (3.1)$$

After stopping with N_1 observations, we construct the interval

$$I_{N_1} = \left[\overline{X}_{N_1} - d, \overline{X}_{N_1} + d\right] \text{ for } \theta.$$

In the following theorem, we prove that the sequential procedure (3.1) is 'asymptotically efficient and consistent' in Chow-Robbins (1965) sense.

Theorem 1

$$N_1 \text{ terminates with probability one,} \qquad (3.2)$$

$$\underset{d \to 0}{Lim} \ N_1 = \infty, \qquad (3.3)$$

$$\underset{d \to 0}{Lim} \left(\frac{N_1}{n_0}\right) = 1 \text{ a.s.,} \qquad (3.4)$$

$$\underset{d \to 0}{Lim} \ E\left(\frac{N_1}{n_0}\right) = 1, \quad \text{'asymptotic efficiency'} \qquad (3.5)$$

and

$$\underset{d \to 0}{Lim} \ P\left(\theta \in I_{N_1}\right) = 1 - \alpha, \text{ 'asymptotic consistency'} \qquad (3.6)$$

Proof: Using the fact that $\dfrac{2n_1 \hat{\sigma}_{n_1}}{\sigma} \overset{d}{=} \chi^2_{2(n_1-1)}$, it follows from (3.1) that

$$P(N_1 > n) \leq P\left[n_1 \leq \left(\frac{a}{d}\right)^2 \hat{\sigma}_{n_1}^2\right] = P\left[\hat{\sigma}_{n_1} > \left(\frac{d}{a}\right)n_1^{1/2}\right]$$

$$= P\left[\chi^2_{2(n_1-1)} > 2n_1\left(\frac{n_1}{n_0}\right)^{1/2}\right]$$

$$= P\left[Z_{n_1} > \frac{2n_1\left(\frac{n_1}{n_0}\right)^{1/2} - 2(n_1 - 1)}{\sqrt{4(n_1 - 1)}} \right] \qquad (3.7)$$

where $Z_{n_1} = \dfrac{\left\{\chi^2_{2(n_1-1)} - 2(n_1 - 1)\right\}}{\sqrt{4(n_1 - 1)}}$.

Since $Z_{n_1} \xrightarrow{L} Z$ as $n_1 \to \infty$, where Z is a Standard Normal Variate (SNV) and from Zacks (1971, p.561), $1 - \Phi(x) \approx x^{-1}\varphi(x)$ as $x \to \infty$, where $\varphi(.)$ stands for the p.d.f. of a SNV, we obtain from (3.7) that

$$P(N_1 > n_1) \le 1 - \Phi\left(\frac{2n_1\left(\frac{n_1}{n_0}\right)^{1/2} - 2(n_1 - 1)}{2\sqrt{(n_1 - 1)}} \right)$$

or

$$P(N_1 > n_1) \to \left[\left\{ \frac{2n_1\left(\frac{n_1}{n_0}\right)^{1/2} - 2(n_1 - 1)}{2\sqrt{(n_n - 1)}} \right\} \right] \frac{1}{\sqrt{2\pi}} e^{-\frac{1}{2}\left[2n_1\left(\frac{n_1}{n_0}\right)^{1/2} - 2(n_1 - 1)\right]}$$

$\to 0$ *as* $n_1 \to \infty$, hence the result (3.2) follows.

Result (3.3) follows from the definition of N_1 given at (3.1).

From (3.1) we notice the inequality $\left(\frac{a}{d}\right)^2 \hat{\sigma}^2_{N_1} \le N_1 \le \left(\frac{a}{d}\right)^2 \hat{\sigma}^2_{N_1} + (m - 1)$

or

$$\frac{\left(\frac{a}{d}\right)^2 \hat{\sigma}^2_{N_1}}{\left(\frac{a}{d}\right)^2 \sigma^2} \le \frac{N_1}{n_0} \le \frac{\left(\frac{a}{d}\right)^2 \hat{\sigma}^2_{N_1}}{\left(\frac{a}{d}\right)^2 \sigma^2} + \frac{(m-1)d^2}{a^2\sigma^2}$$

or

$$\frac{\hat{\sigma}^2_{N_1}}{\sigma^2} \le \frac{N_1}{n_0} \le \frac{\hat{\sigma}^2_{N_1}}{\sigma^2} + \frac{(m-1)}{n_0}. \qquad (3.8)$$

Utilizing (3.3), the fact that $\underset{N_1 \to \infty}{Lim}\ \hat{\sigma}_{N_1} = \sigma$ *a.s.*. (Since $\hat{\sigma}_n$ is a consistent estimator of σ) and taking the limit of (3.8) throughout as $d \to 0$, we get

$$1 \le \lim_{d \to 0} \inf \frac{N_1}{n_0} \le \lim_{d \to 0} \sup \frac{N_1}{n_0} \le 1,$$

Hence the result (3.4) follows.

Let, for $0 < \epsilon < 1$, $\theta_1 = (1 - \epsilon)n_0$ and $\theta_2 = (1 + \epsilon)n_0$. Applying Markov's inequality, we get

$$P(N_1 > \theta_1) \le \frac{E(N_1)}{\theta_1}$$

or

$$E\left(\frac{N_1}{n_0}\right) \ge (1 - \epsilon)P(N_1 > \theta_1)$$

or

$$E\left(\frac{N_1}{n_0}\right) \ge (1 - \epsilon)P\left(\frac{N_1}{n_0} > (1 - \epsilon)\right). \tag{3.9}$$

Since ϵ is arbitrary, application of (3.4) to (3.9) leads us to

$$\lim_{d \to 0} \inf E\left(\frac{N_1}{n_0}\right) \ge 1. \tag{3.10}$$

Furthermore, we can write

$$E(N_1) = \sum_{n_1 = m}^{\infty} n_1 P(N_1 = n_1)$$

$$\le \theta_2 P(m \le N_1 \le \theta_2) + \sum_{n_1 \ge \theta_2} (n_1 + 1)P(N_1 = n_1 + 1),$$

or,

$$E\left(\frac{N_1}{n_0}\right) \le (1 + \epsilon) + \frac{1}{n_0} \sum_{n_1 \ge \theta_2} (n_1 + 1)P(N_1 = n_1 + 1) \tag{3.11}$$

Let us denote by

$$T(\theta_2) = \sum_{n_1 \ge \theta_2} (n_1 + 1)P(N_1 = n_1 + 1).$$

It follows from the definition of N_1 given at (3.1) that

$$T(\theta_2) \le \sum_{n_1 \ge \theta_2} (n_1 + 1)P\left[n_1 < \left(\frac{a}{d}\right)^2 \hat{\sigma}_{n_1}^2\right]$$

$$= \sum_{n_1 \ge \theta_2} (n_1 + 1)P\left[\chi_{2(n_1 - 1)}^2 > 2n_1 \left(\frac{n_1}{n_0}\right)^{\frac{1}{2}}\right],$$

which on applying exponential bounds leads us to

$$T(\theta_2) \le \sum_{n_1 \ge \theta_2} (n_1 + 1) \inf_{0 < h < 1/2} \left[\exp\left\{ -2hn_1 \left(\frac{n_1}{n_0} \right)^{\frac{1}{2}} \right\} E\left\{ \exp\left(h\chi^2_{2(n_1-1)} \right) \right\} \right].$$

$$\le \sum_{n_1 \ge \theta_2} (n_1 + 1) \inf_{0 < h < 1/2} \left[\exp\left\{ -2hn_1 \left(\frac{\theta_2}{n_0} \right)^{\frac{1}{2}} \right\} (1 - 2h)^{-(n_1-1)} \right]$$

$$\le \sum_{n_1 \ge \theta_2} (n_1 + 1) \inf_{0 < h < 1/2} \left[\exp\left\{ -2hn_1 (1 + \epsilon)^{\frac{1}{2}} \right\} (1 - 2h)^{-n_1} \right]. \tag{3.12}$$

This inequality is also valid for the value h_0 of h, which minimizes the function

$$g(h) = \exp\left[-2hn_1 (1 + \epsilon)^{\frac{1}{2}} \right] (1 - 2h)^{-n_1}, \text{ i.e. } h_0 = \left(\frac{1}{2} \right) \left[1 - (1 + \epsilon)^{-\frac{1}{2}} \right]$$

and substituting this value of h_0 in (3.12), we get

$$T(\theta_2) \le \sum_{n_1 \ge \theta_2} (n_1 + 1) \left[(1 + \epsilon)^{\frac{1}{2}} \exp\left\{ 1 - (1 + \epsilon)^{\frac{1}{2}} \right\} \right]^{n_1}$$

$$= \sum_{n_1 \ge \theta_2} b_{n_1}, \text{ say }. \tag{3.13}$$

Since $\underset{n_1 \to \infty}{Lim} b_{n_1}^{\frac{1}{n_1}} = (1 + \epsilon)^{\frac{1}{2}} \exp\left\{ 1 - (1 + \epsilon)^{\frac{1}{2}} \right\} < 1$, the series involved on the right hand side of (3.13) is convergent. Hence we conclude that, for a positive constant k,

$$T(\theta_2) \le k. \tag{3.14}$$

Utilizing (3.14), it follows from (3.11) that

$$\underset{d \to 0}{Lim Sup}\ E\left(\frac{N_1}{n_0} \right) \le 1. \tag{3.15}$$

Result (3.5) now follows on combining (3.10) and (3.15).
Finally, we have

$$P(\theta \in I_{N_1}) = P\left[\frac{\left| \overline{X}_{N_1} - (\mu + \sigma) \right|}{\left(\frac{\sigma}{\sqrt{n_0}} \right)} \le \frac{d\sqrt{n_0}}{\sigma} \right]. \tag{3.16}$$

We have shown [see (2.1)] that

$$\frac{\left\{\overline{X}_{n_0} - (\mu + \sigma)\right\}}{\left(\dfrac{\sigma}{\sqrt{n_0}}\right)} \xrightarrow{L} N(0,1) \text{ as } n_0 \to \infty. \tag{3.17}$$

Application of (3.2), (3.3), (3.4) and Theorem 1 of Anscombe (1952) to (3.17) gives that

$$\frac{\left\{\overline{X}_{N_1} - (\mu + \sigma)\right\}}{\left(\dfrac{\sigma}{\sqrt{n_0}}\right)} \xrightarrow{L} N(0,1) \text{ as } d \to 0. \tag{3.18}$$

Since probability measure is bounded by unity, from (3.16), (3.18) and dominated convergence theorem, we get, for Z to be a Standard normal variate

$$\underset{d \to 0}{Lim} P\left(\theta \in I_{N_1}\right) = P\left[|Z| \le a\right] = 2\Phi(a) - 1 = 1 - \alpha.$$

And (3.6) follows.

In the following theorem, we obtain the second-order approximations for the average sample number (ASN) corresponding to the sequential procedure (3.1).

Theorem 2

For all $m \ge 4$, as $d \to 0$,

$$E(N_1) = n_0 + 2v - 3.5 + o(1),$$

where v is specified.

Proof: Utilizing the fact that $\dfrac{2n_1 \hat{\sigma}_{n_1}}{\sigma} = \displaystyle\sum_{j=1}^{n_1-1} Y_j$, with $Y_j \overset{d}{=} \chi^2_{(2)}$, we can re-write the stopping rule (3.1) as

$$N_1 = \inf\left[n_1 \ge m : \sum_{j=1}^{n_1-1}\left(\frac{Y_j}{2}\right) \le n_1^{3/2} n_0^{-1/2}\right]. \tag{3.19}$$

Let us define a new stopping rule N_1^* as

$$N_1^* = \inf\left[n_1 \ge m-1 : \sum_{j=1}^{n_1}\left(\frac{Y_j}{2}\right) \le (n_1+1)^{3/2} n_0^{-1/2}\right].$$

$$= \inf\left[n_1 \ge m-1 : \sum_{j=1}^{n_1}\left(\frac{Y_j}{2}\right) \le n_1^{3/2}\left(1+n_1^{-1}\right)^{3/2} n_0^{-1/2}\right]. \tag{3.20}$$

It follows from a result of Swanepoel and Vanwyk (1982) that N_1 and N_1^* are identically distributed. Comparing (3.20) with equation (1.1) of Woodroofe (1977), we obtain in his notations, $\alpha = \dfrac{3}{2}$, $\beta = 2$ $\mu = E\left(\dfrac{Y_j}{2}\right) = 1$, $\tau^2 = \text{var}\left(\dfrac{Y_j}{2}\right) = 1$, $L_0 = \dfrac{3}{2}$, $C = n_0^{-\frac{1}{2}}$ and $\lambda = n_0$.

Moreover, denoting by $F(x)$, the c.d.f. of Y_j, we have

$$F(x) = P(Y_j \le x) = K \int_0^x e^{-y/2} \, dy \le Kx,$$

so that $a = 1$. Thus we obtain from Theorem 2.4 of Woodroofe (1977) that, for all $m \ge 4$, as $d \to 0$,

$$E(N_1^*) = n_0 + 2v - 4.5 + o(1).$$

Since $N_1^* = N_1 - 1$, we have

$$E(N_1) = n_0 + 2v - 3.5 + o(1).$$

and the theorem follows.

The following theorem provides the asymptotic distribution of the stopping time.

Theorem 3: As $d \to 0$,

$$(n_0)^{-\frac{1}{2}}(N_1 - n_0) \xrightarrow{L} N(0,4).$$

Proof: From the inequality (3.8),

$$\left(\hat{\sigma}_{N_1}^2 - \sigma^2\right) \le \left(\frac{d}{a}\right)^2 (N_1 - n_0) \le \left(\hat{\sigma}_{N_1}^2 - \sigma^2\right) + (m-1)\left(\frac{d}{a}\right)^2,$$

or

$$\frac{\sqrt{n_0}}{2\sigma^2}\left(\hat{\sigma}_{N_1}^2 - \sigma^2\right) \le \frac{(N_1 - n_0)}{2\sqrt{n_0}} \le \frac{\sqrt{n_0}}{2\sigma^2}\left(\hat{\sigma}_{N_1}^2 - \sigma^2\right) + (m-1)\left(\frac{d}{a}\right)^2 \tag{3.21}$$

we have,

$$E\left(\hat{\sigma}_{n_0}^2\right) = \frac{\sigma^2}{4n_o^2} E\left[\chi_{2(n_0-1)}^2\right]^2 = \sigma^2\left(1 - \frac{1}{n_0}\right) \tag{3.22}$$

and

$$E\left(\hat{\sigma}_{n_0}^4\right) = \frac{\sigma^4}{16n_o^4} E\left[\chi_{2(n_0-1)}^2\right]^4 = \sigma^4\left(1 + \frac{2}{n_0} - \frac{1}{n_0^2} - \frac{2}{n_0^3}\right) \tag{3.23}$$

From (3.22) and (3.23),

$$Var\left(\hat{\sigma}_{n_0}^2\right) = \frac{4\sigma^4}{n_0} + o(n_0^{-1}) \tag{3.24}$$

From (3.22), (3.24) and the CLT,

$$\frac{\sqrt{n_0}}{2\sigma^2}\left(\hat{\sigma}^2_{n_0} - \sigma^2\right) \xrightarrow{L} N(0,1), \text{ as } n_0 \to \infty.$$ (3.25)

It follows from (3.2), (3.3), (3.4), (3.25) and Theorem 1 of Anscombe (1952) that, as $d \to 0$,

$$\frac{\sqrt{n_0}}{2\sigma^2}\left(\hat{\sigma}^2_{N_1} - \sigma^2\right) \xrightarrow{L} N(0,1).$$ (3.26)

Application of (3.26) to (3.21) leads to the desired result.

Remarks 1:

One can use the technique of Bhattacharya and Mallik (1973) or Woodroofe (1977) in order to obtain the asymptotic distribution of stopping time. However, our method of obtaining the same is simple and direct. We can also obtain the result (3.5) from Theorem 4.2. But, it requires $m \geq 4$, whereas, (3.5) holds for all $m \geq 2$.

Now we consider the sequential procedure based on the UMVUE of σ.

We take $m(\geq 2)$ as the initial sample size. Then, the stopping time $N_2 \equiv N_2(d)$ is the smallest positive integer $n_2 \geq m$ such that

$$n_2 \geq \left(\frac{a}{d}\right)^2 \hat{\sigma}^{*2}_{n_2}.$$ (3.27)

After stopping with N_2 observations, we construct the confidence interval

$$I_{N_2} = \left[\overline{X}_{N_2} - d, \overline{X}_{N_2} + d\right] \text{ for } \theta.$$

Now we state the following theorems, concerning various results for the stopping time N_2.

Theorem 4:

N_2 terminates with probability one

$$\underset{d \to 0}{Lim} N_2 = \infty,$$

$$\underset{d \to 0}{Lim}\left(\frac{N_2}{n_0}\right) = 1 \text{ a.s.},$$

$$\underset{d \to 0}{Lim} E\left(\frac{N_2}{n_0}\right) = 1, \text{ 'asymptotic efficiency'}$$

and

$$\underset{d \to 0}{Lim} P\left(\theta \in I_{N_2}\right) = 1 - \alpha, \text{ 'asymptotic consistency'}$$

Proof: The proof is similar to that of Theorem 1.

Theorem 5: For all $m \geq 4$, as $d \to 0$,

$$E(N_2) = n_0 + 2\nu - 3 + 0(1),$$

where v is same as in Theorem 2.

Proof: The proof can be obtained along the lines of that of Theorem 2.

Remarks 2:

It is to be noted here that N_2 enjoys all the 'optimal' properties of N_1. However, if we compare Theorems 2 and 5, we conclude that ASN for N_2 is slightly higher than that of N_1.

Theorem 6: As $d \to 0$, $(n_0)^{-\frac{1}{2}}(N_2 - n_0) \xrightarrow{L} N(0,4)$.

Proof: The result can be obtained along the lines of that of Theorem 3.

4. Sequential Procedures for the Point Estimation of the Mean Survival Time

First of all, we consider sequential procedure based on the MLE of σ.

We begin with a sample of size $m (\geq 2)$. Then, the stopping time $N_1 \equiv N_1(A)$ is defined by

$$N_1 = \inf\left[n_1 \geq m : n_1 \geq A^{\frac{1}{2}} \hat{\sigma}_{n_1} \right].$$ (4.1)

After stopping, we estimate θ by $\overline{X}_{N_1}$. The risk associated with the sequential procedure (4.1) is

$$R_{N_1}(A) = AE\left[\left(\overline{X}_{N_1} - \theta\right)^2\right] + E(N_1).$$ (4.2)

In what follows, we obtain second-order approximations for the risk corresponding to the sequential procedure (4.1). Before proving the main result, we establish some lemmas.

Lemma 1: For all $m \geq 3$, as $A \to \infty$,

$$E(N_1) = n^* - 1.253 + o(1).$$

Proof: We can re-write the stopping rule (4.1) as

$$N_1 = \inf\left[n_1^* \geq m : \sum_{j=1}^{n_1^*-1}\left(\frac{Y_j}{2}\right) \leq n_1^{*2}\left(n^*\right)^{-1} \right],$$ (4.3)

with $Y_j \overset{d}{=} \chi^2_{(2)}$. Let us define a new stopping rule N_1^* by

$$N_1^* = \inf\left[n_1^* \geq m-1 : \sum_{j=1}^{n_1^*}\left(\frac{Y_j}{2}\right) \leq n_1^{*2}\left(1 + n_1^{*-1}\right)^2\left(n^*\right)^{-1} \right],$$ (4.4)

It follows from Swanepoel and Van Wyk (1982) that N_1 and N_1^* follow the same probability distribution. Comparing (4.4) with equation (1.1) of Woodroofe (1977), we obtain in his notations $\alpha = 2,\ \beta = 1,\ \mu = 1,\ \tau = 1,\ \lambda = n^*,\ L_0 = \left(\dfrac{3}{2}\right),\ C = \left(n^*\right)^{-1}$ and $a = 1$. From Table 2.1 of Woodroofe (1977), $v = .747$. It now follows from Theorem 2.4 of Woodroofe (1977) that, for all $m \geq 3$, as $A \to \infty$,

$$E\left(N_1^*\right) = n^* - 2.253 + 0(1).$$

The lemma now follows on using the result that $N_1^* = N_1 - 1$.

Lemma 2: For $\eta \in (0,1)$, as $A \to \infty$,

$$P\left(N_1 \leq \eta n^*\right) = O\left(A^{-\frac{(m-1)}{2}}\right).$$

Proof: The result is a direct consequence of Lemma 2.3 of Woodroofe (1977).

Lemma 3: Let the random variable 'W' be defined by

$$|W - 1| \leq \left|\left(\frac{N_1}{n^*}\right) - 1\right|.$$

Then,

$$W \xrightarrow{a.s.} 1 \ as \ A \to \infty \tag{4.5}$$

and

$$W^{-4} \text{ is uniformly integrable for all } m \geq 6. \tag{4.6}$$

Proof: From (4.1),

$$A^{\frac{1}{2}} \hat{\sigma}_{N_1} \leq N_1 \leq A^{\frac{1}{2}} \hat{\sigma}_{N_1} + (m-1),$$

or,

$$\left(\frac{\hat{\sigma}_{N_1}}{\sigma}\right) \leq \frac{N_1}{n^*} \leq \left(\frac{\hat{\sigma}_{N_1}}{\sigma}\right) + \frac{(m-1)}{n^*}. \tag{4.7}$$

Applying the result that $\underset{d \to 0}{Lim} N_1 = \infty$ and $\hat{\sigma}_{N_1} \xrightarrow{a.s.} \sigma$ as $N_1 \to \infty$, we obtain from (4.7) that

$$\underset{A \to \infty}{Lim}\left(\frac{N_1}{n^*}\right) = 1 \ \text{a.s.}$$

Result (4.5) now follows from the definition of N_1.

We note that on the event $\left(N_1 \leq \eta n^*\right)$,

$$|W - 1| \leq \left|\left(\frac{N_1}{n^*}\right) - 1\right| \leq 1 - \left(\frac{m}{n^*}\right),$$

i.e. $W^{-1} \leq \left(\dfrac{n^*}{m}\right)$. Thus, denoting by $I(\cdot)$, the usual indicator function and k, any positive generic constant independent of A, we have

$$E\left[W^{-4} I\left(N_1 \leq \eta n^*\right)\right] \leq k\left(n^*\right)^4 P\left(N_1 \leq \eta n^*\right) \tag{4.8}$$

Applying Lemma 3, we obtain from (4.8) that

$$E\left[W^{-4} I\left(N_1 \leq \eta n^*\right)\right] \leq k\left(n^*\right)^4 P\left(N_1 \leq \eta n^*\right) = O\left(A^{\frac{(m-1)}{2}-2}\right)$$

$$= o(1), \text{ as } A \to \infty, \text{ for all } m \geq 6. \tag{4.9}$$

Furthermore, on the event $\left(N_1 \geq \eta n^*\right)$, $W^{-1} \leq \eta^{-1}$. Thus,

$$E\left[W^{-2} I\left(N_1 > \eta n^*\right)\right] \leq k P\left(N_1 > \eta n^*\right)$$

$$= o(1), \text{ as } A \to \infty, \tag{4.10}$$

since N_1 terminates with probability one. Result (4.6) now follows on combining (4.9) and (4.10).

Lemma 4: For $r(> 0)$, $\left(\dfrac{N_1}{n^*}\right)^r$ is uniformly integrable.

Proof: See Lemma 2.1 of Woodroofe (1977).

Lemma 5: For $r(> 0)$, $\left|\dfrac{\left(N_1 - n^*\right)}{\left(n^*\right)^{1/2}}\right|^r$ is uniformly integrable for all $m > 1 + \left(\dfrac{r}{2}\right)$.

Proof: The result follows from Theorem 2.3 of Woodroofe (1977).

In what follows, we denote by $S_n = \displaystyle\sum_{j=1}^{n}\left(\dfrac{Y_j}{2}\right)$.

Lemma 6: For all $m \geq 3$,

$$\dfrac{\left(N_1 - n^*\right)}{\left(n^*\right)^{1/2}} \text{ and } \dfrac{\left(S_{N_1} - N_1\right)^2}{\left(n^*\right)^{1/2}} \text{ are asymptotically uncorrelated,} \tag{4.11}$$

and for all $m \geq 4$,

$$\dfrac{\left(N_1 - n^*\right)^2}{\left(n^*\right)} \text{ and } \dfrac{\left(S_{N_1} - N_1\right)^2}{\left(n^*\right)^{1/2}} \text{ are asymptotically uncorrelated,} \tag{4.12}$$

Proof: By Cauchy-Schwartz inequality, we have

$$Cov^2\left\{\frac{\left(N_1 - n^*\right)}{\left(n^*\right)^{1/2}}, \frac{\left(S_{N_1} - N_1\right)^2}{\left(n^*\right)^{1/2}}\right\} \le Var\left\{\frac{\left(N_1 - n^*\right)}{\left(n^*\right)^{1/2}}\right\} Var\left\{\frac{\left(S_{N_1} - N_1\right)^2}{\left(n^*\right)^{1/2}}\right\}$$

$$\le E\left\{\frac{\left(N_1 - n^*\right)^2}{\left(n^*\right)}\right\} E\left\{\frac{\left(S_{N_1} - N_1\right)^2}{\left(n^*\right)}\right\}. \tag{4.13}$$

It follows from Lemma 5 of Chow and Yu (1981) that $\left\{\frac{\left(S_{N_1} - N_1\right)^2}{\left(n^*\right)}\right\}$ is uniformly

integrable. $\tag{4.14}$

Application of Lemma 5 and (4.14) lead us to (4.11). A similar proof holds for (4.12).

Lemma 7: $\dfrac{\left(N_1 - n^*\right)}{\left(n^*\right)^{1/2}} \xrightarrow{L} N(0,1)$, *as* $A \to \infty$.

Proof: The result follows from Bhattacharya and Mallik (1973). One can also follow the technique of the proof of the Theorem 3.

The main result is now proved in the following theorem, which provides second-order approximations for the risk corresponding to the sequential procedure (4.1)

Theorem 7: For all $m \ge 6$, *as* $A \to \infty$,

$$R_{N_1}(A) = 5n^* + 10.747 + o(1).$$

Proof: We can write (4.2) as

$$R_{N_1}(A) = A\sigma^2 E\left\{\frac{\left(\overline{X}_{N_1} - \mu\right)}{\sigma} - 1\right\}^2 + E(N_1)$$

$$= A\sigma^2 E\left\{\frac{1}{N_1}\sum_{i=1}^{N_1}\frac{\left(X_i - \mu\right)}{\sigma} - 1\right\}^2 + E(N_1)$$

$$= \left(n^*\right)^2 E\left[\frac{1}{N_1^2}\left(S_{N_1} - N_1\right)^2\right] + E(N_1)$$

$$= E\left[f\left(\frac{N_1}{n^*}\right)\left(S_{N_1} - N_1\right)^2\right] + E(N_1),$$

where $f(x) = x^{-2}$. Expanding $f(x)$ around $(x = 1)$ by Taylor's series, we obtain for

$$|W - 1| \le \left|\left(\frac{N_1}{n^*}\right) - 1\right|,$$

$$R_{N_1}(A) = E\left\{(S_{N_1} - N_1)^2\right\} - 2E\left\{\left(\frac{N_1}{n^*} - 1\right)(S_{N_1} - N_1)^2\right\} + 3E\left\{\left(\frac{N_1}{n^*} - 1\right)^2 W^{-4}(S_{N_1} - N_1)^2\right\} + E(N_1). \quad (4.15)$$

It follows from Wald's lemma for cumulative sums that

$$E(S_{N_1} - N_1)^2 = Var(Y_j)E(N_1)$$

$$= 4E(N_1). \quad (4.16)$$

Applying Lemmas 1, 3, 4, 5, 6, 7, and (4.16), we obtain from (4.15) that, for all $m \geq 6$, as $A \to \infty$,

$$R_{N_1}(A) = 5E(N_1) - E\left\{\frac{(N_1 - n^*)}{(n^*)^{1/2}} \cdot \frac{(S_{N_1} - N_1)^2}{(n^*)^{1/2}}\right\} + 3E\left\{\frac{(N_1 - n^*)^2}{(n^*)} \cdot \frac{(S_{N_1} - N_1)^2}{(n^*)} W^{-4}\right\}$$

$$= 5E(N_1) - \frac{4}{n^*}E(N_1 - n^*)E(N_1) + \frac{12}{n^*}E(N_1)$$

$$= 5\{n^* - 1.253 + o(1)\} - \frac{4}{n^*}\{-1.253 + o(1)\}\{n^* - 1.253 + o(1)\} + \frac{12}{n^*}(n^* - 1.253 + o(1))$$

$$= 5n^* + 10.747 + o(1),$$

and the theorem follows.

Remarks 3: The method of obtaining the second-order approximations for the risk presented in Theorem 7 is simpler as compared to that of Woodroofe (1977), as it does not require complicated estimation of various components comprising the risk.

Let us now consider the sequential procedure based on the UMVUE of σ.

Let us take $m(\geq 2)$ to be the initial sample size. Then, the stopping time $N_1 \equiv N_2(A)$ is defined by

$$N_2 = \inf\left[n_2 \geq m : n_2 \geq A^{1/2}\hat{\sigma}_{n_2}^{*2}\right]. \quad (4.17)$$

After stopping, we estimate θ by $\overline{X}_{N_2}$, having the associated risk

$$R_{N_2}(A) = AE\left[(\overline{X}_{N_2} - \theta)^2\right] + E(N_2). \quad (4.18)$$

Now we state the following theorem, which provides second-order approximations for the risk (4.18). The proof of the theorem is similar to that of Theorem 8. We omit the details for brevity.

Theorem 9: For all $m \geq 6$, as $A \to \infty$,

$$R_{N_2}(A) = 5n^* + 11.747 + o(1).$$

Remark 4: From Theorem 8 and 9, we conclude that the risk corresponding to the stopping rule N_2 is higher than that associated with N_1. Thus, the use of MLE of σ is preferred than its UMVUE.

References

Anscombe, F.J. (1952): Large sample theory of sequential estimation. *Proc. Cambridge Philos. Soc.*, 48, 600-607.

Basu, A.P. (1971): On a sequential inspection and statistical decisions. *Jour. Roy. Statist. Soc.*, B16, 151-174.

Bhattacharya, P.K. and Mallik, H. (1973): Asymptotic normality of the stopping times of some sequential procedures. *Ann. Statist.*, 1, 1203-1211.

Chaturvedi, A. and Shukla, P.S. (1990): Sequential point estimation of location parameter of a negative exponential distribution. Jour. Indian Statist. *Assoc.*, 28,41-50.

Chaturvedi, A. (1996): Sequential interval estimation procedures for the mean exponential survival time and reliability function. *Microelectron Reliab.*, 36, 91-96.

Chow, Y.S. and Robbins, H. (1965): On the asymptotic theory of fixed-width sequential confidence intervals for the mean. *Ann. Math. Statist.*, 36, 457-462.

Epstein, B. and Sobel, M. (1953): Life testing. *Jour. Amer. Statist. Assoc.*, 48, 486-502.

Epstein, B. and Sobel, M. (1954): Some theorems relevant to life testing from an exponential distribution. *Ann. Math. Statist.*, 25, 373-381.

Epstein, B. and Sobel, M. (1955): Sequential life tests in the exponential case. *Ann. Math. Statist.*, 26, 82-93.

Epstein, B. (1954): Truncated life tests in the exponential case. *Ann. Math. Statist.*, 25, 555-564.

Epstein, B. (1960): Testing for the validity of the assumption that the underlying distribution of life is exponential. *Technometrics*, 2, 83-101, 167-183.

Gupta, R. and Bhougal, S.(2006): Estimating the largest location parameter of k exponentialpopulations having unequal and unknown scale parameters. *Assam Stat. Rev.*,20,2, 88-111.

Manisha, P., M.M. Ali and J. Woo (2005): Estimation and testing of P(Y>X) in two parameter exponential distribution. *Statistics*, 39,5,415-428.

Mukhopadhayay, N. (1974): Sequential estimation of location parameter in exponential distributions. *Cal. Statist. Assoc. Bull.*, 23, 85-95.

Mukhopadhayay, N. and Hilton, G.F. (1986): Two-stage and sequential procedures for estimating the location parameter of a negative exponential distribution. *South African Statist. Jour.*, 20, 117-136.

Starr, N. and Woodroofe, M. (1972): Further remarks on sequential estimation: The exponential case. *Ann. Math. Statist.*, 43, 1147-1154.

Swanepoel, J.W.H. and Van Wyk, J.W.J. (1982): Fixed width confidence intervals for the location parameter of an exponential distribution. *Commun. Statist.-Theor. Math., All*, 1279-1289.

Woodroofe, M. (1977): Second-order approximations for sequential point and interval estimation. *Ann. Statist.*, 5, 984-995.

Sukhatme, P.V. (1973): Tests of significance for samples of the χ^2 population with two degrees of freedom. *Ann. Eugen.*, 8, 52-56.

Zacks, S. (1971): *The Theory of Statistical inference*. John Wiley and Sons, New York.

In: Applied Statistical Theory and Applications
Editor: Mohammad Ahsanullah

ISBN: 978-1-63321-858-1
© 2014 Nova Science Publishers, Inc.

Chapter 16

CHARACTERIZATIONS OF MIXTURES OF EXPONENTIAL AND GEOMETRIC DISTRIBUTIONS BASED ON THE DOUBLY TRUNCATED MEAN FUNCTION

Zohdy M. Nofal[1] and M. Ahsanullah[2]

[1]Department of Statistics, Faculty of Commerce, Benha University, Egypt
[2]Department of Management Sciences, Rider University, New Jersey, US

Abstract

In this paper we have considered mixtures of exponential and geometric distributions.. Some characterizations of these distributions based on the doubly truncated mean functions are presented.

Keywords: characterization, failure rate, reversed failure rate, conditional expectation, exponential distributions, geometric distributions, mixture distributions, doubly truncated

1. Introduction

Characterizations of distributions have always played an important role in statistical theory and are widely published in the literature, e.g., Arnold (1980), Strivastava (1981), Sreehari (1983), Zijlstra (1983), and Dallas (1987). The survey book by Kagan, Linnik, Rao (1973) and the recent notes by Galambos and Kotz (1978) cover many results. A good discussion of the major directions of characterization is in the Kotz survey (1973). Ahmed (1991) characterized beta, binomial, and Poisson distributions by connecting conitional expectation with hazard rate. Osaki & Li (1988) characterized the gamma and negative binomial distributions. Nassar and Mahmoud(1985) characterized the mixture exponential distributions. EL-Arishi (2005) used the conditional variance characterization of some discrete probability distributions. Shanbhag (1970) characterized the exponential distribution using the linearity of the conditional expectation. Talwalker (1977) has characterized various distributions like Pareto, Power and Burr distributions in terms of conditional expectation of a function of the absolutely continuous random variable, Unnikrishnan and Sudheesh (2010) studied the characterization of continuous distributions by properties of conditional variance. Shanbhag (1970) has characterized the exponential distribution using the linearity of the conditional expectation. Several characterizations based on the properties of the failure rate function have been considered by many authors. Xekalaki (1983) has identified the Pareto distribution through decreasing failure rate, Roy and Mukherjee (1986) have characterized the Weibull distribution via increasing failure rate. Let X be a random variable (r.v.), usually representing the life length fora certain unit (where this unit can have multiple interpretations), then r.v.$(X - x \mid X \geq x)$, represents the residual life of a unit with age x.

Several functions are defined related to the residual life. The failure rate function, defined by:$r(x) = \frac{f(x)}{(1 - F(x))}$ represents the failure rate of X (or F) at age x. We denote the cumulative distribution function (cdf) by F(x) ,where $F(x) = P(X \leq x)$, and f(x) is the probability density function when X is absolutely continuous, or $f(x) = P(X = x)$ when X is discrete.

Another interesting function is the mean residual life function, defined by $E(X - x \mid X \geq x)$, and it represents the expected additional life length for a unit which is alive at age x. This function is equivalent to the left censored mean function, also called vitality function (see Gupta (1975)), defined by $E(X \mid X \geq x)$ .Applications of hazard functions are quite well known in the statistical literature.

Another interesting function is the mean inactivity time function, defined by$E(x - X \mid X \leq x)$ and it is equivalent to the left censored lifetime .it become quite popular among the statisticians, Anderson et al. (1993) showed that the reversed hazard function plays the same role in the analysis of left-censored data as the hazard function plays in the analysis of right-censored data. Interestingly, The properties of the mean inactivity time have been considered by many authors, see, eg., Kayid and Ahmad (2004), and Ahmad , Kayid and Pellery (2005). Several characterizations of probability models have been obtained in the last 30 years based on the univariate failure rate or mean residual life functions. The problems of characterization of distributions are today a substantial part of probability theory and mathematical statistics. The mean inactivity time and mean residual life are applicable in biostatistics, actuarial science, engineering, economics, biometry and applied probability areas. These also are useful in survival analysis studies when we deal with left or right censored data.

In this paper we present some characterization results by using doubly truncated mean function..

2. Main Results

2.1. Characterization of Exponential Distribution

Theorem 2.1

Let F be non-negative random variable with absolutely continuous cdf F(x) and the corresponding pdf f(x). Then X has the pdf f(x) as

$$f(x) = p\lambda_1 e^{-\lambda_1 x} + q\lambda_2 e^{-\lambda_2 x} x > 0, \lambda_i > 0, p + q = 1, 0 \leq p \leq 1$$

If and only if

$$E(X|x \leq X \leq y) = \frac{x\bar{F}(x) - y\bar{F}(y) + a(x) - a(y)}{\bar{F}(x) - \bar{F}(y)} \tag{2.1}$$

$$a(\cdot) = \frac{1}{\lambda_1}\bar{F}(\cdot) + \frac{1}{\lambda_2}\bar{F}(\cdot) - \frac{1}{\lambda_1\lambda_2}f(\cdot).$$

To proof the Theorem we need the following lemma,

Lemma 2.1.

If f(x) $= f(x) = p\lambda_1 e^{-\lambda_1 x} + q\lambda_2 e^{-\lambda_2 x} x > 0, \lambda_i > 0, p + q = 1, 0 \leq p \leq 1$,thgnn

$$p\frac{e^{-\lambda_1 y}}{\lambda_1} + q\frac{e^{-\lambda_2 y}}{\lambda_2} = \left[\frac{1}{\lambda_1} + \frac{1}{\lambda_2}\right]\bar{F}(y) - \frac{1}{\lambda_1\lambda_2}f(y).$$

The proof is given in the Appendix.

Proof of theorem 2.1.

The . Necessity

$$E(X|x \leq X \leq y) = \int_x^y uf(u)du/[F(y) - F(x)] = A/[F(y) - F(x)]$$

Where

$$A = \int_x^y uf(u)du = \int_x^y u\left[p\lambda_1 e^{-\lambda_1 u} + q\lambda_2 e^{-\lambda_2 u}\right]du$$

$$= u\left[p\lambda_1\frac{e^{-\lambda_1 u}}{-\lambda_1} + q\lambda_2\frac{e^{-\lambda_2 u}}{-\lambda_2}\right]\Big|_x^y - \int_x^y\left[p\lambda_1\frac{e^{-\lambda_1 u}}{\lambda_1} + q\lambda_2\frac{e^{-\lambda_2 u}}{\lambda_2}\right]du$$

$$= -y\left[pe^{-\lambda_1 y} + qe^{-\lambda_2 y}\right] + x\left[pe^{-\lambda_1 x} + qe^{-\lambda_2 x}\right] + \left[p\frac{e^{-\lambda_1 u}}{-\lambda_1} + q\frac{e^{-\lambda_2 u}}{-\lambda_2}\right]\Big|_x^y$$

$$= -y\bar{F}(y) + x\bar{F}(x) - \left[p\frac{e^{-\lambda_1 y}}{\lambda_1} + q\frac{e^{-\lambda_2 y}}{\lambda_2}\right] + \left[p\frac{e^{-\lambda_1 x}}{\lambda_1} + q\frac{e^{-\lambda_2 x}}{\lambda_2}\right]$$

Using lemma (2.2) then

$$\int_x^y uf(u)du = -y\bar{F}(y) + x\bar{F}(x) - \left[\frac{1}{\lambda_1} + \frac{1}{\lambda_2}\right]\bar{F}(y) + \left[\frac{1}{\lambda_1} + \frac{1}{\lambda_2}\right]\bar{F}(x)$$

$$+ \frac{1}{\lambda_1\lambda_2}[f(y) - f(x)] \tag{2.2}$$

$$E(X|x \leq X \leq y) = \frac{-y\bar{F}(y)+x\bar{F}(x)+a(x)-a(y)}{\bar{F}(y)-\bar{F}(x)},$$

$$a(\cdot) = \frac{1}{\lambda_1}\bar{F}(\cdot) + \frac{1}{\lambda_2}\bar{F}(\cdot) - \frac{1}{\lambda_1\lambda_2}f(\cdot)$$

B. Sufficiency

Writing

$$E(X \mid x \leq X \leq y) = \frac{\int\limits_x^y uf(u)du}{F(y)-F(x)} = \frac{-y\bar{F}(y)\_x\bar{F}(x)+\int\limits_x^y \bar{F}(u)du}{F(y)-F(x)} \text{ and}$$

Using

$$E(X|x \leq X \leq y) = \frac{x\bar{F}(x) - y\bar{F}(y) + a(x) - a(y)}{\bar{F}(x) - \bar{F}(y)}, we\ obtain$$

$$\int\limits_x^y \bar{F}(u)du = a(x) - a(y). \tag{2,2}$$

By differentiating both sides from equation (2.2) with respect to y, we obtain on simplification

$$\bar{F}(y) = \left[\frac{1}{\lambda_1} + \frac{1}{\lambda_2}\right]f(y) + \frac{1}{\lambda_1\lambda_2}f'(y)$$

We differentiate the above expression once more with respect to y,, then

$$-f(y) = \left[\frac{1}{\lambda_1} + \frac{1}{\lambda_2}\right]f'(y) + \frac{1}{\lambda_1\lambda_2}f''(y)$$

We can write it as

$$f''(y) + (\lambda_1 + \lambda_2)f'(y) + \lambda_1\lambda_2 f(y) = 0 \tag{2.3}$$

The solution of the above differential equation is Which is differential equation and its solution is

$$f(y) = p\lambda_1 e^{-\lambda_1 y} + q\lambda_2 e^{-\lambda_2 y} \quad x > 0, \lambda_i > 0, p + q = 1$$

Corollary 2.1

In Theorem 2.1 if we put $y = \infty$, then we can get the result of(Nassar and Mahmoud(1985)) as

$$E(X|X \geq x) = \frac{x\bar{F}(x)+a(x)}{\bar{F}(x)}$$

$$= x + \frac{1}{\lambda_1} + \frac{1}{\lambda_2} + \frac{1}{\lambda_1\lambda_2}h(x), h(x) = \frac{f(x)}{\bar{F}(x)}$$

2.2. Geometric Distribution

Theorem 2.2

Let X has a geometric distribution with probability mass function (pmf)

$$f(x) = \lambda_1 p_1 q_1{}^x + \lambda_2 p_2 q_2{}^x , x = 0,1,\dots$$

$$p_i + q_i = 1, i = 1,2, \lambda_1 + \lambda_2 = 1, 0 \le \lambda_i \le 1$$

If and only if

$$E(X|x \le X \le y) = \frac{-y\bar{F}(y) + (x-1)\bar{F}(x-1) + c(x-1) - c(y)}{[F(y) - F(x-1)]}, \tag{2.3}$$

$$c(x-1) = \frac{1}{p_1}\bar{F}(x-1) + \frac{1}{p_2}\bar{F}(x-1) - \frac{1}{p_1 p_2}f(x)$$

And

$$c(y) = \frac{1}{p_1}\bar{F}(y) + \frac{1}{p_2}\bar{F}(y) - \frac{1}{p_1 p_2}f(y+1)$$

To proof the Theorem 2.2 we need the following two Lemmas.

Lemma 2.2

$$\sum_{u=0}^{y} uf(u) = \lambda_1\frac{q_1}{p_1} - y\lambda_1 q_1{}^{y+1} - \lambda_1\frac{q_1{}^{y+1}}{p_1} + \lambda_2\frac{q_2}{p_2} - y\lambda_2 q_2{}^{y+1} - \lambda_2\frac{q_2{}^{y+1}}{p_2}$$

Lemma2.3

$$\frac{\lambda_1\bar{F}_1(y)}{p_1} + \frac{\lambda_2\bar{F}_2(y)}{p_2} = \left[\frac{1}{p_1} + \frac{1}{p_2}\right]\bar{F}(y) - \frac{1}{p_1 p_2}f(y+1)$$

The proofs of the Lemmas are given in the Appendix.

Proof of Theorem 2.2.

A. Necessity

$$E(X|x \le X \le y) = \sum_{u=x}^{y} uf(u)du/[F(y) - F(x-1)]$$

$$= A_1/B, say.$$

where,

$$B = [F(y) - F(x-1)],$$

and

$$A_1 = \sum_{u=x}^{y} uf(u)$$

$$= \sum_{u=0}^{y} uf(u) - \sum_{u=0}^{x-1} uf(u)$$

$$= A_2 - A_3$$

where,

$$A_2 = \sum_{u=0}^{y} u f(u)$$

$$A_3 = \sum_{u=0}^{x-1} u f(u)$$

Using lemma (2.1), we have

$$A_2 = \lambda_1 \frac{q_1}{p_1} - y\lambda_1 q_1{}^{y+1} - \lambda_1 \frac{q_1{}^{y+1}}{p_1} + \lambda_2 \frac{q_2}{p_2} - y\lambda_2 q_2{}^{y+1} - \lambda_2 \frac{q_2{}^{y+1}}{p_2}$$

Similarly

$$A_3 = \lambda_1 \frac{q_1}{p_1} - (x-1)\lambda_1 q_1{}^{x} - \lambda_1 \frac{q_1{}^{x}}{p_1} + \lambda_2 \frac{q_2}{p_2} - (x-1)\lambda_2 q_2{}^{x} - \lambda_2 \frac{q_2{}^{x}}{p_2}$$

Then,

$$A_1 = -y\lambda_1 q_1{}^{y+1} - \lambda_1 \frac{q_1{}^{y+1}}{p_1} - y\lambda_2 q_2{}^{y+1} - \lambda_2 \frac{q_2{}^{y+1}}{p_2} + (x-1)\lambda_1 q_1{}^{x}$$

$$+\lambda_1 \frac{q_1{}^{x}}{p_1} + (x-1)\lambda_2 q_2{}^{x} + \lambda_2 \frac{q_2{}^{x}}{p_2},$$

We note that

$$\bar{F}(x) = P(X > x) = \sum_{u=x+1}^{\infty} f(u) = \lambda_1 q_1{}^{x+1} + \lambda_2 q_2{}^{x+1}$$

and

$$A_1 = -y\bar{F}(y) + (x-1)\bar{F}(x-1) - \frac{\lambda_1 \bar{F}_1(y)}{p_1} - \frac{\lambda_2 \bar{F}_2(y)}{p_2} + \frac{\lambda_1 \bar{F}_1(x-1)}{p_1}$$

$$+ \frac{\lambda_2 \bar{F}_2(x-1)}{p_2}$$

Using lemma (2.3), then

$$A_1 = -y\bar{F}(y) + (x-1)\bar{F}(x-1) - \left[\frac{1}{p_1} + \frac{1}{p_2}\right]\bar{F}(y) - \frac{1}{p_1 p_2} f(y+1)$$

$$+ \left[\frac{1}{p_1} + \frac{1}{p_2}\right]\bar{F}(x-1) - \frac{1}{p_1 p_2} f \tag{2.4}$$

Then

$$E(X|x \le X \le y) = \frac{-y\bar{F}(y)+(x-1)\bar{F}(x-1)+c(x-1)-c(y)}{[F(y)-F(x-1)]}, \tag{2.5}$$

$$c(x-1) = \frac{1}{p_1}\bar{F}(x-1) + \frac{1}{p_2}\bar{F}(x-1) - \frac{1}{p_1 p_2} f(x)$$

And

$$c(y) = \frac{1}{p_1}\bar{F}(y) + \frac{1}{p_2}\bar{F}(y) - \frac{1}{p_1 p_2}f(y+1)$$

B. Sufficiency

Equation (2.5) can be written as

$$\sum_{u=k}^{y} uf(u) = -\left[y + \frac{1}{p_1} + \frac{1}{p_2}\right]\bar{F}(y) + \left[(k-1) + \frac{1}{p_1} + \frac{1}{p_2}\right]\bar{F}(k-1)$$

$$+ \frac{1}{p_1 p_2}f(y+1) - \frac{1}{p_1 p_2}f(k) \tag{2.6}$$

Then,

$$kf(k) + \sum_{u=k+1}^{y} uf(u) = -\left[y + \frac{1}{p_1} + \frac{1}{p_2}\right]\bar{F}(y) + \left[(k-1) + \frac{1}{p_1} + \frac{1}{p_2}\right]\bar{F}(k-1)$$

$$+ \frac{1}{p_1 p_2}f(y+1) - \frac{1}{p_1 p_2}f(k) \tag{2.7}$$

Substituting k by k+1 in (2.6), then

$$\sum_{u=k+1}^{y} uf(u) = -\left[y + \frac{1}{p_1} + \frac{1}{p_2}\right]\bar{F}(y) + \left[k + \frac{1}{p_1} + \frac{1}{p_2}\right]\bar{F}(k)$$

$$+ \frac{1}{p_1 p_2}f(y+1) - \frac{1}{p_1 p_2}f(k+1) \tag{2.8}$$

Subtracting (2.8) from (2.7), then

$$\left[k + \frac{1}{p_1 p_2}\right]f(k) = \left[(k-1) + \frac{1}{p_1} + \frac{1}{p_2}\right]\bar{F}(k-1) - \left[k + \frac{1}{p_1} + \frac{1}{p_2}\right]\bar{F}(k)$$

$$+ \frac{1}{p_1 p_2}f(k+1) \tag{2.9}$$

Or

$$\left[k + 1 + \frac{1}{p_1 p_2}\right]f(k+1) = \left[k + \frac{1}{p_1} + \frac{1}{p_2}\right]\bar{F}(k) - \left[k + 1 + \frac{1}{p_1} + \frac{1}{p_2}\right]\bar{F}(k+1)$$

$$+ \frac{1}{p_1 p_2}f(k+2) \tag{2.10}$$

Using the fact $f(y+1) = \bar{F}(y) - \bar{F}(y+1)$, then

$$\left[k + 1 + \frac{1}{p_1 p_2}\right][\bar{F}(k) - \bar{F}(k+1)] = \left[k + \frac{1}{p_1} + \frac{1}{p_2}\right]\bar{F}(k) - \left[k + 1 + \frac{1}{p_1}\right]$$

$$+\frac{1}{p_2}\bigg] \bar{F}(k+1) + \frac{1}{p_1 p_2}[\bar{F}(k+1) - \bar{F}(k+2)] \qquad (2.11)$$

By gathering similar terms one gets

$$\bar{F}(k+2) - (q_1+q_2)\bar{F}(k+1) + (q_1 q_2)\bar{F}(k) = 0 \qquad (2.12)$$

Where,

$$q_i = 1 - p_i \text{ for } i = 1,2$$

Now, (2.12) is a linear is difference equation of order 2. It has the auxiliary equation

$$m^2 - (q_1+q_2)m + (q_1 q_2) = 0$$

Having the two roots q_1 and q_2
The general solution of (15) is

$$\bar{F}(k) = \partial_1 q_1{}^{x+1} + \partial_2 q_2{}^{x+1}$$

The initial condition, $\bar{F}(-1) = 1$ however gives $\partial_1 + \partial_2 = 1$.
Therefore

$$\bar{F}(k) = \lambda_1 q_1{}^{x+1} + \lambda_2 q_2{}^{x+1} \text{ for } x = 0,1,\dots \text{ and } 0 < \lambda_i < 1$$

This completes the proof.

Corollary 2.2
In Theorem 2.2 if we put $y = \infty$, then we can get the result of(Ahmed andYehia (1992))
as

$$E(X|X \geq x) = \frac{(x-1)\bar{F}(x-1)+c(x-1)}{[1-F(x-1)]},$$

$$= x + \frac{1}{p_1} + \frac{1}{p_2} + \frac{1}{p_1 p_2} h(x-1), \ h(x-1) = \frac{f(x-1)}{\bar{F}(x-1)}$$

Appendix

Proof of lemma 2.1

$$p\frac{e^{-\lambda_1 y}}{\lambda_1} + q\frac{e^{-\lambda_2 y}}{\lambda_2} = p\frac{e^{-\lambda_1 y}}{\lambda_1} - q\frac{e^{-\lambda_2 y}}{\lambda_1} + q\frac{e^{-\lambda_2 y}}{\lambda_1} + q\frac{e^{-\lambda_2 y}}{\lambda_2} + p\frac{e^{-\lambda_1 y}}{\lambda_2} - p\frac{e^{-\lambda_1 y}}{\lambda_2}$$

$$= \bigg[p\frac{e^{-\lambda_1 y}}{\lambda_1} + q\frac{e^{-\lambda_2 y}}{\lambda_1}\bigg] - q\frac{e^{-\lambda_2 y}}{\lambda_1} + \bigg[p\frac{e^{-\lambda_1 y}}{\lambda_2} + q\frac{e^{-\lambda_2 y}}{\lambda_2}\bigg] - p\frac{e^{-\lambda_1 y}}{\lambda_2}$$

$$= \frac{1}{\lambda_1}\bar{F}(y) + \frac{1}{\lambda_2}\bar{F}(y) - \frac{1}{\lambda_1 \lambda_2}f(y)$$

Proof of lemma 2.2.

$$A_2 = \sum_{u=0}^{y} u f(u)$$
$$= \sum_{u=0}^{y} u [\lambda_1 p_1 q_1{}^u + \lambda_2 p_2 q_2{}^u]$$

$$= \sum_{u=0}^{y} u \lambda_1 p_1 q_1{}^u + \sum_{u=0}^{y} u \lambda_2 p_2 q_2{}^u$$

$$= A_{21} + A_{22}$$

where,

$$A_{21} = \sum_{u=0}^{y} u \lambda_1 p_1 q_1{}^u$$

$$A_{22} = \sum_{u=0}^{y} u \lambda_2 p_2 q_2{}^u$$

We can compute A_{21}, A_{22} as

$$A_{21} = \sum_{u=0}^{y} u \lambda_1 p_1 q_1{}^u$$

$$= [\lambda_1 p_1 q_1 + 2\lambda_1 p_1 q_1{}^2 + \cdots + \infty] - [(y+1)\lambda_1 p_1 q_1{}^{y+1}$$

$$+ (y+2)\lambda_1 p_1 q_1{}^{y+2} + \cdots + \infty]$$

Rearranging the terms and finding the sum of series, then

$$A_{21} = \lambda_1 \frac{q_1}{p_1} - y\lambda_1 q_1{}^{y+1} - \lambda_1 \frac{q_1{}^{y+1}}{p_1}$$

Similarly

$$A_{22} = \lambda_2 \frac{q_2}{p_2} - y\lambda_2 q_2{}^{y+1} - \lambda_2 \frac{q_2{}^{y+1}}{p_2}$$

Then,

$$A_2 = \lambda_1 \frac{q_1}{p_1} - y\lambda_1 q_1{}^{y+1} - \lambda_1 \frac{q_1{}^{y+1}}{p_1} + \lambda_2 \frac{q_2}{p_2} - y\lambda_2 q_2{}^{y+1} - \lambda_2 \frac{q_2{}^{y+1}}{p_2}$$

Proof of lemma 2.3

$$\frac{\lambda_1 \bar{F}_1(y)}{p_1} + \frac{\lambda_2 \bar{F}_2(y)}{p_2} = \frac{\lambda_1 \bar{F}_1(y)}{p_1} + \frac{\lambda_2 \bar{F}_2(y)}{p_1} - \frac{\lambda_2 \bar{F}_2(y)}{p_1} + \frac{\lambda_2 \bar{F}_2(y)}{p_2}$$

$$+ \frac{\lambda_1 \bar{F}_1(y)}{p_2} - \frac{\lambda_1 \bar{F}_1(y)}{p_2}$$

$$= \left[\frac{1}{p_1} + \frac{1}{p_2} \right] \bar{F}(y) - \frac{1}{p_1 p_2} f(y+1)$$

References

[1]   Ahmed, A.N. (1991). Characterization of Beta, Binomial and Poisson distribution. *IEEE Trans. Reliability* 40 (3), 290-295.

[2]   Ahmed, A.N. and Yehia, A. (1992). Characterization of mixtures of geometric distributions by a predictor and expectations of order statistics. *The Egyptian statistic Journal*, 36, 119-135.

[3]   Arnold, B. (1980). Two characterizations of the geometric distribution. *J. Applied Probability*, vol. 17, pp 570-573.

[4]   Dallas, A. (1987). Characterizing the geometric distribution using expectations of order statistics", *J. Applied Probability*, vol. 24, pp 534-539.

[5]   El-Arishi, S (2005). A conditional variance characterization of some discrete probability distributions, *Statist. Papers*, 46, 31- 45.

[6]   Galambos, J. and Kotz, S. (1978). *Characterization of Probability Distributions*; Springer-Verlage.

[7]   Gupta, R.C. (1975). On characterization of distributions by conditional expectations. *Comm. Statist*. 4 (1), 99-103.

[8]   Gupta, R.C. and Kirmani, S.N.U.A (2004). Some characterization of distributions by functions of failure rates and mean residual life, *Comm. Statist. Theory Methods*, 33, 3115- 3131.

[9]   Kagan, A. M. Linnik, Y. V. Rao, C. R. (1973). *Characterization Problems in Mathematical Statistics*; John Wiley & Sons.

[10]   Kotlarski, I. I. (1972). On a characterization of some probability distributions by conditional expectations. *Sankhya Ser*. A. 34:461–466.

[11]   Kotz, S. (1973). Characterization of statistical distribution: A supplement to recent surveys", *Rev. Znt. Stat.*, vol. 42X, pp 39-65.

[12]   Hitha, N. and Nair, N.U (1989). Characterization of some models by properties of residual life, *Calcutta Statist. Assoc. Bull.*, 38, 219-225.

[13]   Hossain, S.A. and Ahsanullah, M. (2010). Mean residual lives of some discrete distribution. *Pak. J. Statist*. Vol. 26(4), 565-568.

[14]   Muth, E. J. (1980). Memory as a property of probability distributions. *IEEE Trans. Reliability*, vol. R-29, pp160-166.

[15]   Nanda, A.K. (2010). Characterization of distributions through failure rate and mean residual life functions. *Statistics and Probability Letters*, 80, 752-755.

[16]   Nassar, M. M. Mahmoud, M. R. (1985). On characterization of a mixture of exponential distributions", *IEEE Trans. Reliability*, vol. R-34, 1985, pp 484-488.

[17]   Nair, N. U and Sudheesh. K. K (2008). Some Results on Lower Variance Bound Useful in Reliability and Estimation, *Ann. Inst. Stat. Math.*, 60, 591- 603.

[18]   Osaki, S. Li, X. (1988). Characterization of gamma and negative binomial distributions. *IEEE Trans. Reliability*, vol. R-37, pp 379-382.

[19]   Rao, C. and Rubin, H. (1964). On a characterization of the Poisson distribution", *Sankhya A*, vol. 26, pp 295-298.

[20]   Ruiz, J. M. and Navarro, J. (1994). Characterization of distributions by relationships between failure rate and mean residual life. *IEEE Trans. Reliability* 43 (4), 640-644.

[21]   ---- (1995). Characterization of discrete distributions using expected values. *Statist. Papers*. 36 (3), 237-252.

[22]   ---- (1996). Characterizations based on conditional expectations of the doubled truncated distribution. *Ann. Inst. Statist. Math*. 48 (3), 563-572.

[23]   Shanbhag, D. (1972). Some characterizations based on the charya matrix. *J. Applied Probability*, vol. 9, pp 580-587.

[24]   Shanbhag, D. N. and Bhaskara Rao, M. (1975). A note on characterizations of probability distributions based on conditional expected values. *Sankhya Ser. A*. 37: 297–300.

[25]   Shanbhag, D. and Clark, R. (1972). Some characterizations for the Poisson distribution starting with a power-series distribution", *Proc. Camb. Phil. Soc*., pp 517-522.

[26]   Sheetrari, M. (1983). A characterization of the geometric distribution", *J. Applied Probability*, vol. 20, pp 209-212.

[27]   Srivastava, R. (1981). On some characterizations of the geometric distribution in *Statistical Distributions in Scientijc* Work, vol. 4, 981, pp 349-355; Taillie et al., Reidel, Dordrecht.

[28]   Srivastava, R. and Srivastava, A. (1974). On a characterization of a Poisson distribution", *J. Applied Probability*, vol. 7, pp 414-416.

[29]   Zoroa, P., Ruiz, J. M. and Marin, J. (1990). A characterization based on conditional expectations. *Comm. Statist. Theory Methods* 19 (8), 3127-3135.

[30]   Zijlstra, M. (1983). Characterizations of the geometric distribution by distributional properties", *J. Applied Probability*, vol. 20, pp 843-850.

In: Applied Statistical Theory and Applications
Editor: Mohammad Ahsanullah

ISBN: 978-1-63321-858-1
© 2014 Nova Science Publishers, Inc.

Chapter 17

ON GENERALIZED INTERVENED POISSON
DISTRIBUTION

C. Satheesh Kumar* and D. S. Shibu[†]
Department of Statistics, University of Kerala, Trivandrum, India
Department of Statistics, University College, Trivandrum, India

Abstract

A generalization of the well known intervened Poisson distribution (IPD) of Shanmugam (Biometrics, 1985) is discussed here along with some of its important properties such as its probability mass function, mean, variance, expression for factorial moments and recurrence relation for probabilities and factorial moments. Some real life data sets are given to illustrate that the generalized version gives the best fit compared to existing models such as positive Poisson distribution, intervened Poisson distribution and intervened generalized Poisson distribution.

Keywords: Factorial moments; Intervened Poisson distribution; Intervened generalized Poisson distribution; Probability generating function

AMS Subject Classification: Primary 60E05; 60E10

1. Introduction

Shanmugam (1985) considered the intervened Poisson distribution (IPD) as a replacement for the positive Poisson distribution in situations where some intervention process may alter the mean of the rare event generating process under observation. An advantage of the IPD is that it provides information on how effective various preventive actions taken by health service agents, where positive Poisson fails. The IPD is applicable in several areas such as reliability analysis, queuing problems, epidemiological studies, etc. For example, see Shanmugam (1985, 1992) and Huang and Fung (1989). During the observational

---

*E-mail address: drcsatheeshkumar@gmail.com
[†]E-mail address: dsshibu70@ymail.com

period, the failed units are either replaced by new units or rebuilt. This kind of replacement changes the reliability of a system as only some of its components have longer life. Dhanavanthan (1998, 2000) introduced and studied compound IPD and Scollnik (2006) introduced a generalized version of the IPD namely intervened generalized Poisson distribution (IGPD). Kumar and Shibu (2011) considered a modified version of IPD for tackling situations where a second intervention arises. In this paper, we propose a generalized intervened Poisson distribution which extends this modified IPD suitable for situations of more than two interventions.

In section 2, we present the derivation of the IPD and the IGPD and in section 3, we present the derivation of a new generalized version of the IPD, which we call the generalized intervened Poisson distribution (or in short GIPD) and study some of its important properties. Further estimation of parameters of the GIPD by method of factorial moments, method of mixed moments and method of maximum likelihood are discussed in section 4 and illustrated using certain real life data. Further results concerning the statistical inference in case of the GIPD will be published as a sequel.

2.   The IPD and the IGPD

In this section, we present the derivation of the IPD and the IGPD.

Let U_1 be the number of instances of some rare events distributed according to a Poisson distribution with parameter λ. Assume that the observational process is such that only positive values of U_1 are observed. Let $\hat{U}_1$ denote the positive observed number of occurrences of this rare event. Then $\hat{U}_1$ has a positive Poisson distribution with probability mass function (pmf)

$$h_1(u_1) = \frac{\lambda^{u_1}(e^{\lambda}-1)^{-1}}{u_1!}, \tag{1}$$

with $\lambda > 0$ for those values of u_1 on the positive integers, and zero elsewhere.

For example let U_1 be the number of cholera cases in a house hold. $U_1 = 0$ is not observable since the observational apparatus is activated only when $U_1 > 0$. Suppose that health service agencies and others resort to various preventive measures. Thus after $\hat{U}_1$ is generated, some intervention mechanism changes λ to $\lambda\rho$ where $\rho \geq 0$. Let U_2 be the number of occurrences generated after this intervention. The random variable U_2 follows Poisson with mean $\lambda\rho$ and U_2 is statistically independent of U_1. Assume that our observational apparatus has a record of only the random variable $U = \hat{U}_1 + U_2$, the total number of rare events occurred is an intervened Poisson distribution with parameters λ and ρ, which we denoted as $IPD(\lambda, \rho)$. The pmf of the $IPD(\lambda, \rho)$ is given by

$$g_1(u) = P(U = u) = \frac{[(1+\rho)^u - \rho^u]\lambda^u}{(e^{\lambda}-1)e^{\lambda\rho}u!}, \tag{2}$$

with $\lambda > 0$ and $\rho \geq 0$ for those values of u on the positive integers, and zero elsewhere.

A characteristic of the $IPD(\lambda, \rho)$ is its under dispersion (that is its variance is less than its mean) and the under dispersion is really only significant for small values of $\lambda(\lambda < 8)$. As λ increases, the $IPD(\lambda, \rho)$'s variance approaches its mean. Additional properties of the IPD are given in Shanmugam (1985).

A random variable W is said to follow the generalized Poisson distribution (GPD) of Consul (1989) with parameters θ and η, if its pmf is given by

$$h_2(w) = \frac{\theta(\theta + w\eta)^{w-1} e^{-(\theta + w\eta)}}{w!}, \qquad (3)$$

with $\theta > 0$ and $0 \leq \eta < 1$, for those values of w on the non-negative integers, and zero elsewhere. A truncated version of the GPD has been studied by Consul and Famoye (1989). Scollnik (2006) obtained the IGPD as in the following way. Let V_1 follows zero-truncated GPD with parameters θ, η and V_2 follows the GPD with parameters η and $\beta\theta$, for $\beta > 0$. Assume that V_1 and V_2 are independent. Then the random variable $V = V_1 + V_2$ is an IGPD with parameters θ, η and β and its pmf is

$$g_2(v) = \frac{\theta \left[(1+\beta) \left\{ (1+\beta)\theta + v\eta \right\}^{v-1} - \beta \left\{ \beta\theta + v\eta \right\}^{v-1} \right]}{e^{\beta\theta + v\eta}(e^\theta - 1)v!} \qquad (4)$$

with $\theta > 0, \beta > 0$ and $0 \leq \eta < 1$.

3. The GIPD and Its Properties

In this section we define generalized intervened Poisson distribution (GIPD) and derive some of its important properties.

Let Y be a Positive integer valued random variable following the IPD with parameters λ and ρ_1, and let Z be a nonnegative integer valued random variable having Poisson distribution with mean $\lambda\rho_2$, where $\lambda > 0$ and $\rho_2 \geq 0$. Assume that Y and Z are statistically independent. Then for any fixed positive integer k, the distribution of $X = Y + kZ$ is called generalized intervened Poisson distribution with parameters λ, ρ_1 and ρ_2, which we written as $GIPD_k(\lambda, \rho_1, \rho_2)$. Clearly, when $k = 1$, the $GIPD_k(\lambda, \rho_1, \rho_2)$ reduces to the $IPD(\lambda, \rho_1 + \rho_2)$ and for any $k > 1$, the $GIPD_k(\lambda, \rho_1, 0)$ is the $IPD(\lambda, \rho_1)$. Moreover the $GIPD_k(\lambda, 0, \rho_2)$ is a modified version of the $IPD(\lambda, \rho_2)$ and the $GIPD_k(\lambda, 0, 0)$ reduces to positive Poisson distribution with parameter λ. When $k = 2$, the $GIPD_k(\lambda, \rho_1, \rho_2)$ reduces to the modified IPD of Kumar and Shibu (2011). Thus the $GIPD_k(\lambda, \rho_1, \rho_2)$ is a general class of discrete distributions which include both ZTPD and the $IPD(\lambda, \rho)$ as its special case. Also, this type of generalization opens up the possibility of inclusion of k-1 further interventions, since X can be viewed as $X = Y_1 + (k-1)Z$, where Y_1 is $IPD(\lambda, \rho_1 + \rho_2)$ and Z is Poisson with mean $\lambda\rho_2$.

Proposition 3.1 The probability mass function $q_x = P(X = x)$ of the $GIPD_k(\lambda, \rho_1, \rho_2)$ is the following, for $x = 1, 2, ...$, inwhich $\lambda > 0, \rho_1 \geq 0$ and $\rho_2 \geq 0$ and k is a fixed positive integer.

$$p_x = c \sum_{r=0}^{\left[\frac{x-1}{k}\right]} \frac{\delta_{x-kr}(\lambda\rho_2)^r}{(x-kr)!r!}. \qquad (5)$$

where

$$\delta_x = \lambda^x \left[(1+\rho_1)^x - \rho_1^x \right].$$ (6)

and

$$c = (e^\lambda - 1)^{-1} e^{-\lambda(\rho_1+\rho_2)}.$$ (7)

Proof The pmf q_x of X is obtained as given below, for $x = 1, 2, \ldots$.

$$
\begin{aligned}
q_x &= P(X = x) \\
&= \sum_{r=0}^{\left[\frac{x-1}{k}\right]} P(Y = x - kr) P(Z = r/Y = x - kr) \\
&= c \sum_{r=0}^{\left[\frac{x-1}{k}\right]} \frac{\left\{ (1+\rho_1)^{x-kr} - \rho_1^{x-kr} \right\}}{(x-kr)! \, r!} \lambda^{x-kr} (\lambda \rho_2)^r
\end{aligned}
$$

where δ_x and c are given in (6) and (7).

Proposition 3.2 The probability generating function (pgf)$P_X(s)$ of the $GIPD_k(\lambda, \rho_1, \rho_2)$ with pmf (5) is the following.

$$P_X(s) = c(e^{\lambda s} - 1) e^{\lambda(\rho_1 s + \rho_2 s^k)}.$$ (8)

where c is as given in (7).
Proof is simple since the pgf of sum of two independent random variables Y_1 and Y_2 is the product of pgf's of Y_1 and Y_2.

Proposition 3.3 The mean and variance of the $GIPD_k(\lambda, \rho_1, \rho_2)$ are the following.

$$E(X) = \lambda \left[\rho_1 + k\rho_2 + e^\lambda (e^\lambda - 1)^{-1} \right]$$ (9)

and

$$Var(X) = E(X) - \left[\lambda^2 e^\lambda (e^\lambda - 1)^{-2} + k(k-1)\lambda \rho_2 \right]$$ (10)

Proof is simple and hence omitted.
Remark 2.1 From (9) and (10), it is observed that the $GIPD_k(\lambda, \rho_1, \rho_2)$ is under-dispersed for any $\lambda > 0, \rho_1 \geq 0, \rho_2 \geq 0$ and k,a fixed positive integer.

Proposition 3.4 The r-th factorial moment $\mu_{[r]}$ of the $GIPD_k(\lambda,\rho_1,\rho_2)$ with pgf (8) is the following , for $r \geq 0$.

$$\mu_{[r]} = \frac{r!}{(e^\lambda - 1)e^{\lambda\rho_2}} \sum_{j=0}^{\infty} \sum_{x=0}^{r} \binom{kj}{x} \frac{\lambda^{j+r-x}\rho_2^j}{(r-x)!j!} T_{x,\lambda,\rho_1,r} \tag{11}$$

where

$$T_{x,\lambda,\rho_1,r} = e^\lambda(1+\rho_1)^{r-x} - \rho_1^{r-x}. \tag{12}$$

Proof. The factorial moment generating function (fmgf)$F(t)$ of the $GIPD_k(\lambda,\rho_1,\rho_2)$ with pgf (3.5) is

$$\begin{aligned} F(t) &= \sum_{r=0}^{\infty} \mu_{[r]} \frac{t^r}{r!} \\ &= P(1+t) \\ &= c(e^{\lambda(1+t)} - 1)e^{\lambda[\rho_1(1+t)+\rho_2(1+t)^k]} \end{aligned} \tag{13}$$

On expanding exponential functions and using binomial theorem, we obtain the following

$$F(t) = \frac{r!}{(e^\lambda - 1)e^{\lambda\rho_2}} \sum_{r=0}^{\infty} \sum_{j=0}^{\infty} \sum_{x=0}^{r} \binom{kj}{x} \frac{\lambda^{j+r-x}\rho_2^j}{(r-x)!j!} T_{x,\lambda,\rho_1,r} \frac{t^r}{r!}. \tag{14}$$

On equating coefficient of $\frac{t^r}{r!}$ on rigthand expressions of (13) and (14), we obtain (11).

Remark 2.2.When $\rho_2 = 0, \rho_1 = \rho$ in (11), we get

$$\mu_{[r]} = \frac{\lambda^r \left[(1+\rho)^r e^\lambda - \rho^r\right]}{(e^\lambda - 1)}, \tag{15}$$

which is the r-th factorial moment of the $IPD(\lambda,\rho)$.

Proposition 3.5. A simple recurrence relation for the probabilities of the $GIPD_k(\lambda,\rho_1,\rho_2)$ is the following for $x = 1, 2, ...,$ and $x > k-1$ with $q_0 = 0$.

$$(x+1)q_{x+1} = \lambda(1+\rho_1)q_x + k\lambda\rho_2 q_{x-k+1} + \Lambda_{\lambda,\rho_1,\rho_2,j,k}. \tag{16}$$

where

$$\Lambda_{\lambda,\rho_1,\rho_2,j,k} = c \sum_{j=0}^{\left[\frac{x}{k}\right]} \frac{\lambda^{x+1-j(k-1)}\rho_2^j\rho_1^{x-kj}}{(x-kj)!j!}. \tag{17}$$

Proof On differentiating (8) with respect to s, we have

$$
\begin{aligned}
P'(s) &= \sum_{x=1}^{\infty} x s^{x-1} q_x \\
&= \lambda \left[1 + \rho_1 + k\rho_2 s^{k-1} \right] P(s) + c\lambda e^{\lambda(\rho_1 s + \rho_2 s^k)} \\
&= \lambda \left[1 + \rho_1 + k\rho_2 s^{k-1} \right] \sum_{x=1}^{\infty} s^x q_x + \sum_{x=0}^{\infty} \sum_{j=0}^{x} \binom{x}{j} \frac{\lambda^{x+1} (\rho_2 s^k)^x (\rho_1 s)^{x-j}}{x!} \\
&= \lambda \left[1 + \rho_1 + k\rho_2 s^{k-1} \right] \sum_{x=1}^{\infty} s^x p_x + \sum_{x=0}^{\infty} \sum_{j=0}^{\left[\frac{x}{k}\right]} \binom{x}{j} \frac{\lambda^{x+1-j(k-1)} \rho_2^j \rho_1^{x-kj} s^x}{j!(x-kj)!}
\end{aligned}
$$

$$(18)$$

On equating coefficient of s^x on both sides of (18) to obtain (15)

Proposition 3.6. Recurrence relation for factorial moments $\mu_{[r]}$ of the $GIPD_k(\lambda, \rho_1, \rho_2)$ is the following for $r \geq (k-1)$, with $\mu_{[0]} = 1$.

$$
\mu_{[r+1]} = \lambda [1 + \rho_1 + k\rho_2] \mu_{[r]} + k\lambda \rho_2 \sum_{x=1}^{k-1} \binom{k-1}{x} x! \binom{r}{x} \mu_{[r-x]} + \Delta_{\lambda, \rho_1, \rho_2, r, k} \qquad (19)
$$

where

$$
\Delta_{\lambda, \rho_1, \rho_2, r, k} = \frac{r!}{(e^\lambda - 1) e^{\lambda \rho_2}} \sum_{j=0}^{\infty} \sum_{x=0}^{r} \binom{kj}{x} \frac{\lambda^{r+1+j-x} \rho_2^j (1+\rho_1)^{r-x}}{j!(r-x)!}. \qquad (20)
$$

Proof On differentiating (13) with respect to t, we have

$$
\begin{aligned}
F'(t) &= \sum_{r=1}^{\infty} \frac{t^{r-1}}{(r-1)!} \mu_{[r]} \\
&= c\lambda (e^{\lambda(1+t)} - 1) e^{\lambda[\rho_1(1+t) + \rho_2(1+t)^k]} \left[\rho_1 + k\rho_2 (1+t)^{k-1} \right] + c\lambda e^{\lambda[(1+\rho_1)(1+t) + \rho_2(1+t)^k]} \\
&= \lambda [1 + \rho_1 + k\rho_2] \sum_{r=0}^{\infty} \frac{t^r}{r!} \mu_{[r]} + k\lambda \rho_2 \sum_{r=0}^{\infty} \sum_{x=1}^{k-1} \frac{x! \binom{r}{x} \binom{k-1}{x}}{r!} t^{x+r} \\
&\quad + \frac{1}{(e^\lambda - 1) e^{\lambda \rho_2}} \sum_{r=0}^{\infty} \sum_{j=0}^{\infty} \sum_{x=0}^{r} \frac{\binom{kj}{x} \lambda^{r+j-x} \rho_2^j \rho_1^{r-j}}{j!(r-x)!}
\end{aligned}
$$

$$(21)$$

On equating coefficient of $\frac{t^r}{r!}$ on both sides of (21), we get (19).

4. Estimation

Here we discuss the estimation of the parameters λ, ρ_1 and ρ_2 of the $GIPD_k(\lambda, \rho_1, \rho_2)$ for any arbitrary but fixed values of k by method of factorial moments, method of mixed moments and method of maximum likelihood.

The parameters λ, ρ_1 and ρ_2 of the $GIPD_k(\lambda, \rho_1, \rho_2)$ have been estimated by the method of factorial moments for $k = 1, 2$ and 3 as in the following. The first three factorial moments $\mu_{[1]}, \mu_{[2]}$ and $\mu_{[3]}$ of the $GIPD_k(\lambda, \rho_1, \rho_2)$ are equated to the corresponding sample factorial moments $\tau_{[1]}, \tau_{[2]}$ and $\tau_{[3]}$ for fixed value of k. Then we have the following system of equations in which

$$\delta = \frac{e^\lambda}{e^\lambda - 1} \tag{22}$$

.

$$\lambda[\rho_1 + k\rho_2 + \delta] = \tau_{[1]} \tag{23}$$

$$\lambda[1 + \rho_1 + k\rho_2](\mu_{[1]} + \delta\lambda) + k(k-1)\lambda\rho_2 = \tau_{[2]} \tag{24}$$

$$\lambda[1 + \rho_1 + k\rho_2]\mu_{[2]} + 2k(k-1)\lambda\rho_2\mu_{[1]} \\ + \lambda\delta[\lambda^2(1+\rho_1)^2 + 2\lambda^2k\rho_2(1+\rho_1) + k\rho_2(k\rho_2 + k - 1)] = \tau_{[3]} \tag{25}$$

Now estimates of the parameters λ, ρ_1 and ρ_2 are obtained by solving the non-linear system of equations (23),(24) and (25).

In method of mixed moments, the parameters λ, ρ_1 and ρ_2 of the $GIPD_k(\lambda, \rho_1, \rho_2)$ are estimated by using the first two sample factorial moments and the first observed frequency of the distribution. let n_x be the observed frequency of x events, for $x = 1, 2, ..., $.Thus the estimates are obtained by solving the equations (3.24) and (3.25) along with the following equation.

$$c\lambda = \frac{n_1}{N} \tag{26}$$

where n_1 is the observed frequency of the first event, N is the observed total frequency and c is as given in (3.5).

In method of maximum likelihood, the parameters λ, ρ_1 and ρ_2 of the $GIPD_k(\lambda, \rho_1, \rho_2)$ are estimated by maximising the following log-likelihood function with respect to the parameters.

$$\ln L = \sum_{x=1}^{z} n_x \ln q_x \tag{27}$$

$$\sum_{x=1}^{z} \sum_{r=0}^{\left[\frac{x-1}{k}\right]} \frac{f_x}{q_x} \frac{\delta_{x-kr}(x - (k-1)r(\lambda\rho_2)^r}{(x-kr)!r!} = \lambda \sum_{x=1}^{z} \sum_{r=0}^{\left[\frac{x-1}{k}\right]} \frac{f_x}{q_x} \frac{\delta_{x-kr}(\lambda\rho_2)^r}{(x-kr)!r!}\{\delta + \rho_1 + \rho_2\} \tag{28}$$

$$\sum_{x=1}^{z} \sum_{r=0}^{\left[\frac{x-1}{k}\right]} \frac{f_x}{q_x} \frac{\delta_{x-kr-1}(\lambda\rho_2)^r}{(x-kr-1)!r!} = \sum_{x=1}^{z} \sum_{r=0}^{\left[\frac{x-1}{k}\right]} \frac{f_x}{q_x} \frac{\delta_{x-kr}(\lambda\rho_2)^r}{(x-kr)!r!} \tag{29}$$

$$\sum_{x=1}^{z} \sum_{r=1}^{\left[\frac{x-1}{k}\right]} \frac{f_x}{q_x} \frac{\delta_{x-kr-1}(\lambda\rho_2)^r}{(x-kr)!(r-1)!} = \lambda \sum_{x=1}^{z} \sum_{r=0}^{\left[\frac{x-1}{k}\right]} \frac{f_x}{q_x} \frac{\delta_{x-kr}(\lambda\rho_2)^r}{(x-kr)!r!} \tag{30}$$

we present the fitting of positive Poisson distribution(PPD),intervened Poisson distribution (IPD) of Shanmugam (1985), intervened generalized Poisson distribution (IGPD) of Scollnik (2006) and the GIPD for different values of $k(= 1, 2, 3)$ to the following two data sets by the method of factorial moments, method of mixed moments and method of maximum likelihood in Tables 1(a),1(b),1(c) and II(a),II(b),II(c) respectively.

Table 1(a). Comparison of fit of $GIPD_k$ using factorial method of estimation the first data-set

		Expected frequency by factorial moments					
obs.value	frequency	PPD	IPD	IGPD	$GIPD_1$	$GIPD_2$	$GIPD_3$
1	213	210	200	204	200	233	215
2	128	122	134	137	132	111	127
3	37	52	50	43	50	37	42
4	17	11	12	12	15	15	11
5	3	3	3	3	2	3	3
6	2	2	2	1	1	1	2
7	0	0	0	0	0	0	0
Total	400	400	400	400	400	400	400
Estimated value of parameters		$\hat{\lambda}=1.16$	$\hat{\lambda}=0.56$ $\hat{\rho}=0.47$	$\hat{\theta}=0.38$ $\hat{\eta}=0.068$ $\hat{\beta}=1.01$	$\hat{\lambda}=0.56$ $\hat{\rho}_1=0.18$ $\hat{\rho}_2=0.29$	$\hat{\lambda}=0.55$ $\hat{\rho}_1=0.36$ $\hat{\rho}_2=0.10$	$\hat{\lambda}=0.60$ $\hat{\rho}_1=0.48$ $\hat{\rho}_2=0.0288$
χ^2 - value		7.66	7.49	4.83	5.18	4.92	2.174
P-value		0.094	0.101	0.44	0.34	0.35	0.46

Table 1(b). Comparison of fit of $GIPD_k$ using mixed moments estimation for the first data-set

		Expected frequency by factorial moments					
obs.value	frequency	PPD	IPD	IGPD	$GIPD_1$	$GIPD_2$	$GIPD_3$
1	213	213	213	213	213	213	213
2	128	120	123	120	130	112	127
3	37	51	50	48	44	52	41
4	18	12	11	15	11	17	13
5	3	3	3	3	2	5	4
6	1	1	0	1	0	1	2
7	0	0	0	0	0	0	0
Total	400	400	400	400	400	400	400
Estimated value of parameters		$\hat{\lambda}=1.15$	$\hat{\lambda}=0.68$ $\hat{\rho}=0.39$	$\hat{\theta}=0.43$ $\hat{\eta}=0.068$ $\hat{\beta}=1$	$\hat{\lambda}=0.68$ $\hat{\rho}_1=0.17$ $\hat{\rho}_2=0.23$	$\hat{\lambda}=0.55$ $\hat{\rho}_1=0.46$ $\hat{\rho}_2=0.163$	$\hat{\lambda}=0.61$ $\hat{\rho}_1=0.48$ $\hat{\rho}_2=0.028$
χ^2 - value		7.66	6.49	3.36	6.59	7.77	2.98
P-value		0.167	0.133	0.449	0.449	0.148	0.773

The first data set given in Tables 1(a),1(b),1(c) indicate the distribution of number of articles on theoretical Statistics and Probability for years 1940-49 and initial letter N-R of the author's name. for reference, see Kendal (1961).The second data set given in tables II(a),II(b) and II(c) represent the distribution of 1534 biologists according to the number of research papers to their credit in the review of applied entomology, volume 24,1936. For details, see Williams(1944).

Table 1(c). Comparison of fit of $GIPD_k$ using maximum likelihood estimation the first data-set

obs.value	frequency	Expected frequency by factorial moments					
		PPD	IPD	IGPD	$GIPD_1$	$GIPD_2$	$GIPD_3$
1	213	210	191	206	197	217	223
2	128	122	140	134	135	112	120
3	37	52	48	43	51	49	38
4	18	12	17	13	14	16	15
5	3	3	3	3	2	3	3
6	1	1	1	1	1	1	1
7	0	0	0	0	0	0	0
Total	400	400	400	400	400	400	400
Estimated value of parameters		$\hat{\lambda} = 1.16$	$\hat{\lambda} = 0.69$ $\hat{\rho} = 0.47$	$\hat{\theta} = 0.40$ $\hat{\eta} = 0.08$ $\hat{\beta} = 1.1$	$\hat{\lambda} = 0.70$ $\hat{\rho}_1 = 0.22$ $\hat{\rho}_2 = 0.25$	$\hat{\lambda} = 0.53$ $\hat{\rho}_1 = 0.48$ $\hat{\rho}_2 = 0.15$	$\hat{\lambda} = 0.58$ $\hat{\rho}_1 = 0.47$ $\hat{\rho}_2 = 0.018$
χ^2 - value		7.66	6.14	3.36	6.15	5.5	1.61
P-value		0.144	0.224	3.36	6.15	5.5	1.61

Note that $GIPD_1(\lambda, \rho_1, \rho_2)$ is $IPD(\lambda, \rho_1 + \rho_2)$. The consistency of this result is clear from tables. From tables 1(a),1(b) and 1(c), it is seen that chi-square value for $GIPD_k(\lambda, \rho_1, \rho_2)$ with k=3 is minimum and in tables 2(a),2(b) and 2(c) chi-square value is minimum for $GIPD_k(\lambda, \rho_1, \rho_2)$ with k=2. This fact together with the corresponding P-values shows that $GIPD_k(\lambda, \rho_1, \rho_2)$ gives the best fit over positive Poisson distribution, intervened Poisson distribution and intervened generalized Poisson distribution.

Table 2(a). Comparison of fit of $GIPD_k$ using factorial moment estimation for the second data-set

obs.value	frequency	Expected frequency by factorial moments					
		PPD	IPD	IGPD	$GIPD_1$	$GIPD_2$	$GIPD_3$
1	1062	1026	1030	1034	1023	1058	1034
2	263	296	288	277	290	276	295
3	120	138	139	135	142	126	140
4	50	40	40	42	42	44	38
5	22	20	20	29	20	15	16
6	7	8	12	12	12	10	10
7	6	4	4	4	3	5	1
8	2	1	1	1	2	0	0
9	0	0	0	0	0	0	0
10	1	0	0	0	0	0	0
10+	1	0	0	0	0	0	0
Total	1534	1534	1534	1534	1534	1534	1534
Estimated value of parameters		$\hat{\lambda} = 1.02$	$\hat{\lambda} = 0.28$ $\hat{\rho} = 0.85$	$\hat{\theta} = 0.14$ $\hat{\eta} = 0.28$ $\hat{\beta} = 0.003$	$\hat{\lambda} = 0.28$ $\hat{\rho}_1 = 0.61$ $\hat{\rho}_2 = 0.24$	$\hat{\lambda} = 0.30$ $\hat{\rho}_1 = 0.42$ $\hat{\rho}_2 = 0.40$	$\hat{\lambda} = 0.52$ $\hat{\rho}_1 = 0.24$ $\hat{\rho}_2 = 0.236$
χ^2 - value		11.43	10.07	7.102	11.9	4.98	16.17
P-value		0.043	0.016	0.037	0.014	0.20	0.016

Table 2(b). Comparison of fit of $GIPD_k$ using mixed moment estimation for the second data-set

obs.value	frequency	Expected frequency by factorial moments					
		PPD	*IPD*	*IGPD*	*GIPD₁*	*GIPD₂*	*GIPD₃*
1	1062	1062	1062	1062	1062	1062	1062
2	263	284	240	242	244	270	233
3	120	140	146	129	142	114	154
4	50	36	38	50	38	43	46
5	22	32	35	30	32	31	25
6	7	10	13	21	8	20	13
7	6	0	0	0	3	3	1
8	2	0	0	0	0	1	0
9	0	0	0	0	0	0	0
10	1	0	0	0	0	0	0
10+	1	0	0	0	0	0	0
Total	1534	1534	1534	1534	1534	1534	1534
Estimated value of parameters		$\hat{\lambda} = 0.65$	$\hat{\lambda} = 0.60$ $\hat{\rho} = 0.38$	$\hat{\theta} = 0.12$ $\hat{\eta} = 0.30$ $\hat{\beta} = 0.005$	$\hat{\lambda} = 0.60$ $\hat{\rho}_1 = 0.23$ $\hat{\rho}_2 = 0.15$	$\hat{\lambda} = 0.30$ $\hat{\rho}_1 = 0.42$ $\hat{\rho}_2 = 0.40$	$\hat{\lambda} = 0.34$ $\hat{\rho}_1 = 0.23$ $\hat{\rho}_2 = 0.49$
χ^2 - value		18.18	6.66	7.37	7.48	5.59	14.34
P-value		0.03	0.20	0.19	0.15	0.28	0.09

Table 2(c). Comparison of fit of $GIPD_k$ using factorial moment estimation for the second data-set

obs.value	frequency	Expected frequency by factorial moments					
		PPD	*IPD*	*IGPD*	*GIPD₁*	*GIPD₂*	*GIPD₃*
1	1062	1029	1087	1034	1012	1062	1042
2	263	293	236	286	290	258	284
3	120	138	107	128	136	118	135
4	50	40	62	43	61	42	44
5	22	20	30	28	18	30	16
6	7	12	10	11	14	21	10
7	6	1	1	2	2	2	2
8	2	1	1	2	1	1	1
9	0	0	0	0	0	0	0
10	1	0	0	0	0	0	0
10+	1	0	0	0	0	0	0
Total	1534	1534	1534	1534	1534	1534	1534
Estimated value of parameters		$\hat{\lambda} = 1.02$	$\hat{\lambda} = 0.33$ $\hat{\rho} = 0.15$	$\hat{\theta} = 0.12$ $\hat{\eta} = 0.30$ $\hat{\beta} = 0.005$	$\hat{\lambda} = 0.33$ $\hat{\rho}_1 = 0.06$ $\hat{\rho}_2 = 0.09$	$\hat{\lambda} = 0.28$ $\hat{\rho}_1 = 0.40$ $\hat{\rho}_2 = 0.42$	$\hat{\lambda} = 0.40$ $\hat{\rho}_1 = 0.40$ $\hat{\rho}_2 = 0.24$
χ^2 - value		11.43	10.88	6.46	9.82	5.78	9.87
P-value		0.07	0.08	0.18	0.10	0.25	0.09

References

Consul, P.C. *Generalized Poisson distribution: properties and applications*. New York: Marcel Dekke; 1989.

Consul, P.C. and Famoye, F. (1989). The truncated generalized Poisson distribution and its estimation. *Communication Statistics Theory and Methods*, 18, 3635- 3648.

Dhanavananthan, P. (1998). Compound intervened Poisson distribution.*Biometrical Journal*, 40, 641-646.

Dhanavananthan, P. (2000). Estimation of the parameters of compound intervened Poisson distribution. *Biometrical Journal*, 40, 315-320.

Huang , M. and Fung, K. Y. (1989).Intervened truncated Poisson distribution. *Sankhya.* Series B 51, 302- 310.

Kendal, M. G. (1961). Natural law in Science. *Journal of Royal Statistical Society.* Series A, 124,1 18.

Kumar, C. S. and Shibu, D. S. (2011). Modified intervened Poisson distribution. *Statistica*, 71, 489-499.

Scollnik, D. P. M. (1995). Bayesian analysis of an intervened Poisson distribution.*Communication Statistics Theory and Methods*, 24, 735 754.

Scollnik, D. P. M. (1998). On the analysis of the truncated generalized Poisson distribution using a Bayesian method. *Australian Bulletin*, 28, 135- 152.

Scollnik, D. P. M. (2006). On the intervened generalized Poisson distribution. *Communication Statistics Theory and Methods*, 35,953-963.

Shanmugam, R. (1985). An intervened Poisson distribution and its medical application. *Biometrics*, 41, 1025 -1029.

Shanmugam, R. (1992). An inferential procedure for the Poisson intervention parameter. *Biometrics*, 48, 559- 565.

Williams, C. B. (1944). Number of publications written by Biologists. *Annals of Eugenics*, 12, 143-146.

In: Applied Statistical Theory and Applications
Editor: Mohammad Ahsanullah

ISBN: 978-1-63321-858-1
© 2014 Nova Science Publishers, Inc.

Chapter 18

CHARACTERIZATION BY TRANSLATION, CONTRACTION AND DILATION OF DUAL GENERALIZED ORDER STATISTICS

Imtiyaz A. Shah[*] *and A. H. Khan*
Department of Statistics and Operations Research
Aligarh Muslim University, Aligarh, India

Abstract

Generalized logistic distribution $F(x) = [1 + (m + 1) e^{-\alpha x}]^{-\frac{1}{m+1}}$ has been characterized through translation of two non-adjacent dual generalized order statistics($dgos$) and then the characterizing results are obtained for generalized log-logistic distribution through dilation of dual generalized order statistics ($dgos$) and generalized log-logistic distribution through contraction of non-adjacent generalized order statistics (gos). Further, the results are deduced for order statistics and adjacent generalized order statistics and dual generalized order statistics.

Keywords: Order statistics; generalized order statistics; dual generalized order statistics; translation; contraction; dilation. Characterization of distributions; generalized logistic distribution; generalized log-logistic; logistic; log-logistic; exponential; Pareto and power function distributions

Mathematics Subject Classification: 62E10; 62E15; 62G30

1. Introduction

Kamps (1995) introduced the concept of generalized order statistics (gos) as follows:

Let $X_1, X_2, \cdots, X_n$ be a sequence of independent and identically distributed (iid)random variables ($rv's$) with the absolutely continuous distribution function (df)$F(x)$ and the

---

[*] E-mail address: masoom.immy03@gmail.com (Corresponding Author)

probability density function $(pdf)f(x)$, $x \in (a,b)$.Let $n \in N$, $n \geq 2$, $k > 0$, $\tilde{m} = (m_1, m_2, \cdots, m_{n-1}) \in \mathfrak{R}^{n-1}$, $M_r = \sum_{j=r}^{n-1} m_j$, such that $\gamma_r^{(n)} = k + (n-r) + M_r > 0$ for all $r \in \{1, 2, \cdots, n-1\}$. If $m_1 = m_2 = \cdots = m_{n-1} = m$, then $X(r,n,m,k)$ is called the r^{th}m-gos and its pdf is given as:

$$f_{X(r,n,m,k)}(x) = \frac{\gamma_r^{(n)}}{(r-1)!}[\bar{F}(x)]^{\gamma_r^{(n)}-1}\left[\frac{1-[\bar{F}(x)]^{m+1}}{m+1}\right]^{r-1} f(x), a < x < b \qquad (1.1)$$

Based on the generalized order statistics (gos), Burkschat et al. (2003) introduced the concept of the dual generalized order statistics (dgos) where the pdf of the r^{th}m-dgos $X^*(r,n,m,k)$ is given as

$$f_{X^*(r,n,m,k)}(x) = \frac{\gamma_r^{(n)}}{(r-1)!}[F(x)]^{\gamma_r^{(n)}-1}\left[\frac{1-[F(x)]^{m+1}}{m+1}\right]^{r-1} f(x), a < x < b \qquad (1.2)$$

which is obtained just by replacing

$$\bar{F}(x) = 1 - F(x) \text{by } F(x),$$

where

$$\gamma_r^{(n)} = k + (n-r)(m+1), 1 \leq r \leq n \qquad (1.3)$$

$$C_{r-1}^{(n)} = \prod_{i=1}^{r} \gamma_i^{(n)}, 1 \leq r \leq n \qquad (1.4)$$

Ahsanullah (2004) has characterized uniform distribution under random contraction for adjacentdual generalized order statistics (dgos). In this paper, distributioual properties of the dual generalized order statistics (dgos) have been used to characterize distributions for non-adjacent dual generalized order statistics (dgos) under random translation, dilation and contraction, thus generalizing the results of Ahsanullah (2004) and Beutner and Kamps (2008). Further, results in terms of generalized order statistics and order statistics are deduced. One may also refer to Nevzorov (2001); Wesolowskiand Ahsanullah (2004), Once let al. (2005), Arnold et al. (2008), Navarro (2008) Castaño-Martínez et al. (2010), and Khan and Shah (2012) for the related results.

It may be seen that if Y is a measureable function of X with the relation

$$Y = h(X)$$

then

(i) $$Y^*(r,n,m,k) = h[X^*(r,n,m,k)] \qquad (1.5)$$

(ii) $$Y_{r:n} = h(X_{r:n}) \qquad (1.6)$$

if h is an increasing function and

(i) $$Y(r,n,m,k) = h[X^*(r,n,m,k)] \qquad (1.7)$$

(ii) $$Y_{n-r+1:n} = h(X_{r:n}) \qquad (1.8)$$

if h is a decreasing function

where $X_{r:n}$ is the rth order statistic from a sample of size n, $X(r,n,m,k)$ is the rth m-go sand $X^*(r,n,m,k)$ is the rth m- dgos.

If the support of the distribution $F(x)$ be over (a,b) , then by convention, we will write

$$X_{0:n} = a \text{ and } X_{n:n-1} = b \qquad (1.9)$$

Further, we will denote

(i) $X \sim \text{genlogistic}(\alpha)$

if X has a generalized logistic distribution with the df

$$F(x) = [1+(m+1)e^{-\alpha x}]^{-\frac{1}{m+1}}, m > -1, \alpha > 0, -\infty < x < \infty \qquad (1.10)$$

(ii) $X \sim \text{genlog-logistic}(\alpha)$

if X has a generalized log-logistic distribution with the df

$$F(x) = [1+(m+1)x^{-\alpha}]^{-\frac{1}{m+1}}, m > -1, \alpha > 0, 0 < x < \infty \qquad (1.11)$$

(iii) $X \sim \text{logistic}(\alpha)$

if X has a logistic distribution with the df

$$F(x) = [1+e^{-\alpha x}]^{-1}, -\infty < x < \infty, \alpha > 0 \qquad (1.12)$$

(iv) $X \sim \text{log-logistic}(\alpha)$

if X has a log-logistic distribution with the df

$$F(x) = [1+x^{-\alpha}]^{-1}, 0 < x < \infty, \alpha > 0 \qquad (1.13)$$

(v) $X \sim \exp(\alpha)$

if X has an exponential distribution with the df

$$F(x) = 1 - e^{-\alpha x}, 0 < x < \infty, \alpha > 0 \qquad (1.14)$$

(vi) $X \sim \text{Par}(\alpha)$

if X has a Pareto distribution with the df

$$F(x) = 1 - x^{-\alpha}, 1 < x < \infty, \alpha > 0 \qquad (1.15)$$

(vii) $X \sim \text{pow}(\alpha)$

if X has a power function distribution with the df

$$F(x) = x^{\alpha}, 0 < x < 1, \alpha > 0 \qquad (1.16)$$

It may further be noted that

if $\log X \sim genlogistic(\alpha)$ then $X \sim genlog\text{-}logistic(\alpha)$ (1.17)

if $-\log X \sim genlogistic(\alpha)$ then $X \sim genlog\text{-}logistic(\alpha)$ (1.18)

if $\log X \sim logistic(\alpha)$ then $X \sim log\text{-}logistic(\alpha)$ (1.19)

if $-\log X \sim logistic(\alpha)$ then $X \sim log\text{-}logistic(\alpha)$ (1.20)

if $\log X \sim exp(\alpha)$ then $X \sim Par(\alpha)$ (1.21);

and if $-\log X \sim exp(\alpha)$ then $X \sim pow(\alpha)$ (1.22)

It has been assumed here throughout that the *df* is differentiable *w.r.t.* its argument.

2. Characterizing Results

Theorem 2.1 Let $X^*(s,n,m,k)$ be the sth *m-dgos* from a sample of size n drawn from a continuous population with the *pdf* $f(x)$ and the *df* $F(x)$, then for $1 \le r < s \le n$,

$$X^*(s-r+j, n-r+j, m, k) \overset{d}{=} X^*(s,n,m,k) + Y_{r-j:s-1}, j = 0,1 \quad (2.1)$$

where $Y_{r-j:s-1}$ is the $(r-j)^{th}$ order statistic from a sample of size $(s-1)$ drawn from an $exp(\alpha)$ distribution and is independent of $X^*(s,n,m,k)$ if and only if $X_1 \sim genlogistic(\alpha)$.

Proof. To prove the necessary part, let the moment generating function (*mgf*) of $X^*(s,n,m,k)$ be $M_{X^*_{(s,n,m,k)}}(t)$, then

$$X^*(s-r, n-r, m, k) \overset{d}{=} X^*(s,n,m,k) + Y$$

implies

$$M_{X^*_{(s-r,n-r,m,k)}}(t) \overset{d}{=} M_{X^*_{(s,n,m,k)}}(t) \cdot M_Y(t)$$

Since for the *genlogistic*(α) distribution.

$$M_{X^*_{(s,n,m,k)}}(t) = \frac{(m+1)^{\frac{t}{\alpha}}}{(s-1)!} \frac{\Gamma\left(\frac{\gamma_s^{(n)}}{(m+1)} + \frac{t}{\alpha}\right)\Gamma\left(s - \frac{t}{\alpha}\right)}{\Gamma\left(\frac{\gamma_s^{(n)}}{(m+1)}\right)}$$

Therefore,

$$M_Y(t) = \frac{M_{X^*_{(s-r,n-r,m,k)}}(t)}{M_{X^*_{(s,n,m,k)}}(t)} = \frac{\Gamma(s)}{\Gamma(s-r)} \frac{\Gamma\left(s-r-\frac{t}{\alpha}\right)}{\Gamma\left(s-\frac{t}{\alpha}\right)}$$

as $\gamma_{s-r+j}^{(n-r)} = k + (n-s-j)(m+1) = \gamma_{s+j}^{(n)}$

But this is the *mgf* of $Y_{r:s-1}$, the rth order statistic from a sample of size $(s-1)$ drawn from $exp(\alpha)$ and hence the result.

For the proof of sufficiency part, we have by the convolution method

$$f_{X^*_{(s-r,n-r,m,k)}}(x) = \int_0^x f_{X^*_{(s,n,m,k)}}(y) \cdot f_{Y_{r:s-1}}(x-y)dy \tag{2.2}$$

$$= \frac{\alpha\,(s-1)!}{(r-1)!(s-r-1)!}\int_0^x [e^{-\alpha(x-y)}]^{s-r}[1-e^{-\alpha(x-y)}]^{r-1}$$

$$\times f_{X^*_{(s,n,m,k)}}(y)dy. \tag{2.3}$$

Differentiating both the sides of (2.3) $w.r.t.x$, we get

$$\frac{d}{dx}f_{X^*_{(s-r,n-r,m,k)}}(x) = \frac{\alpha\,(r-1)(s-1)!}{(r-1)!(s-r-1)!}\int_0^x \alpha[e^{-\alpha(x-y)}]^{s-r+1}[1-e^{-\alpha(x-y)}]^{r-2}$$
$$\times f_{X^*_{(s,n,m,k)}}(y)dy$$

$$\frac{\alpha\,(s-r)(s-1)!}{(r-1)!(s-r-1)!}\int_0^x \alpha[e^{-\alpha(x-y)}]^{s-r}[1-e^{-\alpha(x-y)}]^{r-1}$$

$$\times f_{X^*_{(s,n,m,k)}}(y)dy$$

which leads to

$$\frac{d}{dx}f_{X^*_{(s-r,n-r,m,k)}}(x) = \alpha(s-r)[\,f_{X^*_{(s-r+1,n-r+1,m,k)}}(x) - f_{X^*_{(s-r,n-r,m,k)}}(x)] \tag{2.4}$$

or, $$f_{X^*_{(s-r,n-r,m,k)}}(x) = \alpha(s-r)[F_{X^*_{(s-r+1,n-r+1,m,k)}}(x) - F_{X^*_{(s-r,n-r,m,k)}}(x)]. \tag{2.5}$$

Now, since (Kamps, 1995)

$$[F_{X^*_{(s-r+1,n-r+1,m,k)}}(x) - F_{X^*_{(s-r,n-r,m,k)}}(x)] =$$

$$\frac{C^{(n-r)}_{s-r-1}}{(s-r)!(m+1)^{s-r}}[F(x)]^{\gamma^{(n)}_s}[1-(F(x))^{m+1}]^{s-r}. \tag{2.6}$$

Therefore, in view of (1.2), (2.5) and (2.6), we have

$$(m+1)f(x) = \alpha[F(x)][1-(F(x))^{m+1}]$$

But this is the characterization result for *genlogistic* distribution$F(x) = [1+(m+1)e^{-\alpha x}]^{-\frac{1}{m+1}}$and hence the Theorem.

Remark 2.1 We can get the corresponding characterizing result for the order statistics at$m = 0$ is:

Let $X_{r:n}$ be the r^{th}order statistic from a sample of size$n$ drawn from a continuous population with the *pdf*$f(x)$ and the *df*$F(x)$, then for $1 \le r < s < n$,

$$X_{n-s+1:n-r+j} \overset{d}{=} X_{n-s+1:n} + Y_{r-j:s-1} \quad j = 0,1$$

where $Y_{r-j:s-1}$is the$(r-j)^{th}$order statistic from a sample of size$(s-1)$drawn from $exp\,(\alpha)$ distribution and is independent of $X_{n-s+1:n}$ if and only if $X_1 \sim logistic(\alpha)$, if we replace $(n-s+1)$ by r and $(n-r)$ by$m$, as obtained by Khan and Shah (2012).

Corollary 2.1 Let $X^*(s,n,m,k)$ be the $s^{th}m$-dgos from a sample of size n drawn from a continuous population with the $pdf f(x)$and the $df F(x)$, then for$1 \leq r < s \leq n$,

$$X^*(s-r+j,n-r+j,m,k)\overset{d}{=}X^*(s,n,m,k)\cdot Y_{r-j:s-1}\,,j=0,1 \qquad (2.7)$$

where $Y_{r-j:s-1}$ is the $(r-j)^{th}$ order statistic from a sample of size $(s-1)$ drawn from $Par(\alpha)$ distribution and is independent of$X^*(s,n,m,k)$if and only if $X_1 \sim genlog$-$logistic(\alpha)$. Here the product $X^*(s,n,m,k)\cdot Y_{r-j:s-1}$in (2.7) is called random dilation of $X^*(s,n,m,k)$ (Beutner and Kamps, 2008).

Proof.Note that

$$\log X^*(s-r,n-r,m,k)\overset{d}{=}\;\log X^*(s,n,m,k)+\log Y_{r:s-1}$$

then

$$X^*(s-r,n-r,m,k)\overset{d}{=}\;X^*(s,n,m,k)\cdot Y_{r:s-1}$$

and the result follows in view of (1.5), (1.6), (1.17) and (1.21).

Remark 2.2 In case of ordinary order statistics, i.e., at $m=0$, Corollary 2.1 reduces to

$$X_{r:m+j}\overset{d}{=}X_{r:n}\cdot Y_{n-m-j:n-r}\,,j=0,1;1\leq r\leq m<n \qquad (2.8)$$

where $Y_{n-m-j:n-r}$ is the $(n-m-j)^{th}$ order statistic from a sample of size $(n-r)$ drawn from the $Par(\alpha)$ distribution and is independent of $X_{r:n}$if and only if $X_1 \sim log$-$logistic(\alpha)$, as obtained by Khan and Shah (2012).

Corollary 2.2 Let $X(s,n,m,k)$ be the $s^{th}m$-gos from a sample of size n drawn from a continuous population with the $pdf\,F(x)$and the $df\,F(x)$, then for $1 \leq r < s \leq n$,

$$X(s-r+j,n-r+j,m,k)\;\overset{d}{=}X(s,n,m,k)\cdot Y_{s-r+j:s-1}\,,j=0,1 \qquad (2.9)$$

where $Y_{s-r+j:s-1}$ is the $(s-r+j)^{th}$ order statistic from a sample of size $(s-1)$ drawn from $pow(\alpha)$distribution and is independent of $X(s,n,m,k)$if and only if $X_1 \sim genlog$-$logistic(\alpha)$. Here the product $X(s,n,m,k)\cdot Y_{s-r+j:s-1}$in (2.9) is called random contraction of $X(s-r+j,n-r+j,m,k)$ (Beutner and Kamps, 2008).

Proof. It may be noted that

$$-\log X^*(s-r,n-r,m,k)\overset{d}{=}\;-\log X^*(s,n,m,k)-\log Y_{r:s-1}$$

implies

$$X(s-r,n-r,m,k)\overset{d}{=}\;X(s,n,m,k)\cdot Y_{s-r:s-1}$$

andhence the result follows in view of (1.7), (1.8), (1.18) and (1.22).

Remark 2.3 At $j = 0$ and $r = 1$, Corollary 2.2 reduces to the result given by Beutner and Kamps (2008)

$$X(s - 1, n - 1, m, k) \stackrel{d}{=} X(s, n, m, k) \cdot Y_{s-1:s-1}$$

for adjacent generalized order statistics.

Remark 2.3 At $m = 0$, Corollary 2.2 reduces for order statistics as obtained by Khan and Shah (2012).

References

[1]   Ahsanullah, M. (2004): A characterization of the uniform distribution by dual generalized order statistics, *Commun.Statist.Theor.Meth*.33: 2921-2928.

[2]   Ahsanullah, M. (2006). The generalized order statistics from exponential distribution. *Pak. J. Statist*. 22(2):121-128.

[3]   Ahsanullah, M. (2006).On generalized order statistics from exponential distribution, *J. Statist Res*, 40, 21-27.

[4]   Arnold, B.C., Castillo, E. and Sarabia, J.M. (2008). Some characterizations involving uniform and powers of uniform random variables. *Statist*. 42(6): 527-534.

[5]   Burkschat, M., Cramer, E and Kamps, U. (2003). Dual generalized order statistics. *Metron-International Journal of Statistics*, LXI(I), 13-26.

[6]   Beutner, E. and Kamps, U. (2008). Random contraction and random dilation of generalized order statistics. *Commun.Statist.Theor.Meth*.37:2185-2201.

[7]   Castaño-Martínez, A., López-Blázquez, F. and Salamanca-Miño, B. (2010).Random translations, contractions and dilations of order statistics and records.*Statist*.: 1-11.DOI: 10.1080/02331888.2010.495406

[8]   Kamps, U. (1995). *A Concept of Generalized Order Statistics*. B. G. Teubner, Stuttgart.

[9]   Khan, A. H., and Shah Imtiyaz, A. (2012). Characterization *Through Distributional Properties of Order Statistics*.Communicated for publication.

[10]   Nevzorov, V. B. (2001). Record: Mathematical Theory. *Translation of Mathematical Monographs* 194.Providence: American Mathematical Society.

[11]   Navarro, J. (2008). Characteriozations by power contraction of order statistics.Commun. *Statist. Theor. Meth*.37:987-997.

[12]   Oncel S.Y., Ahsanullah, M., Aliev, F.A. and Aygun, F. (2005).Switching record and order statistics via random contraction. *Statist. Probab. Lett*.73:207-217.

[13]   Wesolowski, J. and Ahsanullah, M. (2004). Switching order statistics through random power contractions.Aust. N. Z. J. *Statist*.46:297-303.

In: Applied Statistical Theory and Applications
Editor: Mohammad Ahsanullah

ISBN: 978-1-63321-858-1
© 2014 Nova Science Publishers, Inc.

Chapter 19

ESTIMATION OF THE PARAMETER OF BINOMIAL DISTRIBUTION IN THE PRESENCE OF OUTLIERS

Ulhas J. Dixit* and Shailaja G. Kelkar[†]
Department of Statistics, University of Mumbai, Mumbai-India

Abstract

The maximum likelihood and moment estimators are derived for samples from the binomial distribution in the presence of outliers. We have shown that moment estimators are consistent. Further, it is shown that these estimators are better than MLE by using simulation technique. At the end we have given an example of Shooters.

Keywords: Binomial distribution, method of moment, method of maximum likelihood, outliers

1. Introduction

The standard problem associated with the binomial distribution is that of estimating its probability 'p' of success. See for details Steinhaus (1957) and Chew (1971). In this paper we try to estimate 'p' in the presence of outliers. See, Dixit (1989), Dixit, Ali and Woo(2003).

Let $X_1, X_2, ..., X_m$ be the number of successful attempts made by the shooter. It is found that the shooter has changed the position on some attempts, say k(known).

Thus, we assume that these k random variables are distributed with probability mass function $g(x, n, p)$, where

$$g(x, n, p) = C(n, x)(\alpha p)^x q_1^{n-x}; \quad x = 0, 1, ..., n, \ 0 < p < 1,$$
$$0 < \alpha p < 1, \ q_1 = 1 - \alpha p, \tag{1.1}$$

and the remaining $(m - k)$ random variables are distributed with probability mass function $f(x, n, p)$, where

$$f(x, n, p) = C(n, x)p^x q^{n-x}; \quad x = 0, 1, ..., n \ 0 < p < 1, \ q = 1 - p \tag{1.2}$$

---

*E-mail address: ulhasdixit@yahoo.co.in
[†]E-mail address: kelkar_shailaja@yahoo.com

where, p = probability the shooter hits the target, n = number of attempts and $C(n,x) = \frac{n!}{(n-x)!x!}$.

In this paper we estimate p, and α by using method of moments (MM) and maximum likelihood (ML).

At the end, if k is unknown we have given a criteria to estimate k.

2. Estimation of p and α

The joint distribution of $(X_1, X_2, ..., X_m)$ is given by using (1.1) and (1.2)

$$f(x_1, x_2, ...x_m, p, \alpha) = \frac{1}{C(m,k)} \prod_{i=1}^{m} C(n,x_i) p^T q^{mn-T} (\frac{q_1}{q})^{(nk)} G(x, \alpha, p) \tag{2.1}$$

where, $C(m,k) = \frac{m!}{(m-k)!k!}$, k known

$$G(x, \alpha, p) = \sum_{A_1=1}^{m-k+1} \sum_{A_2=A_1+1}^{m-k+2} ... \sum_{A_k=A_{k-1}+1}^{m} (\frac{\alpha q}{q_1})^{\sum_{i=1}^{k} x_{A_i}} \tag{2.2}$$

and $T = \sum_{i=1}^{m} x_i$

Case (1). Method of Moments

$$m'_1 = bn\alpha p + \bar{b}np \tag{2.3}$$

$$m'_2 = n(n-1)p^2(b\alpha^2 + \bar{b}) + np(b\alpha + \bar{b}) \tag{2.4}$$

where

$$m'_i = m^{-1} \sum_{j=1}^{m} x_j{}^i; \quad i = 1, 2 \ and \ b = k/m, \bar{b} = 1 - b \tag{2.5}$$

From (2.3)

$$\hat{\alpha} = \frac{1}{b}[\frac{m'_1}{n\hat{p}} - \bar{b}] \tag{2.6}$$

If $\frac{m'_1}{n} < \hat{p}\bar{b}$ then $\tilde{\alpha} = Max(0, \hat{\alpha})$.
Substitute (2.6) in (2.4)

$$\hat{p}^2[\frac{n(n-1)\bar{b}}{b}] - \hat{p}[\frac{2(n-1)m'_1\bar{b}}{b}] + \frac{(n-1)m'_1{}^2}{nb} + m'_1 - m'_2 = 0 \tag{2.7}$$

$$A_1\hat{p}^2 + A_2\hat{p} + A_3 = 0$$

$$\hat{p} = \frac{-A_2 \pm \sqrt{A_2^2 - 4A_1A_3}}{2A_1} \tag{2.8}$$

where $A_1 = \frac{n(n-1)\bar{b}}{b}$, $A_2 = \frac{-2(n-1)m'_1\bar{b}}{b}$ and $A_3 = \frac{(n-1)m'_1{}^2}{nb} + m'_1 - m'_2$

If $\hat{p} < 0$ then define $\tilde{p} = Max(0,\hat{p})$

Theorem 2.1. *$\hat{p}$ and $\hat{\alpha}$ are consistent estimators.*

Proof. Case (i) $\hat{p}$ is consistent.

Let $\hat{p} = f(w_1,w_2)$ where $w_1 = m'_1$ and $w_2 = m'_2$.

Suppose that $Ew_1 = \lambda_1$ and $Ew_2 = \lambda_2$.

Expand the function $f(w_1,w_2)$ around (λ_1,λ_2) by Taylor series.

$$
\begin{aligned}
f(w_1,w_2) &= f(\lambda_1,\lambda_2) + (w_1 - \lambda_1)\frac{\partial f}{\partial w_1}|_{w_1=\lambda_1,w_2=\lambda_2} \\
&+ (w_2 - \lambda_2)\frac{\partial f}{\partial w_2}|_{w_1=\lambda_1,w_2=\lambda_2} + ...
\end{aligned}
\tag{2.9}
$$

$$
E(\hat{p}) = f(\lambda_1,\lambda_2) + o(m^{-1}),
$$

where

$$
\lambda_1 = np(b\alpha + \bar{b})
$$

$$
\lambda_2 = n(n-1)p^2(b\alpha^2 + \bar{b}) + np(b\alpha + \bar{b})
$$

$$
\hat{p} = \frac{\lambda_1}{n} \pm \frac{\sqrt{-(n-1)^2\bar{b}b^{-1}\lambda_1^2 - n(n-1)\bar{b}b^{-1}(\lambda_1 - \lambda_2)}}{n(n-1)bb^{-1}}
\tag{2.10}
$$

After some algebra

$$
E\hat{p} = p(b\alpha + \bar{b}) \pm p\frac{\sqrt{b^2(1-\alpha)^2}}{bb^{-1}} + o(m^{-1})
$$

$$
E\hat{p} = p + o(m^{-1})
\tag{2.11}
$$

As m and k tends to infinity, then $E\hat{p}$ tends to p.

From (2.9),

$$
\hat{p} = p + (w_1 - \lambda_1)\frac{\partial f}{\partial w_1}|_{w_1=\lambda_1,w_2=\lambda_2} + (w_2 - \lambda_2)\frac{\partial f}{\partial w_2}|_{w_1=\lambda_1,w_2=\lambda_2} + ...
$$

$$
\begin{aligned}
E(\hat{p} - p)^2 &= V(w_1)(\frac{\partial f}{\partial w_1})^2 + V(w_2)(\frac{\partial f}{\partial w_2})^2 \\
&+ Cov(w_1,w_2)(\frac{\partial f}{\partial w_1})(\frac{\partial f}{\partial w_2}) + o(m^{-2})
\end{aligned}
\tag{2.12}
$$

Further

$$mV(w_1) = np(b\alpha + \bar{b}) - np^2(b\alpha^2 + \bar{b}) \tag{2.13}$$

$$\begin{aligned} mV(w_2) &= p^4(b\alpha^4 + \bar{b})n(n-1)(-4n+6) + p^3(b\alpha^3 + \bar{b})2n(n-1)(2n-6) \\ &+ p^2(b\alpha^2 + \bar{b})n(6n-7) + np(b\alpha + \bar{b}) \end{aligned} \tag{2.14}$$

$$\begin{aligned} mCov(w_1, w_2) &= -2n(n-1)p^3(b\alpha^3 + \bar{b}) + n(2n-3)p^2(b\alpha^2 + \bar{b}) \\ &+ n(b\alpha + \bar{b})p \end{aligned} \tag{2.15}$$

$$\frac{\partial f}{\partial w_1} = \frac{1}{n} - \frac{2(n-1)(b\alpha + \bar{b})p + 1}{2n(n-1)b|1-\alpha|p}$$

$$\frac{\partial f}{\partial w_2} = \frac{1}{2n(n-1)b|1-\alpha|p}$$

We can see that $E(\hat{p} - p)^2$ tends to zero as m and k tends to infinity. Therefore $\hat{p}$ is a consistent estimator.

Case(ii). $\hat{\alpha}$ is consistent.

Using the Taylor series expansion as in (2.9),

$$E\hat{\alpha} = \frac{1}{b}\left[\frac{p(b\alpha + \bar{b})}{p(b\alpha + b) + pb(1-\alpha)} - \bar{b}\right] + o(m^{-1}) \tag{2.16}$$

$$E\hat{\alpha} = \alpha + o(m^{-1})$$

As m and k tends to infinity,

$$E\hat{\alpha} \to \alpha$$

Similarly, as we have done in (2.12),

$$E(\hat{\alpha} - \alpha)^2 = V(w_1)(\frac{\partial f}{\partial w_1})^2 + V(w_2)(\frac{\partial f}{\partial w_2})^2 + Cov(w_1, w_2)(\frac{\partial f}{\partial w_1})(\frac{\partial f}{\partial w_2}) + o(m^{-2})$$

where

$$\frac{\delta f}{\delta w_1} = \frac{[2(n-1)p(b\alpha^2 + \bar{b}) + (b\alpha + \bar{b})]}{2bb|1-\alpha|n(n-1)p^2}$$

$$\frac{\delta f}{\delta w_2} = \frac{-(b\alpha + \bar{b})}{2bb|1-\alpha|n(n-1)p^2}$$

$V(w_1)$, $V(w_2)$ and $Cov(w_1, w_2)$ are given in (2.13), (2.14) and (2.15).

Hence, $E(\hat{\alpha} - \alpha)^2$ tends to zero as m and k tends to infinity.
Therefore, $\hat{\alpha}$ is a consistent estimator.

Theorem 2.2. Let

$$A = \begin{pmatrix} V(\hat{p}) & Cov(\hat{p}, \hat{\alpha}) \\ Cov(\hat{p}, \hat{\alpha}) & V(\hat{\alpha}) \end{pmatrix}. \tag{2.17}$$

Then $|A| \to 0$ as m and k tends to infinity.

Proof.

$$Cov(\hat{p}, \hat{\alpha}) = E\hat{p}\hat{\alpha} - E\hat{p}E\hat{\alpha} \tag{2.18}$$

From (2.6)

$$\hat{\alpha} = \frac{1}{b}[\frac{\bar{x}}{n\hat{p}} - \bar{b}]$$

where $\hat{p}$ is given in (2.8).

$$\hat{\alpha}\hat{p} = \frac{1}{b}[\frac{\bar{x}}{n} - \bar{b}\hat{p}] \tag{2.19}$$

By using $\hat{p}$ given in (2.8),

$$\hat{\alpha}\hat{p} = \frac{1}{b}\left[\frac{m'_1}{n} - \bar{b}\{\frac{m'_1}{n} - \frac{\sqrt{-(n-1)^2 m'_1{}^2 \bar{b}b^{-1} - n(n-1)\bar{b}b^{-1}(m'_1 - m'_2)}}{n(n-1)bb^{-1}}\}\right]$$

$$\hat{\alpha}\hat{p} = \frac{m'_1}{n} - \frac{\sqrt{-(n-1)^2 m'_1{}^2 \bar{b}b^{-1} - n(n-1)\bar{b}b^{-1}(m'_1 - m'_2)}}{n(n-1)}$$

Using Taylors series expansion as in (2.10),

$$E(\hat{\alpha}\hat{p}) = p(b\alpha + \bar{b}) + p\sqrt{\bar{b}b^{-1}[(b\alpha^2 + \bar{b}) - (b\alpha + \bar{b})^2]} + o(m^{-2})$$

After some algebra,

$$E(\hat{\alpha}\hat{p}) = \alpha p + o(m^{-2})$$

as m tends to infinity and k tends to infinity

$$E(\hat{\alpha}\hat{p}) \to \alpha p$$

Therefore

$$Cov(\hat{p}, \hat{\alpha}) \to 0 \tag{2.20}$$

$$det|A| = |V(\hat{p})V(\hat{\alpha}) - Cov(\hat{p}, \hat{\alpha})^2| \tag{2.21}$$

$$|A| \to 0$$

as m and k tends to infinity.

Note. $\hat{p}$ and $\hat{\alpha}$ are jointly consistent.

Case (2). Method of Maximum Likelihood

From (2.1) and (2.2)

$$L(p,\alpha) = \frac{1}{C(m,k)} \prod_{i=1}^{m} C(n,x_i).p^T q^{mn-T} (\frac{q_1}{q})^{(nk)} \overset{*}{\sum} (\frac{\alpha q}{q_1})^X \tag{2.22}$$

where $T = \sum_{i=1}^{m} x_i$, $X = \sum_{i=1}^{k} x_{A_i}$

$$\overset{*}{\sum} = \sum_{A_1=1}^{m-k+1} \sum_{A_2=A_1+1}^{m-k+2} \cdots \sum_{A_k=A_{k-1}+1}^{m}$$

$$\ln L(p,\alpha) \simeq T\ln p + (mn-T)\ln q + nk[\ln q_1 - \ln q] + \ln \overset{*}{\sum}(\frac{\alpha q}{q_1})^X \tag{2.23}$$

Let

$$\overset{*}{\sum}(\frac{\alpha q}{q_1})^X = S, \quad \overset{*}{\sum} X(\frac{\alpha q}{q_1})^X = S_x, \quad \overset{*}{\sum} X^2(\frac{\alpha q}{q_1})^X = S_{xx}$$

The likelihood Equations are as follows:

$$\frac{T}{p} - \frac{mn-T}{q} + nk[\frac{-\alpha}{q_1} + \frac{1}{q}] + \frac{\alpha-1}{qq_1}\frac{S_x}{S} = 0 \tag{2.24}$$

$$\frac{-nkp}{q_1} + \frac{1}{\alpha q_1}\frac{S_x}{S} = 0 \tag{2.25}$$

From (2.24) and (2.25) we get one more equation

$$m_1' = np(b\alpha + \bar{b}) \tag{2.26}$$

write (2.25) as

$$nkp\alpha - \frac{S_x}{S} = 0 \tag{2.27}$$

Let

$$t_1(p,\alpha) = \bar{x} - np(b\alpha + \bar{b}) \tag{2.28}$$

and

$$t_2(p, \alpha) = \frac{S_x}{S} - nkp\alpha \tag{2.29}$$

Expanding the equations (2.28) and (2.29) by Taylor series around (p_0, α_0),

$$t_1(p, \alpha) = t_1(p_0, \alpha_0) + \triangle p t'_{1p}(p_0, \alpha_0) + \triangle \alpha t'_{1\alpha}(p_0, \alpha_0) + o(m^{-1}) \tag{2.30}$$

$$t_2(p, \alpha) = t_2(p_0, \alpha_0) + \triangle p t'_{2p}(p_0, \alpha_0) + \triangle \alpha t'_{2\alpha}(p_0, \alpha_0) + o(m^{-1}) \tag{2.31}$$

where $\triangle \alpha = \alpha - \alpha_0$, $\triangle p = p - p_0$,$t'_{1p}(p, \alpha)$ and $t'_{1\alpha}(p, \alpha)$ are the first order derivative of $t_1(p, \alpha)$ with respect to p and α respectively.

Similarly $t'_{2p}(p, \alpha)$ and $t'_{2\alpha}(p, \alpha)$ are the first order derivative of $t_2(p, \alpha)$ with respect to p and α respectively.

$$t'_{1p} = -n(b\alpha + \bar{b})$$

$$t'_{1\alpha} = -npb$$

$$t'_{2p} = \frac{\alpha - 1}{qq_1} [\frac{S_{xx}}{S} - (\frac{S_x}{S})^2] - nk\alpha$$

and

$$t'_{2\alpha} = \frac{1}{\alpha q_1} [\frac{S_{xx}}{S} - (\frac{S_x}{S})^2] - nkp$$

write (2.30) and (2.31) as follows

$$t_1(p, \alpha) = c_1 + g\triangle p + h\triangle \alpha = 0 \tag{2.32}$$

$$t_2(p, \alpha) = c_2 + e\triangle p + f\triangle \alpha = 0 \tag{2.33}$$

Solving (2.31) and (2.32)

$$\triangle \alpha = \frac{-c_2 g + c_1 e}{fg - eh}$$

and

$$\triangle p = \frac{-c_2 h + c_1 f}{eh - fg}$$

The corrections $\triangle p$ and $\triangle \alpha$ are obtained such that we may expect

$$p^* = \triangle p + p_0$$

$$\alpha^* = \triangle \alpha + \alpha_0$$

These are the improved approximations of p and α.

Remark. *Estimation of k:* If k is unknown, then k can be selected by evaluating the likelihood for different values of k choosing the one that maximises the likelihood.

3. Numerical Study and Example

In order to get the idea of efficiency between the two types of estimation i.e Method of Moments and MLE. We have generated a sample of size m=10(10)40 from the Binomial distribution with $n = 10$, p=0.4(0.2)0.8, α=0.3(0.2)0.7 and k=1,2,3. We have calculated variance-covariance matrix of the estimate of p and α. Generalised variance-covariance matrix is $V(\hat{p})V(\hat{\alpha}) - Cov(\hat{p}, \hat{\alpha})^2$. We have given graphs based on one thousand independent replications of each experiment.

From the graphs, it has been seen that moment estimators are more efficient than maximum likelihood estimators.

Example. Following data give the number of successful attempts made by three shooters to hit the target. The shooter has changed the position on some attempts. The shooter has given $m = 10$ attempts.In each attempt he is hitting $n = 10$ times at the target and the entries X_i denote the number of successful shots made out of n shots. Now the problem is to choose the best shooter on the basis of probability of hitting the target.

Shooter	X_1	X_2	X_3	X_4	X_5	X_6	X_7	X_8	X_9	X_{10}
1	2	7	7	6	7	8	8	9	6	7
2	6	6	5	2	5	6	1	6	5	5
3	5	2	6	2	7	5	4	4	7	7

Since the moment estimators are more efficient ,$\hat{p}$ and $\hat{\alpha}$ are calculated by using (2.6) and (2.8).Further k is estimated by using likelihood.

For First shooter

k	$\hat{p}$	$\hat{\alpha}$	L
1	0.705119	0.501944	.241385E-7
2	0.722678	0.635534	.789916E-8
3	0.738972	0.688883	.488225E-8

For Second shooter

k	$\hat{p}$	$\hat{\alpha}$	L
1	0.489845	0.594870	.571544E-8
2	0.499768	0.702185	.490987E-8
3	0.508975	0.744749	.431211E-8

For Third shooter

k	$\hat{p}$	$\hat{\alpha}$	L
1	0.521250	0.400485	.2617241E-8
2	0.536875	0.563450	.3213714E-8
3	0.551373	0.628968	.3054450E-8

The efficient estimator on the basis of Likelihood are as follows

Shooter	k	$\hat{p}$	$\hat{\alpha}$	L
1	1	0.705119	0.501944	.241385E-7
2	1	0.489845	0.594870	.571544E-8
3	2	0.536875	0.563450	.321371E-8

We select the Shooter 1 as the Best Shooter on the basis of Maximum $\hat{p}$.

Generalized variance of $\hat{p}$ and $\hat{\alpha}$ for k=1

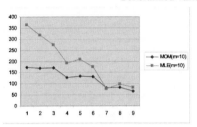
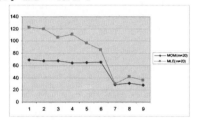

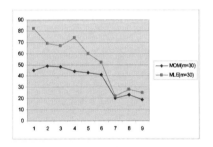
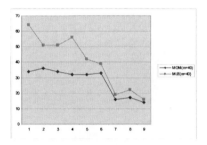

Generalized variance of $\hat{p}$ and $\hat{\alpha}$ for k=2

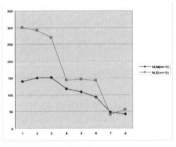
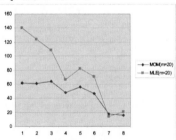

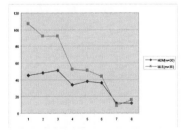
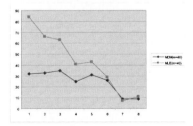

Generalized variance of $\hat{p}$ and $\hat{\alpha}$ for k=3

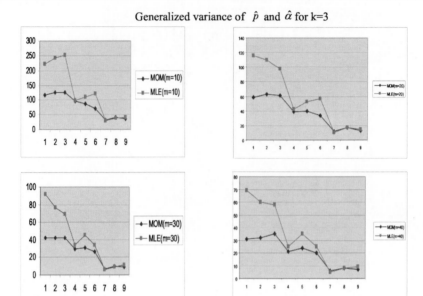

Acknowledgment

The authors are grateful to the referees and the editors.

References

[1] Dixit, U.J., (1989). Estimation of parameters of the gamma distribution in the presence of outliers. *Commun. Statist. Theor. Meth.* 18, 3071-3085.

[2] Dixit, U.J., Ali M. Masoom and Woo Jungsoo, (2003). Efficient estimation of parameters of a uniform distribution in the presence of outliers. *Soochow journal of mathematics*, 29(4), 363-369.

[3] Steinhaus, H.(1957). The Problem of Estimation. *The Annals of Mathematical Statistics*, 28: 633-648.

[4] Chew Victor, (1971). Point Estimation of the Parameter of Binomial Distribution. *The American Statistician*, 25(5): 47-50.

INDEX